THE BEVERLY HILLS
PARTY PLANNER

The National Directory For Party Services

A Creative Resource Guide
To Over 1700 Sources For Planning Celebrations,
Fund Raisers, Festivals,
Grand Openings and Corporate Events

JAN ROBERTS

The Beverly Hills Party Planner
139 South Beverly Drive, Suite 312
Beverly Hills, CA 90212

The Beverly Hills Party Planner
139 South Beverly Drive., Suite 312
Beverly Hills, CA 90212
310.271.7641

Researched, compiled and edited by Jan Roberts
Art direction, cover design and typography by 411 Graphics
Illustrations by 411 Graphics
Cover photograph by Rosemary Weller, provided by Tony Stone Worldwide

Printed in the United States of America
First edition

Dedicated to my grandparents,
Janet and Nate,
for their love and support.

ACKNOWLEDGEMENTS

Love and thanks to the following people for their help, time, recommendations and support which has made this book possible.

JERRY ASTOURIAN

CARL BERELLI

BONNIE BLOCH

BONNIE BOYD

PATTI COONS

ANDREA CLASTER

ANNETTE DAOUST

MARY FREVELE

LIESE GARDNER

AUDREY GORDON

SUSAN GORDON

STEVE GUSSMAN

MICHELLE HICKEY

JOHN JAKOB

VALERIE KERSH

TREY MOYNIHAN

LISA MONTGOMERY

NANCE MARTIN

MONA MERETSKY

CAROLINE MILLARD

ANITA NELSON

LIZ NEUMARK

AVA NEWBURGER

DON RAPOSA

ANNIE REVEL

LUANN ROBERTO

SALLY SCHWARTZ

SPECIAL EVENTS MAGAZINE

JENNIFER STEWART

MARY TRIBBLE

SANDY VILLANO

SHEILA WATNICK

411 GRAPHICS

DISCLAIMER

This Directory is intended to provide certain information to the general public with respect to the subject matter described in this Directory. All information contained in this Directory was compiled by invitation of the Author over the telephone, by mail and/or facsimile, was accepted in good faith and no advertising or other fees were accepted in connection therewith. Accordingly, neither the Author not the Publisher guarantee or recommend the services or goods of the providers described herein or assume any liability or responsibility for any credentials stated or claims made by any such providers. Additionally, although every reasonable effort has been made to make this Directory as accurate and informative as possible, this Directory may contain certain errors and /or inaccuracies, both within and beyond the control of the Author and/or Publisher.

The businesses, services and providers listed in this Directory were included at the sole discretion of the Author, are not meant to be exhaustive of the particular fields and no slight is intended to any business, service provider or organization not included in this Directory. Additionally, all information submitted to the Author had been edited by the Author for purposes of conciseness and clarity and certain of such submitted information has been necessarily omitted (for which neither the Author not the Publisher accept any liability or responsibility) and no inference should be drawn with respect thereto or with respect to the size of the particular description of any business, service or provider described herein. Lastly, neither the Author nor the Publisher assume any liability or responsibility to any person or entity with respect to any loss or damage caused, or alleged to have been caused, either directly or indirectly, by anything included in, or omitted from, this Directory.

TABLE OF CONTENTS

INTRODUCTION

Planning parties is always an exciting and unpredictable adventure. I have created carnival themed murder mystery events for law school graduates, luxury "Day of Beauty" events for the homeless, audience participation Hollywood theme events for attorneys and Irish birthday parties complete with bagpipe players and leprechauns.

I have provided comedic speakers for indoctrinations, stunt performers disguised as waiters for dinner parties, comedic Jewish yentas for Chamber of Commerce mixers and singing Santas and elves for corporate Christmas parties.

Through all this I have had the pleasure to work with and meet a diversified number of event specialists and clients, all of whom make being in the special event field an endless source of creative inspiration and fun.

It is my hope that everyone who uses this book will also find planning their celebrations as much of a creative joy as I have had in helping my clients plan theirs.

May all your parties be perfect.

Jan Roberts

HOW TO USE THIS BOOK

The Beverly Hills Party Planner is intended to be a helpful resource guide for anyone who entertains. All of the businesses, individuals and services listed inside volunteered the information at my invitation. The information was accepted on good faith and in most cases edited to be as concise and informative as possible. The length of the descriptions in no way reflect the calibre of the services provided and although every effort has been made to ensure the accuracy of the descriptions, I do not take responsibility for any inaccuracies that may have occurred.

Each chapter contains a variety of the following categories and sub-categories:

Audiovisual & Technical Services	**Invitations & Accessories**
Balloons	**Lighting, Staging & Sound**
Books	**Limousine & Transportation**
Cakes & Baked Goods	❧ **Pet Transportation**
Calligraphy	**Linens**
Catering	**Music & Entertainment**
❧**Bar Catering**	❧ **Animals**
❧**Pet Catering**	❧ **Caricatures & Drawings**
❧**Private Chefs**	❧ **Celebrity Look-alikes**
Celebrity Acquisition	❧ **Circus**
Chocolates & Confections	❧ **Comedy**
Classes & Seminars	❧ **DJs & Karaoke**
Costumes	❧ **Dance Troupes**
Delicacies	❧ **Entertainment Production & Booking**
Destination Management	
Equipment Rentals & Tenting	❧ **Magic, Hypnosis & Psychics**
Event Planning	❧ **Music**
Favors	❧ **Novelty**
Fireworks & Special Effects	**Party Sites**
Florists & Floral Designs	❧ **Beachfront**
Formal Wear	❧ **Galleries**
❧ **Pet Formal Wear**	❧ **Hotels**
Gifts & Gift Baskets	❧ **Location Bureaus**
Ice Services	❧ **Mansions & Garden Settings**

- Museums
- Novelty
- Private Clubs
- Restaurants
- Theatres & Auditoriums
- Zoos & Theme Parks

Party Supplies
Personnel & Staffing
Photography & Video
Plant Rentals

Props & Decor
Publications
Public Relations
Security
Signage
Speakers
Tabletop Accessories & Kitchenware
Uniforms
Valet Parking
Wine & Spirits
Yacht & Boat Charters

For specific pages and more information, please consult the index.

The Beverly Hills Party Planner
139 South Beverly Drive
Suite 312
Beverly Hills CA 90212
310.271.7641

❧ ❧ ❧

BEVERLY HILLS

BALLOONS

EXCLUSIVE GIFT BASKETS 'N' BALLOONS
8827 W. Olympic Blvd.
Suite 100
Beverly Hills, CA 90211
310.659.5680
Inggrit Hidajat
Areas served: Los Angeles County
Balloon bouquets, balloon decorations, gift baskets, invitations, calligraphy.

BOOKS

WILLIAMS-SONOMA
317 N. Beverly Drive
Beverly Hills, CA 90210
310.274.9127
An authoritative selection of the best for the kitchen. Complete line of cookware, bakeware, electrics, glassware, tabletop, kitchen furniture, cookbooks, packaged foods. Knowledgeable staff will help choose equipment, plan parties. Most of their merchandise is exclusive to Williams-Sonoma.

CAKES & BAKED GOODS

AMOUREX INTERNATIONAL, INC.
9567 Wilshire Blvd.
Beverly Hills, CA 90212
310.247.9774
Rebecca Lewis
Custom-designed, computerized women's formal wear and bridal wear. Design your own evening gown and bridal wear. In-house designers work with you to create the dress of your dreams. Delivery within six weeks. Jewelry, accessories, gifts, invitations, calligraphy services, floral design, custom-designed cakes, catering and photography services.

MISS GRACE LEMON CAKE CO.
422 N. Canon Drive
Beverly Hills, CA 90210
310.281.8096
800.367.2253 (mail order)
Mindy Moss

Areas served: Los Angeles, West Side, Valley; ship mail order anywhere. Highest quality baked goods made exclusively from scratch. Known for their lemon cake. Wedding cakes, decorated cakes for all occasions, gift baskets.

MUFFINS, ETC.
8950 W. Olympic Blvd.
Beverly Hills, CA 90211
310.274.5888
Janet Acquaro
Gourmet gift shop specializing in muffins baked on the premises, gift baskets and a large selection of gifts, cookware and tabletop accessories. For ages two to ninety-two. Local and UPS shipping. Specializing in sugar-free and sugar/fat-free muffins.

CALLIGRAPHY

AMOUREX INTERNATIONAL, INC.
9567 Wilshire Blvd.
Beverly Hills, CA 90212
310.247.9774
Rebecca Lewis
Custom-designed, computerized women's formal wear and bridal wear. Design your own evening gown and bridal wear. In-house designers work with you to create the dress of your dreams. Delivery within six weeks. Jewelry, accessories, gifts, invitations, calligraphy services, floral design, custom-designed cakes, catering and photography services.

EXCLUSIVE GIFT BASKETS 'N' BALLOONS
8827 W. Olympic Blvd.
Suite 100
Beverly Hills, CA 90211
310.659.5680
Inggrit Hidajat
Areas served: Los Angeles County
Balloon bouquets, balloon decorations, gift baskets, invitations, calligraphy.

FRANCIS ORR STATIONERY
320 N. Camden Drive
Beverly Hills, CA 90210
310.271.6106
213.272.2013

BEVERLY HILLS

Invitatons & calligraphy services for all occasions.

JUST ROBIN STUDIOS
9025 Wilshire Blvd.
Beverly Hills, CA 90211
310.273.9736
Robin Wagner
Areas served: National
Custom-designed invitations, calligraphy and accesssories for the most discriminating tastes. They carry a huge selection of imported papers from all over the world. Clients include celebrities, top corporations, high-end weddings and Bar Mitzvahs. Showroom viewing available by appointment.

WILLIAM ERNEST BROWN
442 N. Canon Drive
Beverly Hills, CA 90210
310.278.5620
Areas served: International
Custom-designed and catalogue invitations, seating charts, accessories, place cards and party supplies for all special events. They also provide calligraphy services. Known for their high quality products and special services. Clients all over the United States and Europe.

CATERING

AMOUREX INTERNATIONAL, INC.
9567 Wilshire Blvd.
Beverly Hills, CA 90212
310.247.9774
Rebecca Lewis
Custom-designed, computerized women's formal wear and bridal wear. Design your own evening gown and bridal wear. In-house designers work with you to create the dress of your dreams. Delivery within six weeks. Jewelry, accessories, gifts, invitations, calligraphy services, floral design, custom-designed cakes, catering and photography services.

**CHEESE STORE OF BEVERLY HILLS
LA FROMAGERIE**
419 N. Beverly Drive
Beverly Hills, CA 90210

310.278.2855
800.547.1515
Areas served: National
One of the largest selection of cheese, catering, wines and gourmet products. Custom-designed baskets. Delivery anywhere.

THE GRILL ON THE ALLEY
9560 Dayton Way
Beverly Hills, CA 90212
310.276.0615
Leslie Weill
Areas served: Los Angeles, Orange County
Restaurant known for outstanding classic American food. Provides full service catering for $75 per person all inclusive, ten person minimum. The Grill is brought to any location, home or office. Grilled steaks and fish.

RANGOON RACQUET CLUB
9474 Santa Monica Blvd.
Beverly Hills, CA 90210
310.274.8926
Jerry Prendergast
Areas served: Los Angeles
Restaurant and bar featuring traditional fare of steaks, chops and seafood. Classic California 1920's architecture. Full service catering. Semi-private banquet facilities. Sit down: 24 people.

❧ BAR CATERING

FROZEN DRINKS UNLIMITED
9923 Santa Monica Blvd.
Suite 339
Beverly Hills, CA 90212
310.312.0707
Robert Weinburg
Areas served: Los Angeles, Orange County
Margueritas, bar catering and machine rentals. Parties and events from 20 to 20,000 people. Write ups in *LA Magazine* and *Hollywood Reporter*.

[Continued on next page.]

❧ PET CATERING

CRITTER CATERERS
9405 Brighton Way
Suite 34
Beverly Hills, CA 90210
310.288.0882
Tracy Parsons
Areas served: Los Angeles County
Full service pet catering and formal wear.
Dog birthday parties, bone-shaped birthday
cakes, bakery goods for dogs and cats.

CELEBRITY ACQUISITION

THE ENTERTAINMENT CONNECTION, INC.
204 S. Clark Drive
Beverly Hills, CA 90211
310.652.1996
Penny Bigelow
Areas served: International
Special event production and coordination,
entertainment, catering, decoration, sound
systems, lighting, special effects, laser
shows, press/special event photographers,
limousine service, bus charters, parking
attendants, security. Entertainment at
every price level —celebrities, singers,
dancers, bands, musical groups, comics,
speakers, sports stars, complete shows.

MARCI WEINER
450 S. Maple Drive
Suite 204
Beverly Hills, CA 90212
310.276.5070
Areas served: Beverly Hills, Los Angeles,
Bel Air, Malibu, Palm Springs, San Diego
and Santa Barbara.
Columnist with many newspapers and
publications serving the affluent West Side
and Beverly Hills areas. She can provide
copy in any of her various publications as
well as celebrity acquisition services for
special events.

CHOCOLATES & CONFECTIONS

EDELWEISS CHOCOLATES
444 N. Canon Drive
Beverly Hills, CA 90210
310.275.0341
Sam Rosen
Areas served: National
Finest handmade chocolates,
marshmallows, fresh nuts, specially
designed nuts, chocolate favors, place
cards, specialty mints, gift boxes, custom-
designed candy plates, monogrammed mint
disks, eighty varieties of chocolates and
truffles handmade on the premises,
chocolate seating cards. Clients all over the
country, featured in *The Chocolate Bible*,
over twenty magazine articles, TV shows,
etc. In business over fifty years.

JUDI KAUFMAN AND COMPANY
400 S. Beverly Drive
Suite 214
Beverly Hills, CA 90212
310.858.7787
800.475.7787
Judi Kaufman
Areas served: National
Grand chocolate pizzas delivered anywhere.
Non-perishable. Environmental emphasis.
Chocolate centerpieces.

LEE GELFOND CHOCOLATES
275 S. Robertson Blvd.
Beverly Hills, CA 90211
310.854.3524
Lee Gelfond
Areas served: National
Custom-designed chocolates for all
occasions —favors, gift baskets, corporate
gifts, etc.

TEUSCHER CHOCOLATES
9548 Brighton Way
Beverly Hills, CA 90210
310.276.2776
Aviva Covitz
Janet Surmi
Areas served: International
Imported truffles, pralines, gianduja and
marzipan chocolates from Zurich,
Switzerland. Known for their champagne
truffles filled with a center of Dom Perignon

creme, handmade decorated gift boxes from Switzerland, gift baskets and elegant packaging with personalized service. They provide local and international delivery.

CLASSES & SEMINARS

AT HOME
310.858.0773
Shelby Goodman

Custom-created seminars on all aspects of entertaining and running a home. Shelby is an accomplished party planner and interior designer who includes every aspect of designing and running a household in her private seminars. She specializes in old-world elegance and tradition and has been written about in *Vanity Fair, California Homes and Lifestyles, Angeles* and *213*.

THE WINE MERCHANT
9701 Santa Monica Blvd.
Beverly Hills, CA 90210
310.278.7322
Lucille Dash

Areas served: Los Angeles County
One of the finest purveyors of wines and spirits. Their staff of wine experts and consultants are ready to serve all needs. They offer delivery, gift wrap, custom gift baskets, a huge underground wine locker facility, a unique wine of the month club by mail, wine classes, tastings and dinners.

DELICACIES

CAVIARTERIA WEST, INC.
247 N. Beverly Drive
Beverly Hills, CA 90210
310.288.9773

Mail order and store sale of caviar, Scotch salmon, fresh foie gras, gourmet foods, gift baskets, champagne delivered or shipped anywhere in California. Won Chefs in America Gold Medal, Confrerie de Chain des Rotisseurs Award of Excellence.

CHEESE STORE OF BEVERLY HILLS
LA FROMAGERIE
419 N. Beverly Drive
Beverly Hills, CA 90210
310.278.2855
800.547.1515

Areas served: National
One of the largest selection of cheese, catering, wines and gourmet products. Custom-designed baskets. Delivery anywhere.

EQUIPMENT RENTALS & TENTING

FROZEN DRINKS UNLIMITED
9923 Santa Monica Blvd.
Suite 339
Beverly Hills, CA 90212
310.312.0707
Robert Weinburg

Areas served: Los Angeles, Orange County
Margueritas, bar catering and machine rentals. Parties and events from 20 to 20,000 people. Write ups in *LA Magazine* and *Hollywood Reporter*.

EVENT PLANNING

BOB GAIL ORCHESTRAS AND ENTERTAINMENT
9454 Wilshire Blvd.
Suite M-4
Beverly Hills, CA 90212
310.276.3300
Bob Levine

Areas served: All areas
All kinds of music and entertainment for all kinds of events, and event planning from concept to clean-up. #1 entertainment agency in Los Angeles by *Beverly Hills 213 Magazine* five years in a row.

FLORAL CREATIONS
The Regent Beverly Wilshire Hotel
9500 Wilshire Blvd.
Beverly Hills, CA 90212

3351 LaCienega Place
Los Angeles, CA 90016

310.204.1700
Dee Kartoon
Teri Abelson
Areas served: Greater Los Angeles and
surrounding communities
Full service florist providing floral design,
party planning, gourmet baskets and plants
for parties, weddings, Bar Mitzvahs, theme
events and corporate dinners. They are the
premier florist at The Regent Beverly
Wilshire Hotel and are responsible for all
the flowers in the Main Room. Delivery is
provided.

THE FLOWER MEADOWS
9627 Brighton Way
Beverly Hills, CA 90210
310.247.6040
Jef Hackbarth, AIFD
Areas served: National
Elegant floral design, decor and props for
weddings, corporate events, movie and TV
set dressings, theme celebrations, premiere
galas and corporate image. They have over
thirty-five years experience in dressing
movie sets and the Academy Awards'
Governors Ball. In addition to flowers, they
also provide plants and trees. Jef
Hackbarth, AIFD, is the past National
President of the American Institute of
Floral Designers, and his work has
appeared in over forty Academy Award-
winning films.

JOAN LUTHER & ASSOCIATES
407 N. Maple Drive
Bevery Hills, CA 90210
310.273.4936
Susan Gordon
Areas served: Los Angeles
Special event planning and coordination.
Publicity for special events. Specializing in
charities, restaurants, fundraisers, fashion
and retail.

RENT AN EVENT
139 S. Beverly Drive
Suite 312
Bevery Hills, CA 90212
310.271.7641
Jan Roberts
Full service event planning for all occasions.

FAVORS

A SPECIAL FAVOR
617 N. Beverly Drive
Bevery Hills, CA 90210
310.273.3010
Maxx Komack
Gretchen DiNapoli
Areas served: National
Custom-designed party favors, invitations,
bridal attendant gifts, hostess gifts and
elegant accessories for all special occasions.
Previous clients include Lee Iacoca, The
Beverly Hills Hotel, The Bistro Garden and
many more.

EDELWEISS CHOCOLATES
444 N. Canon Drive
Beverly Hills, CA 90210
310.275.0341
Sam Rosen
Areas served: National
Finest handmade chocolates,
marshmallows, fresh nuts, specially
designed nuts, chocolate favors, place
cards, specialty mints, gift boxes, custom-
designed candy plates, monogrammed mint
disks, eighty varieties of chocolates and
truffles handmade on the premises,
chocolate seating cards. Clients all over the
country, featured in *The Chocolate Bible*,
over twenty magazine articles, TV shows,
etc. In business over fifty years.

LEE GELFOND CHOCOLATES
275 S. Robertson Blvd.
Beverly Hills, CA 90211
310.854.3524
Lee Gelfond
Areas served: National
Custom-designed chocolates for all
occasions — favors, gift baskets, corporate
gifts, etc.

LINENS ET AL
165 N. Robertson Blvd.
Beverly Hills, CA 90211
310.652.7970
Marilyn Snyder
Areas served: National
Fine tabletop accessories and linens, favors
and gift items. Engraving and
monogramming.

TEUSCHER CHOCOLATES
9548 Brighton Way
Beverly Hills, CA 90210
310.276.2776
Aviva Covitz
Janet Surmi
Areas served: International
Imported truffles, pralines, gianduja and marzipan chocolates from Zurich, Switzerland. Known for their champagne truffles filled with a center of Dom Perignoncreme, handmade decorated gift boxes from Switzerland, gift baskets and elegant packaging with personalized service. They provide local and international delivery.

TIFFANY & COMPANY
210 N. Rodeo Drive
Beverly Hills, CA 90210
310.273.8880
Michele Sheid
The finest in engraved invitations, favors, accessories, stationery, bridal registry, fine crystal and china, Tiffany flatware and gifts for all occasions.

FLORISTS & FLORAL DESIGNS

AMOUREX INTERNATIONAL, INC.
9567 Wilshire Blvd.
Beverly Hills, CA 90212
310.247.9774
Rebecca Lewis
Custom-designed, computerized women's formal wear and bridal wear. Design your own evening gown and bridal wear. In-house designers work with you to create the dress of your dreams. Delivery within six weeks. Jewelry, accessories, gifts, invitations, calligraphy services, floral design, custom-designed cakes, catering and photography services.

FLORAL CREATIONS
The Regent Beverly Wilshire Hotel
9500 Wilshire Blvd.
Beverly Hills, CA 90212

3351 LaCienega Place
Los Angeles, CA 90016

310.204.1700
Dee Kartoon
Teri Abelson
Areas served: Greater Los Angeles and surrounding communities
Full service florist providing floral design, party planning, gourmet baskets and plants for parties, weddings, Bar Mitzvahs, theme events and corporate dinners. They are the premier florist at The Regent Beverly Wilshire Hotel and are responsible for all the flowers in the Main Room. Delivery is provided.

LA PREMIERE FLOWERS
8928 W. Olympic Blvd.
Beverly Hills, CA 90211
310.276.4665
Kevin Lee
Areas served: Beverly Hills, Los Angeles, Santa Monica, Encino and surrounding areas
Full service florist and floral designer. They carry full lines of party decorations, including wedding and theme parties, and have won both national and international awards for floral design.

FORMAL WEAR

AMOUREX INTERNATIONAL, INC.
9567 Wilshire Blvd.
Beverly Hills, CA 90212
310.247.9774
Rebecca Lewis
Custom-designed, computerized women's formal wear and bridal wear. Design your own evening gown and bridal wear. In-house designers work with you to create the dress of your dreams. Delivery within six weeks. Jewelry, accessories, gifts, invitations, calligraphy services, floral design, custom-designed cakes, catering and photography services.

GARY'S TUX SHOPS
8621 Wilshire Blvd.
Beverly Hills, CA 90211
310.652.7296
Tuxedo sales and rentals. Large selection of fine formal wear including Christian Dior, Henry Grethel, Pierre Cardin, Lord West and more. Specializing in weddings and

corporate events/conventions, offering special discounts and services for large groups. Served over 250,000 "newly-weds" since 1933. Supplied over 700 tuxedos for Super Bowl in San Diego and all tuxes for opening ceremonies of Los Angeles Olympics.

STARLIT SOIREE
8950 W. Olympic Blvd.
Suite 213
Beverly Hills, CA 90211
310.275.5570
Sherry Morgan
Ladies designer formal rentals. Designer party dresses, cocktail dresses, dinner suits and gowns for rent. Also rent shoes, evening bags and jewelry. Pageant, prom and black tie attire are their specialty. Featured on AMCA, CNN, CH7, CH4, etc.

PET FORMAL WEAR

CRITTER CATERERS
9405 Brighton Way
Suite 34
Beverly Hills, CA 90210
310.288.0882
Tracy Parsons
Areas served: Los Angeles County
Full service pet catering and formal wear. Dog birthday parties, bone-shaped birthday cakes, bakery goods for dogs and cats.

GIFTS & GIFT BASKETS

AMOUREX INTERNATIONAL, INC.
9567 Wilshire Blvd.
Beverly Hills, CA 90212
310.247.9774
Rebecca Lewis
Custom-designed, computerized women's formal wear and bridal wear. Design your own evening gown and bridal wear. In-house designers work with you to create the dress of your dreams. Delivery within six weeks. Jewelry, accessories, gifts, invitations, calligraphy services, floral design, custom-designed cakes, catering and photography services.

CAVIARTERIA WEST, INC.
247 N. Beverly Drive
Beverly Hills, CA 90210
310.288.9773
Mail order and store sale of caviar, Scotch salmon, fresh foie gras, gourmet foods, gift baskets, champagne delivered or shipped anywhere in California. Won Chefs in America Gold Medal, Confrerie de Chain des Rotisseurs Award of Excellence.

CHEESE STORE OF BEVERLY HILLS LA FROMMAGERIE
419 N. Beverly Drive
Beverly Hills, CA 90210
310.278.2855
800.547.1515
Areas served: National
One of the largest selection of cheese, catering, wines and gourmet products. Custom-designed baskets. Delivery anywhere.

EDELWEISS CHOCOLATES
444 N. Canon Drive
Beverly Hills, CA 90210
310.275.0341
Sam Rosen
Areas served: National
Finest handmade chocolates, marshmallows, fresh nuts, specially designed nuts, chocolate favors, place cards, specialty mints, gift boxes, custom-designed candy plates, monogrammed mint disks, eighty varieties of chocolates and truffles handmade on the premises, chocolate seating cards. Clients all over the country, featured in *The Chocolate Bible*, over twenty magazine articles, TV shows, etc. In business over fifty years.

EXCLUSIVE GIFT BASKETS 'N' BALLOONS
8827 W. Olympic Blvd.
Suite 100
Beverly Hills, CA 90211
310.659.5680
Inggrit Hidajat
Areas served: Los Angeles County
Balloon bouquets, balloon decorations, gift baskets, invitations, calligraphy.

FLORAL CREATIONS
The Regent Beverly Wilshire Hotel
9500 Wilshire Blvd.
Beverly Hills, CA 90212

3351 LaCienega Place
Los Angeles, CA 90016
310.204.1700
Dee Kartoon
Teri Abelson
Areas served: Greater Los Angeles and surrounding communities
Full service florist providing floral design, party planning, gourmet baskets and plants for parties, weddings, Bar Mitzvahs, theme events and corporate dinners. They are the premier florist at The Regent Beverly Wilshire Hotel and are responsible for all the flowers in the Main Room. Delivery is provided.

JUDI KAUFMAN AND COMPANY
400 S. Beverly Drive
Suite 214
Beverly Hills, CA 90212
310.858.7787
800.475.7787
Judi Kaufman
Areas served: National
Grand chocolate pizzas delivered anywhere. Non-perishable. Environmental emphasis. Chocolate centerpieces.

LEE GELFOND CHOCOLATES
275 S. Robertson Blvd.
Beverly Hills, CA 90211
310.854.3524
Lee Gelfond
Areas served: National
Custom-designed chocolates for all occasions — favors, gift baskets, corporate gifts, etc.

LINENS ET AL
165 N. Robertson Blvd.
Beverly Hills, CA 90211
310.652.7970
Marilyn Snyder
Areas served: National
Fine tabletop accessories and linens, favors and gift items. Engraving and monogramming.

MISS GRACE LEMON CAKE CO.
422 N. Canon Drive
Beverly Hills, CA 90210
310.281.8096
800.367.2253 (mail order)
Mindy Moss
Areas served: Los Angeles, West Side,

Valley; ship mail order anywhere. Highest quality baked goods made exclusively from scratch. Known for their lemon cake. Wedding cakes, decorated cakes for all occasions, gift baskets.

MUFFINS, ETC.
8950 W. Olympic Blvd.
Beverly Hills, CA 90211
310.274.5888
Janet Acquaro
Gourmet gift shop specializing in muffins baked on the premises, gift baskets and a large selection of gifts, cookware and tabletop accessories. For ages two to ninety-two. Local and UPS shipping. Specializing in sugar-free and sugar/fat-free muffins.

STEVE/BEVERLY HILLS
9530 Santa Monica Blvd.
Beverly Hills, CA 90210
310.274.6567
Mark Krasne
Steve Rieman
Incredible selection of unusual tabletop accessories, giftware, dinnerware, American crafts, linens, settings and props. Prop rentals for events as well as a corporate gift registry and bridal registry.

TEUSCHER CHOCOLATES
9548 Brighton Way
Beverly Hills, CA 90210
310.276.2776
Aviva Covitz
Janet Surmi
Areas served: International
Imported truffles, pralines, gianduja and marzipan chocolates from Zurich, Switzerland. Known for their champagne truffles filled with a center of Dom Perignon creme, handmade decorated gift boxes from Switzerland, gift baskets and elegant packaging with personalized service. They provide local and international delivery.

TIFFANY & COMPANY
210 N. Rodeo Drive
Beverly Hills, CA 90210
310.273.8880
Michele Sheid
The finest in engraved invitations, favors, accessories, stationery, bridal registry, fine

crystal and china, Tiffany flatware and gifts for all occasions.

THE WINE MERCHANT
9701 Santa Monica Blvd.
Beverly Hills, CA 90210
310.278.7322
Lucille Dash

Areas served: Los Angeles County
One of the finest purveyors of wines andand spirits. Their staff of wine experts and consultants are ready to serve all needs. They offer delivery, gift wrap, custom gift baskets, a huge underground wine locker facility, a unique wine of the month club by mail, wine classes, tastings and dinners.

INVITATIONS & ACCESSORIES

A SPECIAL FAVOR
617 N. Beverly Drive
Bevery Hills, CA 90210
310.273.3010
Maxx Komack
Gretchen DiNapoli

Areas served: National
Custom-designed party favors, invitations, bridal attendant gifts, hostess gifts and elegant accessories for all special occasions. Previous clients include Lee Iacoca, The Beverly Hills Hotel, The Bistro Garden and many more.

AMOUREX INTERNATIONAL, INC.
9567 Wilshire Blvd.
Beverly Hills, CA 90212
310.247.9774
Rebecca Lewis

Custom-designed, computerized women's formal wear and bridal wear. Design your own evening gown and bridal wear. In-house designers work with you to create the dress of your dreams. Delivery within six weeks. Jewelry, accessories, gifts, invitations, calligraphy services, floral design, custom-designed cakes, catering and photography services.

EDELWEISS CHOCOLATES
444 N. Canon Drive
Beverly Hills, CA 90210

310.275.0341
Sam Rosen

Areas served: National
Finest handmade chocolates, marshmallows, fresh nuts, specially designed nuts, chocolate favors, place cards, specialty mints, gift boxes, custom-designed candy plates, monogrammed mint disks, eighty varieties of chocolates and truffles handmade on the premises, chocolate seating cards. Clients all over the country, featured in *The Chocolate Bible*, over twenty magazine articles, TV shows, etc. In business over fifty years.

EXCLUSIVE GIFT BASKETS 'N' BALLOONS
8827 W. Olympic Blvd.
Suite 100
Beverly Hills, CA 90211
310.659.5680
Inggrit Hidajat

Areas served: Los Angeles County
Balloon bouquets, balloon decorations, gift baskets, invitations, calligraphy.

FRANCIS ORR STATIONERY
320 N. Camden Drive
Beverly Hills, CA 90210
310.271.6106
213.272.2013

Invitations and calligraphy services for all occasions.

JUST ROBIN STUDIOS
9025 Wilshire Blvd.
Beverly Hills, CA 90211
310.273.9736
Robin Wagner

Areas served: National
Custom-designed invitations, calligraphy and accesssories for the most discriminating tastes. They carry a huge selection of imported papers from all over the world. Clients include celebrities, top corporations, high-end weddings and Bar Mitzvahs. Showroom viewing available by appointment.

TIFFANY & COMPANY
210 N. Rodeo Drive
Beverly Hills, CA 90210
310.273.8880
Michele Sheid

The finest in engraved invitations, favors, accessories, stationery, bridal registry, fine crystal and china, Tiffany flatware and gifts for all occasions.

WILLIAM ERNEST BROWN
442 N. Canon Drive
Beverly Hills, CA 90210
310.278.5620
Areas served: International
Custom-designed and catalogue invitations, seating charts, accessories, place cards and party supplies for all special events. They also provide calligraphy services. Known for their high quality products and special services. Clients all over the United States and Europe.

LIMOUSINE & TRANSPORTATION

DAV EL CHAUFFEURED TRANSPORTATION NETWORK
9641 Sunset Blvd.
Beverly Hills, CA 90210
310.642.6666 (Local)
800.328.3526 (Outside CA)
800.826.5779 (Inside CA)
Katie Cotton
Areas served: International
Luxury chauffeured services in over 350 cities worldwide. Centralized reservations and billing. Airport concierge services.

CAREY LIMOUSINE
9350 Civic Center Drive
Suite 100
Beverly Hills, CA 90210
310.275.4153
800.336.4646
Areas served: International
Privately chauffeured sedans, limousines, vans and mini buses in 372 cities.

DIVA LIMOUSINE
400 S. Beverly Drive
Suite 214
Beverly Hills, CA 90212
310.278.3482
Ron Zowgi

Areas served: Southern California
Limousine and car service specializing in corporate accounts.

SIMPLY CORPORATE AFFORDABLE LUXURY TRANSPORTATION
P.O. Box 9099
Beverly Hills, CA 90212-1099
310.274.7070
George Heyman, President
Robert DiCicco
Patrick Murphy
Areas served: All areas
Twenty-four hour affordable luxury transportation that provides corporate-oriented chauffeur. Company has station wagons, Lincoln Town Cars and stretch limousines with cellular telephones available. They specialize in coordinating, planning and moving large groups in the corporate and entertainment industries.

LINENS

ACCENT PARTY LINEN RENTALS
270 N. Canon Drive
Suite 1328
Beverly Hills, CA 90210
310.273.8191
Debbie Baker
Areas served: National
Local and nationwide rental of fancy overlay tablecloths. Wholesale only to special event professionals.

LINENS ET AL
165 N. Robertson Blvd.
Beverly Hills, CA 90211
310.652.7970
Marilyn Snyder
Areas served: National
Fine tabletop accessories and linens, favors and gift items. Engraving and monogramming.

STEVE/BEVERLY HILLS
9530 Santa Monica Blvd.
Beverly Hills, CA 90210
310.274.6567
Mark Krasne
Steve Rieman

BEVERLY HILLS

Incredible selection of unusual tabletop accessories, giftware, dinnerware, American crafts, linens, settings and props. Prop rentals for events as well as a corporate gift registry and bridal registry.

MUSIC & ENTERTAINMENT

BOB GAIL ORCHESTRAS AND ENTERTAINMENT
9454 Wilshire Blvd.
Suite M-4
Beverly Hills, CA 90212
310.276.3300
Bob Levine
Areas served: All areas
All kinds of music and entertainment for all kinds of events, and event planning from concept to clean-up. #1 entertainment agency in Los Angeles *by Beverly Hills 213 Magazine* five years in a row.

THE ENTERTAINMENT CONNECTION, INC.
204 S. Clark Drive
Beverly Hills, CA 90211
310.652.1996
Penny Bigelow
Areas served: National and International
Special event production and coordination, entertainment, catering, decoration, sound systems, lighting, special effects, laser shows, press/special event photographers, limousine service, bus charters, parking attendants, security. Entertainment at every price level – celebrities, singers, dancers, bands, musical groups, comics, speakers, sports stars, complete shows.

ESP PRODUCTIONS
P.O. Box 5790
Beverly Hills, CA 90209
310.273.9476
Josh Zellner
Areas served: Southern California
Variety, circus, novelty entertainment. Theme and holiday performers; most entertainers have been featured in TV and film, etc.

LEE HAHN
320 N. Maple Drive
Suite 201
Beverly Hills, CA 90210
310.276.8068
Areas served: Los Angeles and Orange County
Musical entertainer and singer. Show called "Broadway and Me", featuring great songs from musical theatre.

TRIBUTES UNLIMITED OF BEVERLY HILLS
229 S. Elm Drive
Suite 1
Beverly Hills, CA 90212
310.275.8407
Shirley Siegel
Areas served: Southern California
Custom entertainment: "Your Life Set To Music" with personalized, engraved gold-leaf Oscar figure; Bar and Bat Mitzvah candle-lightings, Broadway-style with coaching and microphone training for the youngster. Corporate awards ceremonies a specialty. Corporate and professional achievement awards set to a musical bio theme. "The Best of LA" most ingenious special event service.

PARTY SITES

BICE BEVERLY HILLS
301 N. Canon Drive
Beverly Hills, CA 90210
310.272.2423
Pepe Amespil
Restaurant and banquet facility. Indoor and oudoor dining. Northern Italian cuisine. Facilities for up to 150 people. In business in Milan since 1926.

THE BISTRO
246 N. Canon Drive
Beverly Hills, CA 90210
310.273.5633
Freddy Kernbach
Renowned restaurant. 4500 square feet, holds up to 300 people.

BEVERLY HILLS

THE BISTRO GARDEN
176 N. Canon Drive
Beverly Hills, CA 90210
310.550.3900
Christopher Niklas
Renowned restaurant. 9000 square feet.
Receptions: 400 people. Sit down: 350
people.

CIRCLE GALLERY
329 N. Beverly Drive
Beverly Hills, CA 90210
310.273.1461
Robert Sibulkin
Contemporary art and sculpture. Two
private viewing/conference rooms,
hardwood floors, open-air ceilings, perfect
for unique cocktail parties. 35,000 square
feet. Receptions: 250 people. Sit down:
100 people.

FOUR SEASONS HOTEL
AT BEVERLY HILLS
300 S. Doheny Drive
Los Angeles, CA 90048
310.273.2222
Judy James
Images of a manor house come to mind at
the four Seasons Hotel at Beverly Hills.
The sixteen-story hotel is like a grand
residence, bringing an East Coast and
European flavor to the city. The residential
size and style of the hotel caters to smaller
and mid-sized groups in assorted salons and
meeting rooms. The largest of the hotel's
function areas are the ballroom and nearby
Wetherly Garden. The latter, a beautifully
landscaped court of white camellias and
bougainvillea, is popular for outdoor social
events, ie., weddings. Total square footage,
all meeting rooms and ballroom: 9650 (10
meeting rooms). Receptions: 500 people in
ballroom. Sit down: 280 people in
ballroom, 400 people theatre-style in
ballroom. Mobil Five Star 1991-92; AAA
Four Diamond 1990-92. California
Restaurant Writers Association Four Star
1990-92. Calibre Award for Excellence in
Design 1988. LA Beautiful Award for
Landscaping in 1988.

THE GRILL ON THE ALLEY
9560 Dayton Way
Beverly Hills, CA 90212

310.276.0615
Leslie Weill
Areas served: Los Angeles, Orange County
Restaurant known for outstanding classic
American food. Provides full service
catering for $75 per person all inclusive, ten
person minimum. The Grill is brought to
any location, home or office. Grilled steaks
and fish.

HOTEL NIKKO AT BEVERLY HILLS
465 S. LaCienega Blvd.
Los Angeles, CA 90048
Howard Feldman
Banquet facilities for social and business
events. State-of-the-art facilities. Unique
thunder and lightening special effect light
show. Named "Best New Discover" by *San
Francisco Focus Magazine*. Receptions:
125 people. Sit down: 125 people.

L'ERMITAGE HOTEL
9291 Burton Way
Beverly Hills, CA 90212
310.278.3344
Karen Michaels
Banquet facilities. "Grande classe"
hospitality. Weddings, receptions,
meetings. Executive Chef, Dennis Burrage,
personally creates signature dishes for each
memorable affair.

LARRY PARKER'S DINER
206 S. Beverly Drive
Beverly Hills, CA 90212
310.274.5655
Karen
Twenty-four hour diner, 1950s, jukeboxes.

MEDITERANEAN VILLA
310.858.0773
Shelby Goodman
Large garden and exquisite interior
surrounded by rose trees and rose gardens.
Romantic arches, flower encircled
pool/garden area. 55,000 square feet plus
cottage. Holds up to 300 people. Chosen by
LA County Museum as an exceptionally fine
example of its style. Write ups in *Vanity
Fair, Angeles, California Homes*, etc.

[Continued on next page.]

RANGOON RACQUET CLUB
9474 Santa Monica Blvd.
Beverly Hills, CA 90210
310.274.8926
Jerry Prendergast
Areas served: Los Angeles
Restaurant and bar featuring traditional
fare of steaks, chops and seafood. Classic
California 1920's architecture. Full service
catering. Semi-private banquet facilities.
Sit down: 24 people.

REGENT BEVERLY WILSHIRE HOTEL
9500 Wilshire Blvd.
Beverly Hills, CA 90212
310.275.5200
Ann Flowers
World renowned hotel. Full event planning
facilities. First class service and style.
Stunning architecture and design.
Meetings, weddings, fundraisers, parties.
Receptions: 1100 people. Sit down: 850
people.

VIRGINIA ROBINSON GARDENS
310.276.3302
John Copeland
Botanical gardens available for small
daytime events Tuesday through Friday.
No weddings. Hold up to 100 people.

PARTY SUPPLIES

WILLIAM ERNEST BROWN
442 N. Canon Drive
Beverly Hills, CA 90210
310.278.5620
Areas served: International
Custom-designed and catalogue invitations,
seating charts, accessories, place cards and
party supplies for all special events. They
also provide calligraphy services. Known
for their high quality products and special
services. Clients all over the United States
and Europe.

PERSONNEL & STAFFING

THE PARTY STAFF
9328 Civic Center Drive
Suite A
Beverly Hills, CA 90210
310.859.6500
Tom Sifuentes
Brian Lillie
Areas served: Southern California
Temporary food service employees, waiters,
waitresses, bartenders.

PHOTOGRAPHY & VIDEO

AMOUREX INTERNATIONAL, INC.
9567 Wilshire Blvd.
Beverly Hills, CA 90212
310.247.9774
Rebecca Lewis
Custom-designed, computerized women's
formal wear and bridal wear. Design
your own evening gown and bridal wear.
In-house designers work with you to create
the dress of your dreams. Delivery within
six weeks. Jewelry, accessories, gifts,
invitations, calligraphy services, floral
design, custom-designed cakes, catering and
photography services.

PLANT RENTALS

THE FLOWER MEADOWS
9627 Brighton Way
Beverly Hills, CA 90210
310.247.6040
Jef Hackbarth, AIFD
Areas served: National
Elegant floral design, decor and props for
weddings, corporate events, movie and TV
set dressings, theme celebrations, premiere
galas and corporate image. They have over
thirty-five years experience in dressing
movie sets and the Academy Awards'
Governors Ball. In addition to flowers, they
also provide plants and trees. Jef
Hackbarth, AIFD, is the past National
President of the American Institute of
Floral Designers, and his work has

appeared in over forty Academy Award-winning films.

PROPS & DECOR

JUDI KAUFMAN AND COMPANY
      400 S. Beverly Drive
      Suite 214
      Beverly Hills, CA 90212
      310.858.7787
      800.475.7787
      Judi Kaufman
Areas served: National
Grand chocolate pizzas delivered anywhere.
Non-perishable. Environmental emphasis.
Chocolate centerpieces.

THE FLOWER MEADOWS
      9627 Brighton Way
      Beverly Hills, CA 90210
      310.247.6040
      Jef Hackbarth, AIFD
Areas served: National
Elegant floral design, decor and props for
weddings, corporate events, movie and TV
set dressings, theme celebrations, premiere
galas and corporate image. They have over
thirty-five years experience in dressing
movie sets and the Academy Awards'
Governors Ball. In addition to flowers, they
also provide plants and trees. Jef
Hackbarth, AIFD, is the past National
President of the American Institute of
Floral Designers, and his work has
appeared in over forty Academy Award-
winning films.

LA PREMIERE FLOWERS
      8928 W. Olympic Blvd.
      Beverly Hills, CA 90211
      310.276.4665
      Kevin Lee
Areas served: Beverly Hills, Los Angeles,
Santa Monica, Encino and surrounding
areas.
Full service florist and floral designer.
They carry full lines of party decorations,
including wedding and theme parties, and
have won both national and international
awards for floral design.

STEVE/BEVERLY HILLS
      9530 Santa Monica Blvd.
      Beverly Hills, CA 90210
      310.274.6567
      Mark Krasne
      Steve Rieman
Incredible selection of unusual tabletop
accessories, giftware, dinnerware, American
crafts, linens, settings and props. Prop
rentals for events as well as a corporate gift
registry and bridal registry.

PUBLIC RELATIONS

JOAN LUTHER & ASSOCIATES
      407 N. Maple Drive
      Bevery Hills, CA 90210
      310.273.4936
      Susan Gordon
Areas served: Los Angeles
Special event planning and coordination.
Publicity for special events. Specializing in
charities, restaurants, fundraisers, fashion
and retail.

MARCI WEINER
      450 S. Maple Drive
      Suite 204
      Beverly Hills, CA 90212
      310.276.5070
Areas served: Beverly Hills, Los Angeles,
Bel Air, Malibu, Palm Springs, San Diego
and Santa Barbara.
Columnist with many newspapers and
publications serving the affluent West Side
and Beverly Hills areas. She can provide
copy in any of her various publications as
well as celebrity acquisition services for
special events.

[Continued on next page.]

SECURITY

EXCLUSIVE PROTECTION
331 N. Rodeo Drive
Suite 3
Beverly Hills, CA 90210
310.859.8248
Jackie Fox
Areas served: Los Angeles
Armed and unarmed, uniformed or
plainclothes security officers.

TABLETOP ACCESSORIES & KITCHENWARE

LINENS ET AL
165 N. Robertson Blvd.
Beverly Hills, CA 90211
310.652.7970
Marilyn Snyder
Areas served: National
Fine tabletop accessories and linens, favors
and gift items. Engraving and
monogramming.

MUFFINS, ETC.
8950 W. Olympic Blvd.
Beverly Hills, CA 90211
310.274.5888
Janet Acquaro
Gourmet gift shop specializing in muffins
baked on the premises, gift baskets and a
large selection of gifts, cookware and
tabletop accessories. For ages two to
ninety-two. Local and UPS shipping.
Specializing in sugar-free and sugar/fat-free
muffins.

WILLIAMS-SONOMA
317 N. Beverly Drive
Beverly Hills, CA 90210
310.274.9127
An authoritative selection of the best for the
kitchen. Complete line of cookware,
bakeware, electrics, glassware, tabletop,
kitchen furniture, cookbooks, packaged
foods. Knowledgeable staff will help choose
equipment, plan parties. Most of their
merchandise is exclusive to Williams-
Sonoma.

STEVE/BEVERLY HILLS
9530 Santa Monica Blvd.
Beverly Hills, CA 90210
310.274.6567
Mark Krasne
Steve Rieman
Incredible selection of unusual tabletop
accessories, giftware, dinnerware, American
crafts, linens, settings and props. Prop
rentals for events as well as a corporate gift
registry and bridal registry.

TIFFANY & COMPANY
210 N. Rodeo Drive
Beverly Hills, CA 90210
310.273.8880
Michele Sheid
The finest in engraved invitations, favors,
accessories, stationery, bridal registry, fine
crystal and china, Tiffany flatware and gifts
for all occasions.

WINE & SPIRITS

CHEESE STORE OF BEVERLY HILLS
LA FROMAGERIE
419 N. Beverly Drive
Beverly Hills, CA 90210
310.278.2855
800.547.1515
Areas served: National
One of the largest selection of cheese,
catering, wines and gourmet products.
Custom-designed
baskets. Delivery anywhere.

THE WINE MERCHANT
9701 Santa Monica Blvd.
Beverly Hills, CA 90210
310.278.7322
Lucille Dash
Areas served: Los Angeles County
One of the finest purveyors of wines and
spirits. Their staff of wine experts and
consultants are ready to serve all needs.
They offer delivery, gift wrap, custom gift
baskets, a huge underground wine locker
facility, a unique wine of the month club by
mail, wine classes, tastings and dinners.

LOS ANGELES

AUDIOVISUAL & TECHNICAL SERVICES

ACADEMY TENT AND CANVAS, INC.
2910 S. Alameda Street
Los Angeles, CA 90058
213.234.4060
800.228.3687 (inside CA)
800.222.4535 (outside CA)
Maury Rice
Areas served: National
Provide complete facility hospitality
equipment for private, commercial,
institutional, and corporate hospitality
events, including tents, flooring, ground
covering, staging, lighting, heating, air
conditioning, and power. Founded 1981.

EVENT TECHNICAL SERVICES, INC.
6600 Bandini Blvd.
City of Commerce, CA 90040
800.521.8368
Chris Coe
Areas served: National
State licensed contractor. Portable
restrooms, temporary plumbing,
generators, power distribution, platforms,
stages, portable wood floors, air
conditioning, heating, pool scaffolds.
Specializing in outdoor events.

KUSHNER AND ASSOCIATES
1104 S. Robertson Blvd.
Los Angeles, CA 90035
310.274.8819
Linda Kushner
Areas served: Southern California
Corporate event, meeting and full service
destination management company. Handle
transportation, sight seeing, companion
programs, sports and special events, music,
novelty entertainment, celebrity
acquisition, registration and hospitality
staff. Theme parties and technical support.

McCUNE AUDIO VISUAL
1562 Embassy Street
Anaheim, CA 92802
714.523.7650
Areas served: International
Complete audiovisual services, sound
systems, videos, multi-media, etc. for
corporate events, meetings and conventions.

PARTY PLANNERS WEST, INC.
4141 Glencoe Avenue
Building C
Marina Del Rey, CA 90292
310.305.1000
Patricia Ryan
Robyn Leuthe
Areas served: National
Full service corporate event planning
company providing innovative concept
development, in-house production
department, set and lighting design, theme
parties, in-house floral department, menu
development and coordination with
caterers, entertainment bookings,
audiovisual coordination, technical and
special effects. Customized events to client's
specific needs. Named fifteenth largest
woman owned business in Los Angeles
County by the *Los Angeles Business
Journal*. Named in *Inc. Magazine's* Top
500 Private Corporations.

BALLOONS

AAH's
1083-1087 Broxton Avenue
Westwood, CA 90024
310.824.1688

3223 Wilshire Blvd.
Santa Monica, CA 90403
310.829.1807

14548 Ventura Blvd.
Sherman Oaks, CA 91403
818.907.0300
Jack Sing
Lesley Chapman
Party supplies, gift wrap, balloons,
novelties, unusual gifts.

BALLOONS BY MAGIC WORLD
10122 Topanga Canyon Blvd.
Chatsworth, CA 91311
818.700.8100
Areas served: Greater Los Angeles area
Balloons, helium tank rentals, paper
supplies, balloon decorating (small & large),
costumes, magic themes. Twenty years in
business. Duplicated Brooklyn Bridge for
Paramount Studios with balloons.

BALLOONS BY TIC-TOCK
1601-1/2 N. La Brea Avenue
Los Angeles, CA 90028
213.874.3034
Eddie Zaratsian
Areas served: National
Elegant balloon decorations for events and parties. Custom concept, design and production. Uses 100% biodegradable balloons. Winner of several awards including Best Sculpture.

BALLOONS TO REMEMBER
18504 Erwin Street
Suite 24
Reseda, CA 91335
818.342.0833
Bill Beckett
Bernice Beckett
Areas served: Southern California
Complete custom balloon decorating for weddings, Bar/Bat Mitzvahs, conventions, trade shows, parties, etc. Award winning custom made centerpieces. Four years in business. Specialty decorating, such as balloon murals and sculptures. Complete theme decorating.

CALIFORNIA TOY TIME BALLOONS
554 W. Seventh Street
Suite 4
Los Angeles, CA 90014
310.548.1234
Janice Pusateri
Areas served: California
Custom balloon printing for advertising, weddings, birthdays, etc.

PARTY MANIA
818.609.8633
Linda Drew
Areas served: Los Angeles
Custom decorations to fit any event. Balloon decorations, sculptures, arches, prop centerpieces, theme related prop rental, gift deliveries, costume deliveries, invitations. Balloon decorations to fit any budget. Member of the National Association of Balloon Artists for five years.

PARTY WORLD
19450 Business Center Drive
Northridge, CA 91324
818.993.3033

2011 Hollywood Way
Burbank, CA 91505
818.846.6202

1754 Moorpark Road
Thousand Oaks, CA 91360
805.496.6611

19816 Ventura Blvd.
Woodland Hills, CA 91364
818.716.1266

11910 W. Pico Blvd.
West Los Angeles, CA 90064
310.473.8822

17843 Colima Road
City of Industry, CA 91748
818.810.8877

18681 Main Street
Huntington Beach, CA 92648
714.841.2999

25375 Crenshaw Blvd.
Torrance, CA 90505
310.530.0566

5509 Woodruff Avenue
Lakewood, CA 90713
310.925.9777

1521 S. Harbor Blvd.
Fullterton, CA 92632
714.526.3855

25410 Marguerite Pkwy.
Mission Viejo, CA 92691
714.768.3850

1026 W. Covina Pkwy.
West Covina, CA 91790
818.813.0039

1060 Commerce Center Drive
Lancaster, CA 93534
805.940.7079

5840 Sepulveda Blvd.
Van Nuys, CA 91411
818.909.0799

500 W. Broadway
Glendale, CA 91204
818.241.6464

3404 E. Chapman
Orange, CA 92669
714.633.6693

LOS ANGELES

PARTY WORLD (CONTINUED)
2011 Via del Norte
Oxnard, CA 93030
805.485.0714

349 S. Mountain
Upland CA 91786
714.946.8090

3675 E. Colorado Blvd.
Pasadena, CA 91107
818.796.8022

3480 La Sierra
Riverside, CA 92503
714.687.7734
Stanley Tauber
One-stop center for all your party needs at
20 - 50% discount.

STREAMERS
North County Fair
272 E. Via Rancho Pkwy.
Suite 463
Escondido, CA 92025
619.737.8408

Main Place
2800 N. Main Street
Space 284
Santa Ana, CA 92701
714.647.1356

Sherman Oaks Fashion Square
14006 Riverside Drive
Space 116
Sherman Oaks, CA 91423
818.784.8724

284 Del Amo Fashion Center
Torrance, CA 90503
213.542.3566
One-stop shopping for party supplies,
invitations, balloons, paper supplies,
imprinting, machine calligraphy,
decorations.

BOOKS

BRISTOL FARMS COOK'N'THINGS GOURMET COOKWARE STORE
606 Fair Oaks Avenue
South Pasadena, CA 91030
818.441.5588
David Gronsky
Areas served: San Gabriel Valley, Los
Angeles County, San Fernando Valley
Complete selection of the finest gourmet
cookware and accessories, fine china and
stemware, linens, cookbook library. On-
going demonstrations of the latest in
gourmet cookware, guest appearances of
cookbook authors, professional cooking
school on premises.

THE COOK'S LIBRARY
8373 W. Third Street
Los Angeles, CA 90048
213.655.3141
Ellen Rose
Areas served: International
Culinary bookstore with over 3500 titles.
Everything from how to put on a bake sale,
to a party for thousands.

WILLIAMS-SONOMA
317 N. Beverly Drive
Beverly Hills, CA 90210
310.274.9127

Beverly Center
131 N. LaCienega Blvd.
Los Angeles, CA 90048
310.652.9117

The Commons
146 S. Lake Avenue
Pasadena, CA 91101
818.795.5045

273 Promenade
Woodland Hills, CA 91367
818.887.4355

La Cumbre Place
3835 State Street
Santa Barbara, CA 93105
805.563.0767

14006 Riverside Drive
Sherman Oaks, CA 91423
818.981.1044

1112 Glendale Galleria
Glendale, CA 91210
818.241.0154

South Coast Plaza
3333 S. Bristol Street
Costa Mesa, CA 92626
714.751.1166

Main Place
2800 N. Main Street
Suite 552
Santa Ana, CA 92701
714.542.8852

The Shops at Palos Verdes
550 Deep Valley Drive
Rolling Hills Estates, CA 90274
310.541.9545

1016 Brea Mall
Brea, CA 92621
714.256.9301

An authoritative selection of the best for the kitchen. Complete line of cookware, bakeware, electrics, glassware, tabletop, kitchen furniture, cookbooks, packaged foods. Knowledgeable staff will help choose equipment, plan parties. Most merchandise is exclusive to Williams-Sonoma.

CAKES & BAKED GOODS

BLACK FOREST BAKERY AND CAFE OF DANA POINT
32515 Golden Lantern
Suite A
Dana Point, CA 92629
714.240.7100
Evi Rosen
Areas served: Orange County
Customized cakes and confections for all special events. Second location in Lake Forest, CA.

BRISTOL FARMS SPECIALTY FOOD MARKET
837 Silver Spur Road
Rolling Hills, CA 90274
310.541.9157
Tom Lo Grande

606 Fair Oaks Avenue
South Pasadena, CA 91030
818.441.5450

David Gronsky

1570 Rosecrans Blvd.
Manhattan Beach, CA 90266
310.643.5229
Bruce Mannis
Areas served: South Bay, West Side, Los Angeles County, San Gabriel Valley, parts of Orange County
Full service deli, bakery, meat departments. One of the largest selections of fresh produce in Southern California, restaurant facility, over 200 different imported cheeses, fresh sushi bar, full service catering. Wine tasting seminars, imported gourmet specialty grocery items, large selection of domestic and imported wines, on-going free cooking classes. Voted in 1991-92 as number one supermarket chain in the United States by *Supermarket News*, a national publication. Voted Best of Pasadena by *The Pasadena Weekly* in deli, produce, meat departments for five consecutive years.

CAKE AND ART
8709 Santa Monica Blvd.
Santa Monica, CA 90404
310.657.8694
Glenn Von Kicher
Painted and sculptured cakes. Write-ups in major magazines. Glenn Von Kicher has been interviewed on thirty talk shows in fifteen years and on the cover of *Life Magazine*, August 1988 with cover credit. Cake designs on camera in major films, TV shows and commercials for fifteen years.

THE CAKE PLACE
2221 S. Barry Avenue
Los Angeles, CA 90064
310.479.7783
Areas served: Los Angeles County
Retail and wholesale bakery providing dessert cakes, decorated cakes, wedding cakes and artwork. Paintings and sculptures done with cakes. Featured in *Los Angeles Magazine*, Best Kept Secret.

[Continued on next page.]

LOS ANGELES

CRYSTAL CAKE TOPS
>818.447.3021
>714.599.0627
>Bill Barton

Areas served: Southern California
Over 250 designs. Largest selection of
crystal cake tops on the West Coast.
Individually handmade crystals, made in
Southern California. Crystal cake tops are
annealed, fired inside a furnace, to add
extra strength and everlasting beauty.
Becomes a family heirloom and keepsake.
Crystal cake tops for all occasions:
weddings, shower gifts, anniversaries, etc.

MISS GRACE LEMON CAKE CO.
>16571 Ventura Blvd.
>Encino, CA 91436
>818.885.1987
>Mindy Moss

>422 N. Canon Drive
>Beverly Hills, CA 90210
>310.281.8096
>800.367.2253 (mail order)
>Mindy Moss

Areas served: Los Angeles, West Side,
Valley. Ship mail order anywhere.
Highest quality baked goods made
exclusively from scratch. Known for their
lemon cake. Wedding cakes, decorated
cakes for all occasions, gift baskets.

MUFFINS, ETC.
>12634 Ventura Blvd.
>Studio City, CA 91604
>818.762.6343
>Janet Acquaro

Areas served: Local and UPS shipping
Meal size and mini muffins baked daily on
premises, gourmet coffee, gift baskets.
Sugar free and sugar/fat free muffins a
specialty. Awarded Studio City Business of
the Month.

CALLIGRAPHY
AMD GRAPHICS
>Los Angeles (South Bay)
>310.318.9378

>Orange County
>714.774.3318
>Annette Daoust

Calligraphic and graphic services.
Custom-designed invitations. Hand lettered
envelopes, place cards, menu cards, name
tags. Computer-generated event programs,
wedding booklets, invitations. Stationery,
business cards and logos. Color laser
printing. Presentation materials.

ANN FIEDLER CREATIONS
>10544 W. Pico Blvd.
>Los Angeles, CA 90064
>310.838.1857
>Ann Fiedler

Areas served: International
Fine quality invitations, calligraphy,
personalized gifts, place cards, accessories
for corporate and charity invites. Unique
custom designs with a creative flair at every
price. One of the largest retailers of
invitations in the United States with a huge
selection of catalogues.

CALLIGRAPHY BY MARY LOU
>818.355.4639
>Mary Lou Barton-Boner

Areas served: Southern California
Artistic writing for all occasions. Serving
discriminating brides and clientele
throughout Los Angeles and Orange
County. Unique and custom designs.
Place cards, weddings, envelope addressing,
shower invitations, announcements, poems,
invitations, reception or thank you cards,
parties, marriage certificates,
award/achievement certificates.

KAREN JEWELL FINE INVITATIONS
>10568 -1/2 Ayres Avenue
>Los Angeles, CA 90064
>310.558.4938
>Karen Jewell

Areas served: United States, Japan
Personalized wedding counsel with each
invite order, hand done calligraphy, rush
orders, foreign languages. Specialize in
custom and catalogue, 16 different hand

calligraphy styles; menus, programs, signage. Clients include: Fred Hayman, Lee Radziwill, Giorgio, Marvin Davis.

NOTEWORTHY
Beverly Center
131 N. LaCienega Blvd.
Los Angeles, CA 90048
310.652.3775
Maureen Malone
Invitations, laser printing and calligraphy.

PURE POETRY
P.O. Box 3592
Granada Hills, CA 91394
818.360.0583
Gloria Nash
Areas served: San Fernando Valley area
Custom made and catalogue invitations, weddings at twenty-five percent off, announcements, accessories, calligraphy.

RHYMES AND DESIGNS
1838 S. Robertson Blvd.
Los Angeles, CA 90035
310.838.7755
Sandra Gutterman
Areas served: Greater Los Angeles
Party coordinator, florist, custom-designed and catalogue invitations, calligraphy services, custom escort cards, table numbers, complete room decoration, centerpieces, lighting, etc. Past clients include Michelle Lee, Vidal Sassoon, Kaufman & Broad, Bob Dylan, Falcon Cable, Germaine Jackson.

SCRIBBLES
714.283.4568
Annette Ertel
Areas served: Southern California
Calligraphy specialists for all printed party supplies. Many different styles and colors available. Invitations, seating cards, weddings, programs, certificates.

STREAMERS
North County Fair
272 E. Via Rancho Pkwy.
Suite 463
Escondido, CA 92025
619.737.8408

Main Place
2800 N. Main Street

Space 284
Santa Ana, CA 92701
714.647.1356

Sherman Oaks Fashion Square
14006 Riverside Drive
Space 116
Sherman Oaks, CA 91423
818.784.8724

284 Del Amo Fashion Center
Torrance, CA 90503
213.542.3566
One-stop shopping for party supplies, invitations, balloons, paper supplies, imprinting, machine calligraphy, decorations.

WILLIAM ERNEST BROWN
South Coast Plaza
3333 S. Bristol Street
Costa Mesa, CA 92626
714.540.2265

The Market Place
6529 E. Pacific Coast Hwy.
Long Beach, CA 90803
310.598.1725
Custom-designed and catalogue invitations, seating charts, accessories, place cards and party supplies for all special events. They also provide calligraphy services. Known for their high quality products and special services. Clients all over the United States and Europe.

WORDSTYLE
714.838.4969
Miriam Prell
Areas served: Southern California
Calligraphy for all occasions. Name tags, custom maps, unique custom invitations, place cards, menu cards, programs, certificates. Staff includes writers, designers and graphic specialists.

[Continued on next page.]

CATERING

ALONG CAME MARY
5265 W. Pico Blvd.
Los Angeles, CA 90019
213.931.9082
Mary Micucci
Areas served: Southern California
Complete party planning, event
coordinating and gourmet food from Los
Angeles's finest caterer. Over seventeen
years experience. Named Top Business
Woman by the *LA Business Journal* 1992.

AMBROSIA
1717 Stewart Street
Santa Monica, CA 90404
310.453.7007
David Corwin
Areas served: Catering: California,
Nevada, Colorado, Arizona
Provide catering, event planning and
production. Ultra high-end quality catering
combined with detail oriented coordination.
Environmentally and socially conscious
planning. Original themes. Forty full-time
employees. Eight event producers and
party coordinators. Received three Gala
Awards, seven nominations. Catered the
sixtieth and sixty-first Academy Awards
Governor's Ball, the opening of the Nixon
Library, countless celebrities' weddings,
and private functions for movers and
shakers of the entertainment and corporate
worlds.

BRISTOL FARMS CATERING
837 Silver Spur Road
Rolling Hills, CA 90274
310.544.2155
Florence Bell

606 Fair Oaks Avenue
South Pasadena, CA 91030
818.441.5450
Eric Chan

1570 Rosecrans Blvd.
Manhattan Beach, CA 90266
310.643.5229
Susie Bratton
Areas served: South Bay, Los Angeles
County, San Gabriel Valley, San Fernando
Valley, parts of Orange County

Menu items from breakfast, sandwiches,
salads, entrees, side dishes, hors d'oeuvres,
platters, gourmet picnics, elegant tea
menus, and party bars. Specialize in
gourmet picnics, menu and fresh food
prepared to specification. Arrangements
for service personnel, beverages, valet
parking, rentals, music and flowers
available upon request.

CALIFORNIA CELEBRATIONS
4051 Glencoe Avenue
Suite 7
Marina Del Rey, CA 90292
310.305.8849
David Stephens
Areas served: Southern California and
beyond
Custom catering, event planning, decor,
locations, specialty lighting, any or all
services needed for a special event.
Specialize in custom menus of fine quality
foods cooked fresh at party site, stylized
elegant food presentations and settings,
theme events, wedding coordination, social
and corporate buffets, stations and seated
dinners. National award winning in-house
art director. National *Special Events
Magazine* awards nominee.

CATERED OCCASIONS
920 Venice Blvd.
Suite 106
Venice, CA 90291
310.821.6864
Marilyn Caldwell
Areas served: Southern California
Catering and party planning. Specialize in
Creole/Cajun, Mexican, Italian, barbecue,
cuisine of the 90's, themes, corporate.

CHASEN'S
9039 Beverly Blvd.
W. Hollywood, CA 90048
310.271.2168
Ronnie Clint
Areas served: International
Complete catering both off the premises and
at the restaurant. Catered the opening of
the two presidential libraries (Reagan &
Nixon). Served five presidents and their
families. Holiday Award from
Distinguished Restaurants of North
America. Restaurant Writers Award.

Serving only the finest cuisine for over fifty-six years.

CHEZ MELANGE
1716 Pacific Coast Hwy.
Redondo Beach, CA 90277
310.540.1222
Michael Franks

Areas served: South Bay, Orange County, Los Angeles County
Banquet rooms, off-premise catering, full service event management. Specialize in gourmet wine dinners, ethnic menus, first class service. Distinctions include Top 100 Restaurant by Epicurean Rendezvous, Top 50 Restaurant in *Zagat* Guide. Owners voted South Bay Citizens of the Year.

CHIN CHIN
13455 Maxella Avenue
Marina Del Rey, CA 90292
310.823.6948
Judy Caspe

Areas served: Los Angeles
Full service catering and banquet facility. Four locations throughout LA. Chinese food prepared fresh and healthful. Dim Sum, tabletop wok cooking, chocolate dipped fortune cookies with personalized messages.

THE DEPOT
1250 Cabrillo Avenue
Torrance, CA 90501
310.787.7501
Michael Shafer

Areas served: South Bay, Los Angeles, Orange County
Banquet facilities and catering. Wide selection of micro-brewery beers. Amazingly creative menu.

GAI KLASS CATERING/ GREAT FOOD AND COMPANY
10335 W. Jefferson Blvd.
Culver City, CA 90232
310.559.6777
Gai Klass

Areas served: Southern California
High-end, gourmet, off-premises, full service catering and party coordination. To-go service for corporate and home. Superior quality in food with a wide repertoire of dishes, integrity and excellence in service, and simply elegant decor with Gai Klass supervising every aspect. Served some of the country's most influential individuals and corporations.

GELSON'S
16450 Ventura Blvd.
Encino, CA 91436
818.906.5780
Greg Hansen

4738 Laurel Canyon Blvd.
N. Hollywood, CA 91607
818.906.5743
Bill Thompson

10250 Santa Monica Blvd.
Los Angeles, CA 90067
310.906.5793
Tim Redmond

5500 Reseda Blvd.
Tarzana, CA 91356
818.906.5752
Mike Lee

1660 San Miguel Drive
Newport Beach, Ca 92660
714.906.5798
Frank Spielberger

15424 Sunset Blvd.
Pacific Palisades, CA 90272
310.906.5795
Jim McCurry

2734 Townsgate Road
Westlake Village, CA 91361
818.906.5790
John Austin

13455 Maxella Avenue
Marina Del Rey, CA 90292
310.906.5771
Rick Imamura

Catering menu contains a broad range of exquisitely prepared foods from poached salmon and cheese and fruit to Crudite and lox and cream cheese. Platters are attractively decorated with hand-carved fruit or vegetable garnishes. Each dish is prepared completely from scratch by Gelson's own chefs. Platter sizes range from 13" to 18". Forty-eight hours notice is preferred.

[Continued on next page.]

LOS ANGELES

GLADSTONE'S 4 FISH
17300 Pacific Coast Hwy.
Pacific Palisades, CA 90272
310.573.0212
Steve Herbert
An LA institution on the ocean. Parties can be held right on the beach for breakfast, lunch, dinner and anytime. Seafood is their specialty, but Mexican, Chinese, or anything can be prepared. Full service catering facility as well. Small dining room seats twenty-five people. Beach available for any size party.

THE GOLDEN TRUFFLE
1767 Newport Blvd.
Costa Mesa, CA 92627
714.645.9858
Louis Manginelli
Areas served: South Los Angeles County, Orange County
Pick-up/drop-off/full service and off-premise catering. Specializing in French-Caribbean cuisine. Distinctions include *Epicurean Rendezvous* 1988-1991, Southern California Restaurant Writers - Gold, 1987 - 1991, DRNA - 1991.

JERRY'S FAMOUS DELI
12655 Ventura Blvd.
Studio City, CA 91604
818.980.4245

16650 Ventura Blvd.
Encino, CA 91436
818.906.1800

13181 Mindanao Way
Marina Del Rey, CA 90292
310.821.6626
Catering, delivery, twenty-four hour service. Party platters, salad trays, desserts.

LA CUISINE
2869 S. Robertson Blvd.
Los Angeles, CA 90034
310.837.8445
Tom Byrne
Full service catering for all occasions.

MASTROIANNI'S/JAY'S CATERING
10581 Garden Grove Blvd.
Garden Grove, CA 92643

714.636.6045
800.585.6045
Norman Meyer
Areas served: Los Angeles, Orange, San Diego, Riverside, Santa Barbara Counties
Catering, full scale props, rentals, flowers, bakery, linens, entertainment.

MISTO CAFFE/CHEZ ALLEZ
24558 Hawthorne Blvd.
Torrance, CA 90505
310.375.3608
Nadia
Areas served: South Bay, Orange County, Los Angeles
Baskets, drop-off buffets, gourmet to-go, full service catering, bakery on site.

MONTANA MERCANTILE
1500 Montana Avenue
Santa Monica, CA 90403
310.451.1418
Rachel Dourec
Areas served: Los Angeles and surrounding communities
Full service catering for private parties as well as prepared foods for meals to take home on a daily basis. For those who love to cook, but hate to waste the time involved in all of the tedious slicing, dicing, cutting and chopping, they provide all of the raw ingredients necessary to prepare a full meal, just assemble them to enjoy a fabulous home-cooked meal.

MORE THAN A MOUTHFUL, CATERING INC.
743 S. Lucerne Blvd.
Los Angeles, CA 90005
213.937.6345
Barry Colman
Areas served: Southern California, travel to Northern California, Nevada, East Coast
Full service event planners including food, decor, rentals, entertainment, banquet facilities for 1000 guests. Specialize in over-abundance of food, mind boggling displays, into the visuals, catering to fantasies. All graduates of the Culinary Institute of America.

LOS ANGELES

NEW YORK FOOD COMPANY
1151 Aviation Blvd.
Hermosa Beach, CA 90254
310.376.6929
Jim Wharton
Areas served: Los Angeles and Orange
Counties with special emphasis on the South
Bay area
Customized catering services, menu
development, staffing, event production,
wedding planning, bartending service,
location assistance. Fourteen years
experience, creative chefs, beautiful
presentation, realistic pricing.

THE OMELETTE KING
P.O. Box 614
Van Nuys, CA 91408
818.780.9943
818.376.1557
John Vernon
Areas served: Los Angeles, Orange,
Ventura Counties
Specialize in omelette brunches, Belgian
waffles, crepes. Offer limited dinner
menus. Formerly owned Chez Vernon, top
rated in *Mobil Travel Guide of Oklahoma*.
Formerly Conseille Culinier, Chaine Des
Rotisseurs, Baillage d'Oklahoma.

RICK ROYCE GOURMET BBQ CATERING
15433 Hart Street
Van Nuys, CA 91406
818.989.9988
Rick Royce
Areas served: Los Angeles, San Fernando
Valley, Ventura, San Diego, Palm Springs,
Orange County
Full service catering specializing in
barbecue. First place "Best Baby Back
Ribs in America" in the National Rib Cook-
off. KABC Talk Radio/Elmer Dills and
Merrill Shindler, first annual BBQ Taste-off
Contest.

ROCOCO, INC.
6734 Valjean Avenue
Van Nuys, CA 91406
818.909.0990
Ray Henderson
Cathee Hickok
Areas served: West Coast from San Diego
to Santa Barbara

Full service caterers specializing in elegant
social affairs, public relations entertaining,
charity benefits and entertainment industry
parties and premiers. Food, bar, decor,
music, parking, etc.

SOMEONE'S IN THE KITCHEN
5973 Reseda Blvd.
Tarzana, CA 91356
818.343.5151
Joann Roth, President
Areas served: Los Angeles, Orange,
Ventura Counties
Full service catering and customized event
planning from 2 - 10,000 guests.
Personalized menus, beautiful presentation
and excellent staff for all occasions.
Distinctions include Mayor's Certificate of
Appreciation, Women in Business
Entrepreneurial Excellence, Woman of the
Year, Tarzana Chamber of Commerce,
County of Los Angeles Commendations for
Dedicated Service to the Affairs of the
Community. Joann Roth is well-known for
her generous support of civic and charitable
activities, which includes the Institute for
Cancer and Blood Research, the LA
Childcare and Development Council, the
Sunshine Mission and the Fred Jordan
Mission.

SPECIAL EVENTS
8736 Canby Avenue
Northridge, CA 91325
818.775.4525
Marcia Smart
Areas served: Los Angeles, Ventura,
Riverside, Orange Counties
Full event production, catering, rentals,
entertainment, decor, themes. All types of
corporate events, picnics, open houses, VIP
receptions, parties. Established in 1980.
Produced world's largest company picnic
for 25,000 guests.

SPECIALTY CATERING
2450 White Road
Irvine, CA 92714
800.675.9629
Marc Mushkin
Areas served: Southern California
Full service catering, rentals, flowers,
entertainers. Specialize in Southwestern
and Mexican food.

LOS ANGELES

⚜ BAR CATERING

BLACK TIE EVENT SERVICES
1454 Third Street Promenade
Suite 212
Santa Monica, CA 90401
310.576.1800
Stephen Plache
Areas served: Southern California
Specialize in custom bar catering, offering
an extensive range of bar menus for both
host and no-host service. Receptions,
premieres, holiday celebrations, weddings,
fund raisers, birthdays and much more.

DUKE OF BOURBON
20908 Roscoe Blvd.
Canoga Park, CA 91304
818.341.1234
David Breitstein
Ron Breitstein
Areas served: San Fernando Valley,
Beverly Hills, West Los Angeles, Malibu,
Westlake Village, Thousand Oaks, Agoura
Wine tasting seminars, executive wine
seminars, party and event planning with
delivery of wine, spirits, beer, wine
collecting consultation, speakers, gift
baskets, newsletter. Specialize in
personalized service. Commendations from
City and County of Los Angeles for twenty-
five years of successful business. Chosen by
The Wine Spectator and *Market Watch* as
one of top twelve wine and spirits shops in
America for 1990. *Beverage Dynamics*
Retailer of the Year 1991.

FROZEN DRINKS UNLIMITED
9923 Santa Monica Blvd.
Suite 339
Beverly Hills, CA 90212
310.312.0707
714.222.0402
Robert Weinburg
Areas served: Los Angeles, Orange County
Margueritas, bar catering and machine
rentals. Parties and events from 20 to
20,000 people. Articles in *LA Magazine* and
Hollywood Reporter.

RED CARPET WINE & SPIRITS MERCHANT
400 E. Glenoaks Blvd.
Glendale, CA 91207
818.247.5544
David Dobbs

Steve Fox
Russell Shin
Areas served: Los Angeles County
Full line beverage catering, wine tasting,
personalized gift baskets, bartending.
Largest gift basket selection. In-store wine
tasting and classes. Best Gift Basket
"Liquors," Kylex Award from New York.
Deliver locally. Ship nationwide.

THE WINE RESERVE
929 S. Brand
Glendale, CA 91204
818.500.8400
Barry Herbst
Areas served: California
Tastings, seminars, outside catering, dining
facilities, wine storage (temperature
controlled). Boutique wineries, eclectic
selection of imported wines, well known
California brands.

⚜ PRIVATE CHEFS

EMILY MILLER
213.460.4908
Areas served: Los Angeles and surrounding
areas
Private chef for small parties from 2-100.
Paris trained chef from La Varenne.
Specializing in French and California
cuisine.

EPICUREAN CONNECTION
8759 Melrose Avenue
Los Angeles, CA 90069
310.659.5990
Shelley Janson
Areas served: Greater Los Angeles
Chef placement in private homes only. No
catering or one time dinners.

MARVIN UGARTE
11933 Ayres Avenue
Suite 2
W. Los Angeles, CA 90064
310.477.2218
Private chef catering small dinners for eight
to twelve people.

CELEBRITY ACQUISITION

DAMON BROOKS ASSOCIATES
1680 N. Vine Street
Suite 910
Hollywood, CA 90028
213.465.3400
Marc Goldman
Areas served: National
Coordination of celebrity involvement with
special events. Tennis, golf, and related
sporting events. Speaking, entertainment,
auction items and personal appearances.
Recognized by California Meetings, Western
Association News, Affordable Meetings,
International Festivals Association,
American Society of Association Executives.

KUSHNER AND ASSOCIATES
1104 S. Robertson Blvd.
Los Angeles, CA 90035
310.274.8819
Linda Kushner
Areas served: Southern California
Corporate event, meeting and full service
destination management company. Handle
transportation, sight seeing, companion
programs, sports and special events, music,
novelty entertainment, celebrity
acquisition, registration and hospitality
staff. Theme parties and technical support.

MIKE VACCARO PRODUCTIONS, INC.
3848-A Atlantic Avenue
Suite 4
Long Beach, CA 90807
310.424.4958
Mike Vaccaro
Areas served: International
Music, entertainment, theme parties, party
planning, site selection, celebrity
entertainment, etc.

WEST COAST COMEDY CONTACT
11362 Reagan Street
Los Alamitos, CA 90720
310.431.6122
Mariana Tilton
Areas served: Southern California
Top notch entertainers, name and novelty
acts, comics, magicians and clowns for
parties, hotels and roasts.

CHOCOLATES & CONFECTIONS

ATELIER DE CHOCOLAT
Malibu Country Mart
3835 Cross Creek Road
Suite 15
Malibu, CA 90265
310.456.0201
Mark Gaffney

442 E. Main Street
Ventura, CA 93001
805.648.5937

6360 Canoga Avenue
Woodland Hills, CA 91367
818.595.1000
European chocolate boutique featuring gift
boxed chocolates with ribbons and roses,
hand-crafted chocolate truffles, sculptured
and traditional chocolates and confections.

COMPARTE'S OF CALIFORNIA
925 Montana Avenue
Santa Monica, CA 90403
310.395.2297
Jill Barker
Areas served: Courier service available for
Los Angeles area, UPS available anywhere
in US.
Hand dipped chocolates, stuffed fruits
(individually wrapped dried fruit with
nuts), gift tins, custom gift baskets, molded
chocolates, candies. Examples of party
items: molded chocolate basket with
chocolate strawberries and raspberries or
assorted truffles, individual boxes (with 2
chocolates) with names to be used as place
cards, chocolates with decorations (holiday,
floral), theme gifts (chocolate tennis racket
or golf balls). Articles in *Bon Apetit*,
English toffee called "Best in Town" *Los
Angeles Magazine*.

DECADENCE FINE CHOCOLATES
24690 Via Buena Suerte
Yorba Linda, CA 92687
714.692.8408
Becky Repic
Areas served: South California
Custom-designed chocolates for special
occasions, holiday parties, corporate
chocolate logos, business cards, favors, gift
baskets.

LOS ANGELES

GODIVA CHOCOLATIER
South Coast Plaza
Costa Mesa
714.556.9055

Mainplace Mall
714.835.4694

Brea Mall
714.671.0793

Los Angeles Area
Beverly Center
213.651.0697

Sherman Oaks
Fashion Square
818.788.4065

Century City
213.277.6154

Citicorp Plaza
213.624.8923

Glendale Galleria
818.545.7282

Pasadena
380 S. Lake Avenue
Suite 7
818.795.1803
World renowned chocolatier. Belgium-style chocolates, gift baskets and party favors.

PSEUDIOS ARTISTIC EDIBLES
2117 Glendale Galleria
Glendale, CA 91210
818.240.4222
Jeanne Goraleski
Areas served: National
Sculptured chocolates, nuts, gourmet food gifts, sugar free and novelty candy.

ULTIMATE NUT & CANDY CO.
11849 Ventura Blvd.
Studio City, CA 91604
818.766.5259
Jerry Donath
Areas served: Southern California
Hand-dipped highest quality chocolates. All natural and no artificial preservatives. Named Best in Southern California by *MGM Grand Air Magazine*. Shipping and delivery.

CLASSES & SEMINARS

THE BILTMORE HOTEL
506 S. Grand Avenue
Los Angeles, CA 90071
213.624.1011
Randy Villareal
Cooking classes, banquet rooms, catering services, children's etiquette classes. Four star hotel and Bernard's restaurant.

BRISTOL FARMS COOK'N'THINGS PROFESSIONAL COOKING SCHOOL
606 Fair Oaks Avenue
South Pasadena, CA 91030
818.441.5588
Judi Munoz-Flores
Professional classes from the top culinary experts in the United States and abroad. Classes are offered four to five nights per week and each class is three hours long. Demonstration with thirty person limit and participation classes with sixteen person limit. Cost is $45 to $75 per class. Schedule of classes available upon request. Voted Number One Cooking School in Southern California by *Los Angeles Magazine*. Member of the International Association of Culinary Professionals.

CULINARY ADVENTURES
23908 DeVilla Way
Malibu, CA 90265
310.456.2484
Doris Felts
Areas served: San Diego to Santa Barbara
Private custom planned cooking lessons, including birthday parties, showers for brides-to-be, shop and cook parties and cooking classes for all levels. Events are held in clients' homes. National third place winner in OTC recipe contest.

DUKE OF BOURBON
20908 Roscoe Blvd.
Canoga Park, CA 91304
818.341.1234
David Breitstein
Ron Breitstein
Areas served: San Fernando Valley, Beverly Hills, West Los Angeles, Malibu, Westlake Village, Thousand Oaks, Agoura
Wine tasting seminars, executive wine seminars, party and event planning with

delivery of wine, spirits, beer, wine collecting consultation, speakers, gift baskets, newsletter. Specialize in personalized service. Commendations from City and County of Los Angeles for twenty-five years of successful business. Chosen by *The Wine Spectator* and *Market Watch* as one of top twelve wine and spirits shops in America for 1990. *Beverage Dynamics* Retailer of the Year 1991.

EPICUREAN
8759 Melrose Avenue
Los Angeles, CA 90069
310.659.5990
Shelley Janson

Professional cooking classes, chef training programs, one night seminars at popular restaurants, as well as theme and baking classes. Provide instruction for all levels and also have a chef placement service. Call for brochure on upcoming seminars.

EVERY WOMAN'S VILLAGE
5650 Sepulveda Blvd.
Van Nuys, CA 91411
818.787.5100
Anita Mathews

Cooking and entertaining classes.

MONTANA MERCANTILE
1500 Montana Avenue
Santa Monica, CA 90403
310.451.1418
Rachel Dourec

Diverse curriculum of cooking classes featuring many different ethnic and American regional cuisines. Both participation workshops and demonstration classes are available. Teachers emphasize recipes that are healthy as well as exciting and in sync with the latest innovations in modern cooking. Customize a class for special occasions and private parties. Call for a complete catalogue of the current semester's offerings.

RED CARPET WINE & SPIRITS MERCHANT
400 E. Glenoaks Blvd.
Glendale, CA 91207
818.247.5544
David Dobbs
Steve Fox

Russell Shin

Areas served: Los Angeles County
Full line beverage catering, wine tasting, personalized gift baskets, bartending. Largest gift basket selection. In-store wine tasting and classes. Best Gift Basket "Liquors," Kylex Award from New York. Deliver locally. Ship nationwide.

THE R.S.V.P. INSTITUTE OF ETIQUETTE
301 E. Fourth Street
Ontario, CA 91764
714.983.1942
Maura Graber

Courses and seminars teaching basic table manners and table settings, how to eat unusual and difficult foods, what to do with finger bowls, seating arrangements, basic social graces. Adult seminars held in the evening, complete with seven course dinner and course book. Inland Empire, Orange County and Southeast Los Angeles County offering children's courses for Beginner, Advanced I and Advanced II. Ontario location only for adult classes. Emphasis on social standards and etiquette for gracious living.

VILLAGE KITCHEN SHOPPE
147 N. Glendora Avenue
Glendora, CA 91740
818.914.7897

Cooking classes ranging from uncomplicated do-ahead cuisine to celebrated chefs and cookbook authors.

THE WINE RESERVE
929 S. Brand
Glendale, CA 91204
818.500.8400
Barry Herbst

Areas served: California
Tastings, seminars, outside catering, dining facilities, wine storage (temperature controlled). Boutique wineries, eclectic selection of imported wines, well known California brands.

[Continued on next page.]

COSTUMES

ADELE'S OF HOLLYWOOD
5034 Hollywood Blvd.
Los Angeles, CA 90027
213.663.2231
Theresa Saidy
Areas served: Southern California
Rentals and sales of costumes. Masquerade
and theatrical costumes and accessories.

BOOK-A-LOOK
324 N. Newport Blvd.
Newport Beach, CA 92663
714.642.9887
Kathy Flores
Areas served: National
Full service entertainment and theatrical
costume facility. Costumes for rent and
custom-created. Makeup, wig room,
alterations and hair styling available. Full
service entertainment agent for celebrity
look-alikes, variety acts, singing telegrams,
children's entertainment, magicians,
clowns, mimes, street performers.

CINEMA SECRETS, INC.
4400 Riverside Drive
Burbank, CA 91505
818.846.0579
Daniel Stein
Areas served: International
Makeup and hair supplies. Professional
makeup artists available. Costume and
Halloween supplies, theatrical supplies,
salon service, temporary tattoos. Top
Hollywood makeup artists with numerous
awards and thousands of motion picture
and TV credits.

COSTUMES BY MAGIC WORLD
10122 Topanga Canyon Blvd.
Chatsworth, CA 91311
818.700.8100
Areas served: Greater Los Angeles area,
Ship anywhere
Costumes for banquets, trade shows,
murder mysteries, balls, theme costume
weddings, promotional, etc. Hundreds of
Best Costume Awards. Thousands of
satisfied customers. Twenty years in
business.

FANTASY COSTUMES
2818 E. Imperial Hwy.
Brea, CA 92621
714.528.3350
Nicki Black
Areas served: Southern California
Over 10,000 costume rentals, makeup, wigs
and accessories. Costume, make-up and
accessories for sale.

GLENDALE COSTUMES
315 N. Brand Blvd.
Glendale, CA 91203
818.244.1161
Jeanne Reith, Costume
Coordinator & Designer
Bryan Leder, Theatrical Rentals
Robin Kissner, Masquerade
Rentals
Areas served: National
Costuming, makeup and costume
construction. Stock of 60,000 costumes.
complete costuming. All time periods,
including animal walk-abouts and novelties.
All categories. Clowns to grapes, soldiers
to gypsies, Romeo's to Draculas. Costume
coordination for theme parties, weddings,
etc. Resident designer holds Drama Critics
Circle and *Dramalogue* Awards for
Costume Design.

HAUNTED STUDIOS
6419 Hollywood Blvd.
Hollywood, CA 90028
213.465.3372
Greg
Costume rentals, wigs, makeup and
complete alteration services. Can transform
anyone into anything. Specialize in movie
glamour from the 20's - 60's and won Best
Costumer for Side by Side by Sonheim
Condide. For best results call for an
appointment.

NOBLITTS COSTUMES
12511 Burbank Blvd.
N. Hollywood, CA 91607
818.769.4737
Gloria Noblitt
Areas served: Southern California
A fantastic selection of over 4000 Halloween
costumes, retail and rentals, Sell makeup,
wigs, accessories.

LOS ANGELES

PARTY MANIA
818.609.8633
Linda Drew
Areas served: Los Angeles
Custom decorations to fit any event.
Balloon decorations, sculptures, arches,
prop centerpieces, theme related prop
rental, gift deliveries, costume deliveries,
invitations. Balloon decorations to fit any
budget. Member of the National
Association of Balloon Artists for five years.

URSULA'S COSTUMES
9069 Venice Blvd.
Los Angeles, CA 90034
310.559.8210
Ursula
Costumes for all occasions, rental and sales.

DELICACIES

BEL-AIR WINE MERCHANT
10421 Santa Monica Blvd.
W. Los Angeles, CA 90025
310.474.9518
Bob Gold
Areas served: Los Angeles, International
Old vintage wines. Fresh Russian caviar.
Full bar supplies. Delivery, shipping
worldwide.

THE BREWERY COFFEE & TEA CO.
263 Santa Monica Place
Santa Monica, CA 90401
310.393.7793
Robert Myers
Dale Myers
John Heinz
Areas served: Santa Monica, Marina Del
Rey, Palisades, Malibu, W. Los Angeles,
Brentwood, Beverly Hills
Gourmet coffee beans, loose and packaged
tea, coffee makers, espresso machines,
replacement parts, coffee and tea
accessories, collector tea pots, large
selection of mugs, cappuccino cups.
Espresso bar with fresh brewed coffee,
muffins, chocolate truffles. Gift baskets.
UPS or local free delivery with minimum
purchase. Serving Santa Monica and the
West Side since 1980.

BRISTOL FARMS SPECIALTY FOOD MARKET
837 Silver Spur Road
Rolling Hills, CA 90274
310.541.9157
Tom Lo Grande

606 Fair Oaks Avenue
South Pasadena, CA 91030
818.441.5450
David Gronsky

1570 Rosecrans Blvd.
Manhattan Beach, CA 90266
310.643.5229
Bruce Mannis
Areas served: South Bay, West Side, Los
Angeles County, San Gabriel Valley, parts
of Orange County
Full service deli, bakery, meat departments.
One of the largest selections of fresh
produce in Southern California, restaurant
facility, over 200 different imported
cheeses, fresh sushi bar, full service
catering. Wine tasting seminars, imported
gourmet specialty grocery items, large
selection of domestic and imported wines,
on-going free cooking classes. Voted in
1991-92 as number one supermarket chain
in the United States by *Supermarket News*,
a national publication. Voted Best of
Pasadena by *The Pasadena Weekly* in deli,
produce, meat departments for five
consecutive years.

COMPARTE'S OF CALIFORNIA
925 Montana Avenue
Santa Monica, CA 90403
310.395.2297
Jill Barker
Areas served: Courier service available for
Los Angeles area, UPS available anywhere
in US.
Hand-dipped chocolates, stuffed fruits
(individually wrapped dried fruit with
nuts), gift tins, custom gift baskets, molded
chocolates, candies. Examples of party
items: molded chocolate basket with chocolate
strawberries and raspberries or assorted
truffles, individual boxes (with 2 chocolates)
with names to be used as place cards,
chocolates with decorations (holiday,
floral), theme gifts (chocolate tennis racket
or golf balls). Written up in *Bon Apetit*,
English toffee called "Best in Town" *Los
Angeles Magazine*.

33

LOS ANGELES

MUFFINS, ETC.
12634 Ventura Blvd.
Studio City, CA 91604
818.762.6343
Janet Acquaro
Areas served: Local and UPS shipping
Meal size and mini muffins baked daily on
premises, gourmet coffee, gift baskets.
Sugar free and sugar/fat free muffins a
specialty. Awarded Studio City Business of
the Month.

PSEUDIOS ARTISTIC EDIBLES
2117 Glendale Galleria
Glendale, CA 91210
818.240.422
Jeanne Goraleski
Areas served: National
Sculptured chocolates, nuts, gourmet food
gifts, sugar free and novelty candy.

SAY CHEESE
2800 Hyperion Avenue
Los Angeles, CA 90027
213.665.0545
Julie Noyes
Areas served: Silverlake, Los Feliz,
Hollywood, Glendale, Delivery by
messenger anywhere
Cheese and pate trays, deli platters,
sandwich trays, gift baskets, catering.
Specialize in European cheeses, fifteen
pates, La Brea Bakery bread, fresh salads,
sandwiches, pastries, chocolates, gourmet
products. Founded in 1973. Features in *Los
Angeles Times, Sunset Magazine*, Gault
Millau *Best of Los Angeles*.

ULTIMATE NUT & CANDY CO.
11849 Ventura Blvd.
Studio City, CA 91604
818.772.8267
Jerry Donath
Areas served: Southern California
Gourmet fresh roasted nuts, hand-dipped
chocolates, unique food gifts and gift
baskets, shipping and delivery.

VILLAGE KITCHEN SHOPPE
147 N. Glendora Avenue
Glendora, CA 91740
818.914.7897
Great variety of imported oils, vinegars,
mustards, jams, difficult to locate gourmet
food items.

DESTINATION MANAGEMENT

**CALIFORNIA LEISURE CONSULTANTS
OF LOS ANGELES**
3605 Long Beach Blvd.
Suite 201
Long Beach, CA 90807-4013
310.427.0414
Ilene Reinhart,
Creative approach to total destination
management services. Specialize in
innovative theme party productions,
customized tour coordination, sporting
events, speakers, entertainment, specialty
gift items and expert service for corporate,
association and incentive meetings and
conventions.

EXTRAORDINARY EVENTS
13437 Ventura Blvd.
Suite 210
Sherman Oaks, CA 91423
818.783.6112
Andrea Michaels
Areas served: International
Full event planning, destination
management, entertainment, decor, location
selection. Numerous awards from *Special
Event Magazine:* "Best Theatrical Show
Production," first and second place awards
for best entertainment concept, theme
decor, fundraising event and tabletop
decor.

KUSHNER AND ASSOCIATES
1104 S. Robertson Blvd.
Los Angeles, CA 90035
310.274.8819
Linda Kushner
Areas served: Southern California
Corporate event, meeting and full service
destination management company. Handle
transportation, sight seeing, companion
programs, sports and special events, music,
novelty entertainment, celebrity
acquisition, registration and hospitality
staff. Theme parties and technical support.

LOS ANGELES

EQUIPMENT RENTALS & TENTING

ABBEY PARTY RENTS
1001 N. La Brea Avenue
Los Angeles, CA 90038
310.652.2760
818.340.2131
Jennifer Austin
Areas served: Los Angeles Basin
Party planning. Rentals: linens, tables, chairs, china, flatware, tenting. Serving Los Angeles since 1924.

ACADEMY TENT AND CANVAS, INC.
2910 S. Alameda Street
Los Angeles, CA 90058
213.234.4060
800.228.3687 (inside CA)
800.222.4535 (outside CA)
Maury Rice
Areas served: National
Provide complete facility hospitality equipment for private, commercial, institutional, and corporate hospitality events nationally. Including tents, flooring, ground covering, staging, lighting, heating, air conditioning, and power. Founded 1981.

CASINO DE PARIS, INC.
9636 Long Beach Blvd.
South Gate, CA 90280
213.566.1001
714.549.3396
Areas served: Southern California
Las Vegas style casino equipment and dealers. In business for thirty-two years.

CLASSIC PARTY RENTALS
8476 Steller Drive
Culver City, CA 90232
310.202.0011
Richard Loguercio, President
Areas served: Southern California
Party and event rentals with an emphasis based quality, service, and creativity. Specializing in logistics and space planning for larger high profile corporate and private events. Board of Directors of ISES and member of Special Events Advisory Board. Richard Loguercio has been engaged as guest speaker for UCLA Extension and lectured on space logistics and event planning, he has also been a guest speaker

for numerous special event conventions speaking on matters relating to event rentals.

E AND M AMUSEMENT
1480 Seabright Avenue
Long Beach, CA 90813
310.427.4327
Earl Kreetel
Areas served: Los Angeles and fifty mile radius.
Party rental casino equipment, game booths, dealers, merchandise, cabana tents.

LA CIRCUS
7531 S. La Salle Avenue
Los Angeles, CA 90047
216.751.3486
Wini McKay
Areas served: International
Customized circus events for all occasions. Equipment rental, seats, tenting, games, performers, elephant rides and acts, as well as complete set-up. Clients include Disney, Yamaha, Pepsi International and many more.

LA PARTY RENTS, INC.
7100 Valjean Avenue
Van Nuys, CA 91406
818.989.4300
310.785.0000
Cindy Giordano
Areas served: Southern California, including Palm Springs, Las Vegas, Northern California
Event equipment rentals including: tents, canopies, caterer's service and kitchen equipment, tables, chairs, linen, china, glassware, flatware, lighting, floor coverings. Twenty-four hour emergency service, free one-on-one consultation, two-way radio dispatched trucks. Distinctions include Reagan Library opening, exclusive rental company to Universal Studios Hollywood, Hugh Hefner's wedding, JFK Premiere, Elizabeth Taylor's birthday at Disneyland, Fantasmic's Grand Opening at Disneyland, Earth Day 1990, Gorbachev's visit to Reagan Library.

[Continued on next page.]

LOS ANGELES

PICO PARTY RENTS
2537 S. Fiarfax Avenue
Culver City, CA 90232
213.936.8268
800.400.8268
Bill Edwards
Area served: Los Angeles County
Party rentals: tents, canopies, chairs, tables, linen, china, silverware. Specialize in wedding arbor and wedding gazebos.

REGAL RENTS
9925 Jefferson Blvd.
Culver City, CA 90232
310.204.3382
Jerry Shanberg
Areas served: California
Tenting, tables, chairs, flatware, dishes, dance floors and stages. Specialize in ballroom chairs, complete party planning and coordinating.

EVENT PLANNING

ALONG CAME MARY
5265 W. Pico Blvd.
Los Angeles, CA 90019
213.931.9082
Mary Micucci
Areas served: Southern California
Complete party planning, event coordinating and gourmet food from Los Angeles's finest caterer. Over seventeen years experience. Named Top Business Woman by the *LA Business Journal* 1992.

AMBROSIA
1717 Stewart Street
Santa Monica, CA 90404
310.453.7007
David Corwin
Areas served: Event planning: National
Provide catering, event planning and production. Ultra high-end quality catering combined with detail oriented coordination. Environmentally and socially conscious planning. Original themes. Forty full-time employees. Eight event producers and party coordinators. Received three Gala Awards, seven nominations. Catered the sixtieth and sixty-first Academy Awards

Governor's Ball, the opening of the Nixon Library, countless celebrities' weddings and private functions for movers and shakers of the entertainment and corporate worlds.

BLACK TIE EVENT SERVICES
1454 Third Street Promenade
Suite 212
Santa Monica, CA 90401
310.576.1800
Stephen Plache
Areas served: Southern California
Bar catering coordination and event staffing services to both industry and private clients, from the informal to the very formal special event. Receptions, premieres, holiday celebrations, weddings, fundraisers, birthdays and much more.

CALIFORNIA CELEBRATIONS
4051 Glencoe Avenue
Suite 7
Marina Del Rey, CA 90292
310.305.8849
David Stephens
Areas served: Southern California and beyond
Custom catering, event planning, decor, locations, specialty lighting, any or all services needed for a special event. Specialize in custom menus of fine quality foods cooked fresh at party site, stylized elegant food presentations and settings, theme events, wedding coordination, social and corporate buffets, stations and seated dinners. National award winning in-house art director. National *Special Events Magazine* awards nominee.

CALIFORNIA LEISURE CONSULTANTS OF LOS ANGELES
3605 Long Beach Blvd.
Suite 201
Long Beach, CA 90807-4013
310.427.0414
Ilene Reinhart
Creative approach to total destination management services. Specialize in innovative theme party productions, customized tour coordination, sporting events, speakers, entertainment, specialty gift items and expert service for corporate, association and incentive meetings and conventions.

CATERED OCCASIONS
920 Venice Blvd.
Suite 106
Venice, CA 90291
310.821.6864
Marilyn Caldwell
Areas served: Southern California
Catering and party planning. Specialize in
Creole/Cajun, Mexican, Italian, barbecue,
cuisine of the 90's, themes, corporate.

CULINARY ADVENTURES
23908 DeVille Way
Malibu, CA 90265
310.456.2484
Doris Felts
Areas served: Southern California
Culinary events. Group tours via van or
bus to places and areas of culinary interest,
including related luncheons, picnics
(catered or restaurant meals). Master chef
cooking demos with lunch. Private culinary
tours of market places, specialty sources,
food processors and plant tours, growers,
wine makers. Featured in *Los Angeles
Magazine, Los Angeles Times, Daily News,
Sunset Magazine, Bon Apetit* and other
media.

ENTERTAINMENT CONTRACTOR
P.O. Box 65151
Los Angeles, CA 90065
213.256.9613
J. Schwartz
Areas served: International
Event coordination, invitations,
decorations, catering, photography,
entertainment, complete party planning,
one call does it all. Specializing in theme
parties.

EVENT WORKS
340 W. 131st Street
Los Angeles, CA 90061
213.321.1793
Janet Elkins
Areas served: Southern California
Event production: music, shows, decor,
floral design. Three time winner of the
Special Event Gala Award.

EXECUTIVE PARTY PLANNERS
1300 Quail Street
Suite 108

Newport Beach, CA 92660
714.955.2922
Jean Studer
Areas served: Orange County
Full service event planning for weddings
through corporate events.

EXTRAORDINARY EVENTS
13437 Ventura Blvd.
Suite 210
Sherman Oaks, CA 91423
818.783.6112
Andrea Michaels
Areas served: International
Full event planning, destination
management, entertainment, decor, location
selection. Numerous awards from *Special
Event Magazine*: "Best Theatrical Show
Production," first and second place awards
for best entertainment concept, theme
decor, fundraising event and tabletop
decor.

IT'S THE MAIN EVENT, INC.
29399 Agoura Road
Suite 105
Agoura Hills, CA 91301
818.706.0340
Cheryl Fish
Areas served: Western States
Full event production company specializing
in corporate and social events. In-house
prop production, graphic arts department
and high styled floral department. Seven
time recipient of *Special Event Magazine*
Gala Awards. Best Floral, three years in a
row, Best Corporate Event over $30,000,
Best Event Done on A Shoestring under
$5,000, Most Imaginative Invitation, two
years in a row.

KAREN JEWELL FINE INVITATIONS
10568 -1/2 Ayres Avenue
Los Angeles, CA 90064
310.558.4938
Karen Jewell
Areas served: United States, Japan
Personalized wedding counsel with each
invite order, hand done calligraphy, rush
orders, foreign languages. Specialize in
custom and catalogue, 16 different hand
calligraphy styles; menus, programs,
signage. Clients include: Fred Hayman,
Lee Radziwill, Giorgio, Marvin Davis.

KUSHNER AND ASSOCIATES
1104 S. Robertson Blvd.
Los Angeles, CA 90035
310.274.8819
Linda Kushner
Areas served: Southern California
Corporate event, meeting and full service
destination management company. Handle
transportation, sight seeing, companion
programs, sports and special events, music,
novelty entertainment, celebrity
acquisition, registration and hospitality
staff. Theme parties and technical support.

LA CIRCUS
7531 S. La Salle Avenue
Los Angeles, CA 90047
216.751.3486
Wini McKay
Areas served: International
Customized circus events for all occasions.
Equipment rental, seats, tenting, games,
performers, elephant rides and acts, as well
as complete set-up. Clients include Disney,
Yamaha, Pepsi International and many
more.

LEHR AND BLACK, INC.
3542 Hayden Avenue
Culver City, CA 90230
310.839.0990
Sol Lehr
Ellen Black
Areas served: National
Custom invitations, table favors,
centerpieces, escort cards, escort boards,
napkins, decorations, party consultation.
Specializing in weddings, Bar Mitzvahs,
theme parties, birthdays, holiday parties.
Received Beverly Hills Chamber of
Commerce First Place Award 1988, 1989,
1990 and 1991 for Christmas decorations.

LOS ANGELES PARTY DESIGNS, INC.
3368 S. Robertson
Los Angeles, CA 90024
310.836.5273
Debra Stevenson
Areas served: National
Event production, decor and floral design.
Gala Award Best Floral Design, Blooming
Inspirations Exhibitor, LA Top 100 Women
Owned Business.

MARC FREDERICKS,
A FLOWER DESIGN FIRM
8441 Warner Drive
Culver City, CA 90232
310.287.2273
800.894.2280
Marc Byrd
Areas served: Los Angeles County, Orange
County, Palm Springs
Event planning and floral decor. Gala
Award 1992 "Best Floral Design."

MARQUIS EVENTS
3007 Washington Blvd.
Suite 225
Marina Del Rey, CA 90292
310.574.6611
Full service event planning company with
exclusive locations including elegant custom
yachts, private homes, castles, mansions,
and estates. Events at land and sea.

MASTROIANNI'S/JAY'S CATERING
10581 Garden Grove Blvd.
Garden Grove, CA 92643
714.636.6045
800.585.6045
Norman Meyer
Areas served: Los Angeles, Orange, San
Diego, Riverside, Santa Barbara Counties
Catering, full scale props, rentals, flowers,
bakery, linens, entertainment.

MIKE VACCARO PRODUCTIONS, INC.
3848-A Atlantic Avenue
Suite 4
Long Beach, CA 90807
310.424.4958
Mike Vaccaro
Areas served: International
Music, entertainment, theme parties, party
planning, site selection, celebrity
entertainment, etc.

MOLLIE MERRELL AND CO.,
WEDDING CONSULTANT
1829 Westchliff Drive
Suite 227
Newport Beach, CA 92660
714.548.1089
Areas served: Orange County
Bridal consultant and bridal show
producer. "Mollie's Brides" column in
Newport News, "Ask Mollie" column in
Weddings West Magazine.

**MORE THAN A MOUTHFUL,
CATERING INC.**
>743 S. Lucerne Blvd.
>Los Angeles, CA 90005
>**213.937.6345**
>Barry Colman

Areas served: Southern California, travel
to Northern California, Nevada, and
the East Coast
Full service event planners including food,
decor , rentals, entertainment, banquet
facilities for 1000 guests. Specialize in
over-abundance of food, mind boggling
displays, into the visuals, catering to
fantasies. All graduates of the Culinary
Institute of America.

PARTY PLANNERS WEST, INC.
>4141 Glencoe Avenue
>Building C
>Marina Del Rey, CA 90292
>**310.305.1000**
>Patricia Ryan
>Robyn Leuthe

Areas served: National
Full service corporate event planning
company providing innovative concept
development, in-house production
department, set and lighting, design, theme
parties, in-house floral department, menu
development and coordination with
caterers, entertainment bookings,
audiovisual coordination, technical and
special effects. Customized events to client's
specific needs. Named fifteenth largest
woman owned business in Los Angeles
County by the *Los Angeles Business
Journal*. Named in *Inc. Magazine's* Top
500 Private Corporations.

RHYMES AND DESIGNS
>1838 S. Robertson Blvd.
>Los Angeles, CA 90035
>**310.838.7755**
>Sandra Gutterman

Areas served: Greater Los Angeles
Party coordinator, florist, custom-designed
and catalogue invitations, calligraphy
services, custom escort cards, table
numbers, complete room decoration,
centerpieces, lighting, etc. Past clients
include Michelle Lee, Vidal Sassoon,
Kaufman & Broad, Bob Dylan, Falcon
Cable, Germaine Jackson.

**RUBIN/JOSEPH ENVIRONMENTAL
DESIGN, INC.**
>11710 Barrington Court
>Los Angeles, CA 90049
>**310.471.3885**
>Edward Joseph

Areas served: Southern California
Complete party planning and floral design
services. Movie premiers, corporate
parties, large and small events. Wide range
of fresh florals, silks and dried materials.

S & R ORIGINALS
>18344 Oxnard Street
>Suite 106
>Tarzana, CA 91356
>**818.705.1778**
>Cindy Symans-Hassel

Areas served: Southern California
Event planning for all occasions. Flowers,
props, invitations, decor, entertainment,
locations and food. Specialize in floral
design and event decor. Props produced
in-house.

SOMEONE'S IN THE KITCHEN
>5973 Reseda Blvd.
>Tarzana, CA 91356
>**818.343.5151**
>Joann Roth, President

Areas served: Los Angeles, Orange,
Ventura Counties
Full service catering and customized event
planning from 2 - 10,000 guests.
Personalized menus, beautiful presentation
and excellent staff for all occasions.
Distinctions include Mayor's Certificate of
Appreciation, Women in Business
Entrepreneurial Excellence, Woman of the
Year, Tarzana Chamber of Commerce,
County of Los Angeles Commendations for
Dedicated Service to the Affairs of the
Community. Joann Roth is well-known for
her generous support of civic and charitable
activities, which includes the Institute for
Cancer and Blood Research, the LA
Childcare and Development Council, the
Sunshine Mission and the Fred Jordan
Mission.

[Continued on next page.]

LOS ANGELES

SPECIAL EVENTS
8736 Canby Avenue
Northridge, CA 91325
818.775.4525
Marcia Smart
Areas served: Los Angeles, Ventura,
Riverside, Orange Counties
Full event production, catering, rentals,
entertainment, decor, themes. All types of
corporate events, picnics, open houses, VIP
receptions, parties. Established in 1980.
Produced world's largest company picnic
for 25,000 guests.

SPECIALTY CATERING
2450 White Road
Irvine, CA 92714
800.675.9629
Marc Mushkin
Areas served: Southern California
Full service catering, rentals, flowers,
entertainers. Specialize in Southwestern
and Mexican food.

SPECTRUM MEETING SERVICES
5900 Wilshire Blvd.
Suite 2555
Los Angeles, CA 90036
213.930.0341
Suzi Patrusky
Complete party design and facilitation
including invitations, decor, local and
celebrity entertainment, transportation,
catering and site selection. By creative and
responsive staff with seventeen years of
experience in Southern California.

FAVORS

COMPARTE'S OF CALIFORNIA
925 Montana Avenue
Santa Monica, CA 90403
310.395.2297
Jill Barker
Areas served: Courier service available for
Los Angeles area, UPS available anywhere
in the United States
Hand dipped chocolates, stuffed fruits
(individually wrapped dried fruit with
nuts), gift tins, custom gift baskets, molded
chocolates, candies. Examples of party
items: molded chocolate basket with

chocolate strawberries and raspberries or
assorted truffles, individual boxes (with 2
chocolates) with names to be used as place
cards, chocolates with decorations (holiday,
floral), theme gifts (chocolate tennis racket
or golf balls). Written up in *Bon Apetit*,
English toffee called "Best in Town" *Los
Angeles Magazine*.

DECADENCE FINE CHOCOLATES
24690 Via Buena Suerte
Yorba Linda, CA 92687
714.692.8408
Becky Repic
Areas served: South California
Custom designed chocolates for special
occasions, holiday parties, corporate
chocolate logos, business cards, favors,
gift baskets.

GODIVA CHOCOLATIER
South Coast Plaza
Costa Mesa
714.556.9055

Mainplace Mall
714.835.4694

Brea Mall
714.671.0793

Los Angeles Area
Beverly Center
213.651.0697

Sherman Oaks
Fashion Square
818.788.4065

Century City
213.277.6154

Citicorp Plaza
213.624.8923

Glendale Galleria
818.545.7282

Pasadena
380 S. Lake Avenue
Suite 7
818.795.1803
World renowned chocolatier. Belgium-style
chocolates, gift baskets and party favors.

LEHR AND BLACK, INC.

3542 Hayden Avenue
Culver City, CA 90230
310.839.0990
Sol Lehr
Ellen Black
Areas served: National
Custom invitations, table favors, centerpieces, escort cards, escort boards, napkins, decorations, party consultation. Specializing in weddings, Bar Mitzvahs, theme parties, birthdays, holiday parties. Received Beverly Hills Chamber of Commerce First Place Award 1988, 1989, 1990 and 1991 for Christmas decorations.

THREE FOXES TROT
23733 Malibu Road
Suite 900
Malibu, CA 90265
310.456.1776
Jeanna Gelston
Areas served: Malibu, San Fernando Valley, Santa Monica, West Los Angeles
Tableware, decor, favors, home furnishings, personal care accessories, audio, gifts, luggage.

TIFFANY & CO.
210 N. Rodeo Drive
Beverly Hills, CA 90210
310.273.8880
Michele Sheid

South Coast Plaza
3333 Bristol Street
Costa Mesa, CA 92626
714.540.5330
The finest in engraved invitations, favors, accessories, stationery, bridal registry, fine crystal and china, Tiffany flatware and gifts for all occasions.

TWIGS
1401 Montana Avenue
Santa Monica, CA 90403
310.451.9934
Angela
Areas served: West Side, Beverly Hills, Malibu, Encino, Pacific Palisades
Favors, wrapping, executive gifts, hostess gifts, custom arrangements, and serving pieces.

ULTIMATE NUT & CANDY CO.

11849 Ventura Blvd.
Studio City, CA 91604
818.772.8267
Jerry Donath
Areas served: Southern California
Gourmet fresh roasted nuts, hand-dipped chocolates, unique food gifts and gift baskets, shipping and delivery.

FIREWORKS & SPECIAL EFFECTS

IMAGES EVENT PRODUCTION
1649 Twelfth Street
Santa Monica, CA 90404
310.392.4240
Jerry Astourian
Areas served: International
Event design, lighting design, set and prop construction. Specializing in Hollywood premiere parties, corporate galas, fundraising events, private affairs. Special Events Magazine Gala Awards: Best Decorated Theme Event, Most Imaginative Use of Lighting & Special Effects (four years), Most Imaginative Use Of A Tent, Most Imaginative Use of Equipment, Special Logistic Award.

PYRO SPECTACULARS
P.O. Box 2329
Rialto, CA 92377
800.322.7732
Kevin Kelley
Areas served: International
Aerial fireworks, displays choreographed to music, low level displays and special effects. Clients include Chinese New Year, Hong Kong (annually), Los Angeles Olympics, Rolling Stones Steel Wheel Tour, America Fest, Statue of Liberty, Macy's, Dodgers, Angels, Giants, A's, Super Bowls, Hollywood Bowl, Magic Mountain and LA County Fair.

[Continued on next page.]

FLORISTS & FLORAL DESIGNS

CASABELLA FLORIST
9040 Santa Monica Blvd.
W. Hollywood, CA 90069
310.274.5440
Joe Benon
Areas served: Los Angeles (west of downtown), San Fernando Valley and Santa Monica
Full service florist. Cut flowers, parties, weddings, etc. Will match or beat any other bid.

COSENTINO FLOWERS & NURSERY
3835 Cross Creek Road
Malibu, CA 90265
310.456.5367
Josephine
Full service florist and floral designs for all occasions.

ELITE FLORIST
4552 Van Nuys Blvd.
Sherman Oaks, CA 91403
818.788.5590
Gale Saul
Areas served: San Fernando Valley, Burbank, Glendale, Beverly Hills, Century City, Bel Air, Santa Monica, Brentwood
Full service florist and floral designers for weddings, parties, corporate imaging. Specializing in European - Holland flowers, gifts, delivery service.

IT'S THE MAIN EVENT, INC.
29399 Agoura Road
Suite 105
Agoura Hills, CA 91301
818.706.0340
Cheryl Fish
Areas served: Western States
Full event production company specializing in corporate and social events. In-house prop production, graphic arts department and high styled floral department. Seven time recipient of *Special Event Magazine* Gala Awards. Best Floral, three years in a row, Best Corporate Event Over $30,000, Best Event Done On A Shoestring Under $5,000, Most Imaginative Invitation, two years in a row.

JOHN DALY INC.
2210 Wilshire Blvd.
Suite 886
Santa Monica, CA 90403
310.459.0586
John Daly
Areas served: International
Design and decor for all events. Gala Awards from The Special Event, Best Table Top, Best Floral, Best Use of Equipment, nominated six years in a row. Twenty-seven years experience in the industry.

LEO'S FLOWER SHOP
8505 W. Santa Monica Blvd.
Los Angeles, CA 90069
213.655.6222
310.652.6307
Areas served: Beverly Hills, West Hollywood, West Los Angeles, Los Angeles, Hollywood, Santa Monica, Studio City, Sherman Oaks, Encino, Toluca Lake
Complete service florist. Highest quality European and tropical flowers. Serving Beverly Hills and West Los Angeles for fifty-three years. Family owned and operated.

LOS ANGELES PARTY DESIGNS, INC.
3368 S. Robertson
Los Angeles, CA 90024
310.836.5273
Debra Stevenson
Areas served: National
Event production, decor and floral design. Gala Award Best Floral Design, Blooming Inspirations Exhibitor, LA Top 100 Women Owned Business.

**MARC FREDERICKS,
A FLOWER DESIGN FIRM**
8441 Warner Drive
Culver City, CA 90232
310.287.2273
800.894.2280
Marc Byrd
Areas served: Los Angeles County, Orange County, Palm Springs
Event planning and floral decor. Gala Award 1992 "Best Floral Design."

MORAIN/GILMORE
1329 Lucile Avenue
Los Angeles, CA 90026
213.667.0846

LOS ANGELES

Craig Gilmore
Malcolm Morain
Areas served: Beverly Hills, Bel Air,
Greater Los Angeles
Cutting edge floral design by one of the
country's top designers. All events and
weekly accounts, weddings, exclusive
intimate occasions. One of a kind
arrangements, using rare and unusual
materials. Old world decadence, beautiful
table arrangements. Clients include Nieman
Marcus Beverly Hills, Ralph Lauren, YSL,
La Maison Francaise. Featured in *Vogue
Entertainment*.

MORE THAN A MOUTHFUL, CATERING INC.
743 S. Lucerne Blvd.
Los Angeles, CA 90005
213.937.6345
Barry Colman
Areas served: Southern California, travel
to Northern California, Nevada,
East Coast
Full service event planners including food,
decor , rentals, entertainment, banquet
facilities for 1000 guests. Specialize in over-
abundance of food, mind boggling displays,
into the visuals, catering to fantasies. All
graduates of the Culinary Institute of
America.

PARTY PLANNERS WEST, INC.
4141 Glencoe Avenue
Building C
Marina Del Rey, CA 90292
310.305.1000
Patricia Ryan
Robyn Leuthe
Areas served: National
Full service corporate event planning
company providing innovative concept
development, in-house production
department, set and lighting, design, theme
parties, in-house floral department, menu
development and coordination with
caterers, entertainment bookings,
audiovisual coordination, technical and
special effects. Customized events to client's
specific needs. Named fifteenth largest
woman owned business in Los Angeles
County by the Los Angeles Business
Journal. Named in *Inc. Magazine's* Top
500 Private Corporations.

RHYMES AND DESIGNS
1838 S. Robertson Blvd.
Los Angeles, CA 90035
310.838.7755
Sandra Gutterman
Areas served: Greater Los Angeles
Party coordinator, florist, custom-designed
and catalogue invitations, calligraphy
services, custom escort cards, table
numbers, complete room decoration,
centerpieces, lighting, etc. Past clients
include Michelle Lee, Vidal Sassoon,
Kaufman & Broad, Bob Dylan, Falcon
Cable, Germaine Jackson.

RUBIN/JOSEPH ENVIRONMENTAL DESIGN, INC.
11710 Barrington Court
Los Angeles, CA 90049
310.471.3885
Edward Joseph
Areas served: Southern California
Complete party planning and floral design
services. Movie premiers, corporate
parties, large and small events. Wide range
of fresh florals, silks and dried materials.

S & R ORIGINALS
18344 Oxnard Street
Suite 106
Tarzana, CA 91356
818.705.1778
Cindy Symans-Hassel
Areas served: Southern California
Event planning for all occasions. Flowers,
props, invitations, decor, entertainment,
locations and food. Specialize in floral
design and event decor. Props produced
in-house.

SILVER BIRCHES
180 E. California Blvd.
Pasadena, CA 91105-3230
818.796.1431
A distinctive floral and design firm, known
for "putting the bloom" on LA grand-
openings, movie producers, mansions and
very private gardens. Projects run the
gamet from interior design, to flowers for
weddings, to set design. Work often with
cottage industry suppliers, and backyarders
to amass the freshest picks available. High
profile clientele.

LOS ANGELES

SOMETHING SPECIAL
14303 Ventura Blvd.
Sherman Oaks, CA 91423
818.905.8664
310.444.9364
800.544.2619
Sean Tanner
Armando Naubandian
Areas served: Los Angeles County
Specializing in unusual and exotic
floral designs.

SYLVIA TIDWELL
1410 Livonia Avenue
Los Angeles, CA 90035
310.659.1817
Sylvia Tidwell
Areas served: Los Angeles, Santa Barbara
to La Jolla
Elegant and unusual floral design for
weddings, parties and events. Specializing
in wedding flowers. Designs featured on two
covers of Flowers & magazine. Rated as
one of twelve Best Wedding Florists
nationally by *Bon Apetit*. Articles in:
*Angeles Magazine, Southern California
Home & Garden*, forthcoming profile in
Garden Design Magazine. Twice an invited
designer in Los Angeles County Museum of
Art's "Blooming Inspirations" tribute to
artistic floral design.

TWIGS
1401 Montana Avenue
Santa Monica, CA 90403
310.451.9934
Angela
Areas served: West Side, Beverly Hills,
Malibu, Encino, Pacific Palisades
Favors, wrapping, executive gifts,
hostess gifts, custom arrangements,
and serving pieces.

FORMAL WEAR

AUNTIE MAME
1102 S. La Cienega Blvd.
Los Angeles, CA 90035
310.652.8430
Murray Goldstein
Areas served: Southern California
Rental and sales of beaded evening wear,
sequined gowns, wedding gowns, studio
costumes, furs (coats, jackets, flings,
stoles), jewelry, accessories, stage wear.
Serving southern California for over
nineteen years, same location. Cater to
the studios and production companies.

GARY'S TUX SHOPS
5621 Wilshire Blvd.
Beverly Hills, CA
310.659.7296

Santa Monica
2838 Wilshire Blvd.
310.453.8705

Hollywood
8371 Sunset Blvd.
310.656.8076

Redondo Beach
South Bay Galleria
310.214.8200

Westchester
8718 Sepulveda Blvd.
213.776.1890

Granada Hills
16917 Devonshire Street
818.368.6206

Northridge
Northridge Fashion Center
818.349.4558

Studio City
12457 Ventura Blvd.
818.980.0108

Encino
17946 Ventura Blvd.
818.987.1636

Van Nuys
6711 Odessa Avenue
818.376.6724

L O S A N G E L E S

Woodland Hills
Promenade Mall
818.888.4878

Pasadena
818.795.0289

Simi Valley
2962 Cochrun Avenue
805.526.7726

Santa Clarita
23220 Lyons Avenue
805.253.2002

Palmdale/Lancaster
Antelope Valley Mall
805.266.9158

West Covina
Fashion Plaza
818.337.5009

Montebello
2617 W. Beverly Blvd.
213.721.4282

Montclair
9015 D Central Avenue
714.621.8441

Montclair Plaza
714.624.1712

Riverside
Riverside Plaza
714.784.5464

Tyler Mall
714.785.8000

San Bernadino
Central City Mall
714.889.9969

Barstow
222 E. Main Street
619.256.7726

Huntington Beach
18583 Beach Blvd.
714.841.0611

Costa Mesa
3845 S. Bristol Street
714.549.2666

Newport Beach
Fashion Island at Phelps
714.644.0280

Santa Ana
2133 N. Main Street
714.547.2266

Mission Viejo
26012 Marguerite Pkwy.
714.562.7780

Laguna Hills
26882 S. La Paz Road
714.831.9730

Tuxedo sales and rentals. Large selection of
fine formal wear including Christian Dior,
Henry Grethel, Pierre Cardin, Lord West
and more. Specializing in weddings and
corporate events/conventions, offering
special discounts and services for large
groups. Served over 250,000 "newly-weds"
since 1933. Supplied over 700 tuxedos for
Super Bowl in San Diego and all tuxedos for
opening ceremonies of Los Angeles Olympics.

TUX DEN AT SEARS
Torrance
Del Amo Mall
310.542.1511

Carson
Carson Mall
310.354.2500

Santa Fe Springs
Santa Fe S;rings Mall
213.903.7074

Los Angeles
Crenshaw Mall
213.292.1700

N. Hollywood
12121 Victory Blvd.
818.766.6745

Northridge
Northridge Fashion Center
818.885.6073

Canoga Park
Fallbrook Mall
818.340.0661

Palmdale/Lancaster
Antelope Valley Mall
805.265.6900

[Continued on next page.]

45

Thousand Oaks
145 W. Hillcrest Street
805.497.4566

Oxnard
Esplanade Mall
805.485.8731

Glendale
236 N. Central Avenue
818.507.7245

Burbank
Burbank Media Center Mall
818.559.6600

Pasadena
3801 E. Football Blvd.
818.357.3546

Alhambra
2500 Commonwealth Avenue
818.576.5261

Brea
Brea Mall
714.256.7300

Buena Park
Buena Park Center
714.828.4400

Cerritos
Los Cerritos Mall
310.860.0511

Costa Mesa
South Coast Plaza
714.850.2100

Mall of Orange
714.637.2100

Westminster Mall
714.698.1411

Laguna Hills Mall
714.586.1100

Tuxedo sales and rentals. Largest selection of fine formal wear including Christina Dior, Henry Grethel, Pierre Cardin, Lord West and more. Specialize in weddings and corporate events/conventions offering special discounts and services for large groups, including on-sight measuring, hotel pick-up and delivery.

GIFTS & GIFT BASKETS
AAH's
1083-1087 Broxton Avenue
Westwood, CA 90024
310.824.1688

3223 Wilshire Blvd.
Santa Monica, CA 90403
310.829.1807

14548 Ventura Blvd.
Sherman Oaks, CA 91403
818.907.0300
Jack Sing
Lesley Chapman
Party supplies, gift wrap, balloons, novelties, unusual gifts.

ANN FIEDLER CREATIONS
10544 W. Pico Blvd.
Los Angeles, CA 90064
310.838.1857
Ann Fiedler
Areas served: International
Fine quality invitations, calligraphy, personalized gifts, place cards, accessories, corporate and charity invites. Unique custom designs with a creative flair at every price. One of the largest retailers of invitations in the United States with a huge selection of catalogues.

ATELIER DE CHOCOLAT
Malibu Country Mart
3835 Cross Creek Road
Suite 15
Malibu, CA 90265
310.456.0201
Mark Gaffney

442 E. Main
Ventura, CA 93001
805.648.5937

6360 Canoga Avenue
Woodland Hills, CA 91367
818.595.1000
European chocolate boutique featuring gift

boxed chocolates with ribbons and roses, hand-crafted chocolate truffles, sculptured and traditional chocolates and confections.

BALLOONS BY TIC-TOCK

1601-1/2 N. La Brea Avenue
Los Angeles, CA 90028
213.874.3034
Eddie Zaratsian
Areas served: National
Custom corporate and personal gift baskets for all occasions

THE BREWERY COFFEE & TEA CO.

263 Santa Monica Place
Santa Monica, CA 90401
310.393.7793
Robert Myers
Dale Myers
John Heinz
Areas served: Santa Monica, Marina Del Rey, Palisades, Malibu, West Los Angeles, Brentwood, Beverly Hills
Gourmet coffee beans, loose and packaged tea, coffee makers, espresso machines, replacement parts, coffee and tea accessories, collector tea pots, large selection of mugs, cappuccino cups. Espresso bar with fresh brewed coffee, muffins, chocolate truffles. Gift baskets. UPS or local free delivery with minimum purchase. Serving Santa Monica and the West Side since 1980.

CALIFORNIA BASKET COMPANY & WINE SHOP

20 S. Raymond Avenue
Old Pasadena, CA 91105
800.992.9992
818.577.9292
Jack Daniel Smith
Areas served: International
Custom-made gift baskets, handle large volumes with ease. Baskets can be made on short notice and can include customer supplied products and goods for special events (company mugs, pens, etc.). Specialize in unique gourmet foods, coffees and teas, chocolates, cheeses and meats, bath products. Also feature a large selection of wines and imported beers. One of the largest gift basket companies in California, each basket is made to order. All bows are hand-made and can be color coordinated for any color scheme. Sixteen page full color catalogue available at no charge.

COMPARTE'S OF CALIFORNIA

925 Montana Avenue
Santa Monica, CA 90403
310.395.2297
Jill Barker
Areas served: Courier service available for Los Angeles area, UPS available anywhere in the United States
Hand dipped chocolates, stuffed fruits (individually wrapped dried fruit with nuts), gift tins, custom gift baskets, molded chocolates, candies. Examples of party items: molded chocolate basket with chocolate strawberries and raspberries or assorted truffles, individual boxes (with two chocolates) with names to be used as place cards, chocolates with decorations (holiday, floral), theme gifts (chocolate tennis racket or golf balls). Written up in *Bon Apetit*, English toffee called "Best in Town" *Los Angeles Magazine*.

DECADENCE FINE CHOCOLATES

24690 Via Buena Suerte
Yorba Linda, CA 92687
714.692.8408
Becky Repic
Areas served: South California
Custom designed chocolates for special occasions, holiday parties, corporate chocolate logos, business cards, favors, gift baskets.

DUKE OF BOURBON

20908 Roscoe Blvd.
Canoga Park, CA 91304
818.341.1234
David Breitstein
Ron Breitstein
Areas served: San Fernando Valley, Beverly Hills, West Los Angeles, Malibu, Westlake Village, Thousand Oaks, Agoura
Wine tasting seminars, executive wine seminars, party and event planning with delivery of wine, spirits, beer, wine collecting consultation, speakers, gift baskets, newsletter. Specialize in personalized service. Commendations from City and County of Los Angeles for twenty-five years of successful business. Chosen by

LOS ANGELES

The Wine Spectator and *Market Watch* as one of top twelve wine and spirits shops in America for 1990. *Beverage Dynamics* Retailer of the Year 1991.

ELITE FLORIST
4552 Van Nuys Blvd.
Sherman Oaks, CA 91403
818.788.5590
Gale Saul
Areas served: San Fernando Valley, Burbank, Glendale, Beverly Hills, Century City, Bel Air, Santa Monica, Brentwood Full service florist and floral designers for weddings, parties, corporate imaging. Specializing in European - Holland flowers, gifts, delivery service.

ENCHANTED BASKETS
1645 N. Vine Street
Suite 606
Hollywood, CA 90028
213.467.2171
800.BASKETS
Phyllis Solomon
Areas served: International
Gift baskets and corporate gifts. Unique basket styles, gourmet, specialty foods, coffees, teas, chocolate, bath baskets, baby baskets, etc. Baskets for all holidays and occasions. Theme baskets - Italian, sport, Southwestern, etc. Customized baskets tailored to specifications and budget.

GELSON'S
16450 Ventura Blvd.
Encino, CA 91436
818.906.5780
Greg Hansen

4738 Laurel Canyon Blvd.
N. Hollywood, CA 91607
818.906.5743
Bill Thompson

10250 Santa Monica Blvd.
Los Angeles, CA 90067
310.906.5793
Tim Redmond

5500 Reseda Blvd.
Tarzana, CA 91356
818.906.5752
Mike Lee

1660 San Miguel Drive
Newport Beach, CA 92660
714.906.5798
Frank Spielberger

15424 Sunset Blvd.
Pacific Palisades, CA 90272
310.906.5795
Jim McCurry

2734 Townsgate Road
Westlake Village, CA 91361
818.906.5790
John Austin

13455 Maxella Avenue
Marina Del Rey, CA 90292
310.906.5771
Rick Imamura
Baskets are elegant, tasteful gifts for family, friends, and business associates alike. They are wonderfully wrapped, beautifully tied, and ready-to-go. Each is filled with Gelson's exceptional quality and taste. Baskets can be ordered by calling 1-800-824-3777. Gelson's charge card, Mastercard and Visa are accepted. Local and out-of-state delivery is available.

GODIVA CHOCOLATIER
South Coast Plaza
Costa Mesa
714.556.9055

Mainplace Mall
714.835.4694

Brea Mall
714.671.0793

Los Angeles Area
Beverly Center
213.651.0697

Sherman Oaks
Fashion Square
818.788.4065

Century City
213.277.6154

Citicorp Plaza
213.624.8923

Glendale Galleria
818.545.7282

Pasadena
380 S. Lake Avenue
Suite 7
818.795.1803
World renowned chocolatier. Belgium-style
chocolates, gift baskets and party favors.

MISS GRACE LEMON CAKE CO.

16571 Ventura Blvd.
Encino, CA 91436
818.885.1987
Mindy Moss

422 N. Canon Drive
Beverly Hills, CA 90210
310.281.8096
800.367.2253 (mail order)
Mindy Moss
Areas served: Los Angeles, West Side,
Valley. Ship mail order anywhere.
Highest quality baked goods made
exclusively from scratch. Known for their
lemon cake. Wedding cakes, decorated
cakes for all occasions, gift baskets.

MONTANA MERCANTILE

1500 Montana Avenue
Santa Monica, CA 90403
310.451.1418
Rachel Dourec
Store is stocked with a full range of high
quality cooking equipment and specialty
foods as well as fine gifts, tabletop
accessories and hand-crafted items.

MUFFINS, ETC.

12634 Ventura Blvd.
Studio City, CA 91604
818.762.6343
Janet Acquaro
Areas served: Local and UPS shipping
Meal size and mini muffins baked daily on
premises, gourmet coffee, gift baskets.
Sugar free and sugar/fat free muffins a
specialty. Awarded Studio City Business of
the Month.

PARTY MANIA

818.609.8633
Linda Drew
Areas served: Los Angeles
Custom decorations to fit any event.
Balloon decorations, sculptures, arches,
prop centerpieces, theme related prop

rental, gift deliveries, costume deliveries,
invitations. Balloon decorations to fit any
budget. Member of the National
Association of Balloon Artists for five years.

PSEUDIOS ARTISTIC EDIBLES

2117 Glendale Galleria
Glendale, CA 91210
818.240.422
Jeanne Goraleski
Areas served: National
Sculptured chocolates, nuts, gourmet food
gifts, sugar free and novelty candy.

RED CARPET WINE
& SPIRITS MERCHANT

400 E. Glenoaks Blvd.
Glendale, CA 91207
818.247.5544
David Dobbs
Steve Fox
Russell Shin
Areas served: Los Angeles County
Full line beverage catering, wine tasting,
personalized gift baskets, bartending.
Largest gift basket selection. In-store wine
tasting and classes. Best Gift Basket
"Liquors," Kylex Award from New York.
Deliver locally. Ship nationwide.

TIFFANY & CO.

210 N. Rodeo Drive
Beverly Hills, CA 90210
310.273.8880
Michele Sheid

South Coast Plaza
3333 Bristol Street
Costa Mesa, CA 92626
714.540.5330
The finest in engraved invitations, favors,
accessories, stationery, bridal registry, fine
crystal and china, Tiffany flatware and gifts
for all occasions.

TWIGS

1401 Montana Avenue
Santa Monica, CA 90403
310.451.9934
Angela
Areas served: West Side, Beverly Hills,
Malibu, Encino, Pacific Palisades
Favors, wrapping, executive gifts, hostess
gifts, custom arrangements, and serving pieces.

ULTIMATE NUT & CANDY CO.
11849 Ventura Blvd.
Studio City, CA 91604
818.766.5259
Jerry Donath
Areas served: Southern California
Gourmet fresh roasted nuts, hand-dipped
chocolates, unique food gifts and gift
baskets, shipping and delivery.

ICE SERVICES

CHIKATO BROTHERS ICE SCULPTURES
2161 Sacramento
Los Angeles, CA 90021
213.622.4181
Mel Chikato
Areas served: Greater Los Angeles, Orange
County
Created ice sculpture in *Edward
Scissorhands*. Sell and deliver all ice
products: packaged ice, cocktail ice, dry ice
and ice sculptures. Sculpture from hearts,
swans to custom pieces, such as Michael
Crawford's 1000th performance of
Phantom Of The Opera party. Phantom
mask in clear ice on the base of black ice.
Make snow scenes on location - holiday
scenes.

MARK DAUKAS DESIGNS
714.760.7271
Ice sculptures. Five times National
Champion of Ice Sculpture. Clients include
movie studios and party planners.

INVITATIONS
& ACCESSORIES

AMD GRAPHICS
Los Angeles (South Bay)
310.318.9378

Orange County
714.774.3318
Annette Daoust
Calligraphic and graphic services.
Custom-designed invitations. Hand lettered
envelopes, place cards, menu cards, name
tags. Computer-generated event programs,

wedding booklets, invitations. Stationery,
business cards and logos. Color laser
printing. Presentation materials.

ANN FIEDLER CREATIONS
10544 W. Pico Blvd.
Los Angeles, CA 90064
310.838.1857
Ann Fiedler
Areas served: International
Fine quality invitations, calligraphy,
personalized gifts, place cards, accessories,
corporate and charity invites. Unique
custom designs with a creative flair at every
price. One of the largest retailers of
invitations in the United States with a huge
selection of catalogues.

CAMPBELL-TOLSTAD STATIONERS
1022 Westwood Blvd.
Los Angeles, CA 90024
310.208.4322

23823 W. Malibu Road
Malibu, CA 90265
310.456.9838
Jeanne Judin
Areas served: Westwood, W. Los Angeles,
Beverly Hills, Los Angeles
Stationery (including Crane's), printing,
party goods, fine gifts, novelties, office
supplies, furniture, pens, etc. Extensive
catalogue available. Free delivery, gift
wrapping, assistance with special events
planning. Westwood branch in business
since 1924.

KAREN JEWELL FINE INVITATIONS
10568 -1/2 Ayres Avenue
Los Angeles, CA 90064
310.558.4938
Karen Jewell
Areas served: United States, Japan
Personalized wedding counsel with each
invite order, hand done calligraphy, rush
orders, foreign languages. Specialize in
custom and catalogue, 16 different hand
calligraphy styles; menus, programs,
signage. Clients include: Fred Hayman,
Lee Radziwill, Giorgio, Marvin Davis.

LEHR AND BLACK, INC.
3542 Hayden Avenue
Culver City, CA 90230

310.839.0990
Sol Lehr
Ellen Black
Areas served: National
Custom invitations, table favors, centerpieces, escort cards, escort boards, napkins, decorations, party consultation. Specializing in weddings, Bar Mitzvahs, theme parties, birthdays, holiday parties. Received Beverly Hills Chamber of Commerce First Place Award 1988, 1989, 1990 and 1991 for Christmas decorations.

WILLIAM ERNEST BROWN
South Coast Plaza
3333 S. Bristol Street
Costa Mesa, CA 92626
714.540.2265

The Market Place
6529 E. Pacific Coast Hwy.
Long Beach, CA 90803
310.598.1725
Custom-designed and catalogue invitations, seating charts, accessories, place cards and party supplies for all special events. They also provide calligraphy services. Known for their high quality products and special services. Clients all over the United States and Europe.

NOTEWORTHY
Beverly Center
131 N. LaCienega Blvd.
Los Angeles, CA 90048
310.652.3775
Maureen Malone
Invitations, laser printing and calligraphy.

PARTY MANIA
818.609.8633
Linda Drew
Areas served: Los Angeles
Invitations, printed napkins, matchbooks, place cards, etc. Offer thirty percent discount off all invitations.

PURE POETRY
P.O. Box 3592
Granada Hills, CA 91394
818.360.0583
Gloria Nash
Areas served: San Fernando Valley area
Custom-made and catalogue invitations,

weddings at twenty-five percent off, announcements, accessories, calligraphy.

RHYMES AND DESIGNS
1838 S. Robertson Blvd.
Los Angeles, CA 90035
310.838.7755
Sandra Gutterman
Areas served: Greater Los Angeles
Party coordinator, florist, custom-designed and catalogue invitations, calligraphy services, custom escort cards, table numbers, complete room decoration, centerpieces, lighting, etc. Past clients include Michelle Lee, Vidal Sassoon, Kaufman & Broad, Bob Dylan, Falcon Cable, Germaine Jackson.

SCRIBBLES
714.283.4568
Annette Ertel
Areas served: Southern California
Calligraphy specialists for all printed party supplies. Many different styles and colors available. Invitations, seating cards, weddings, programs, certificates.

STREAMERS
North County Fair
272 E. Via Rancho Pkwy.
Suite 463
Escondido, CA 92025
619.737.8408

Main Place
2800 N. Main Street
Space 284
Santa Ana, CA 92701
714.647.1356

Sherman Oaks Fashion Square
14006 Riverside Drive
Space 116
Sherman Oaks, CA 91423
818.784.8724

284 Del Amo Fashion Center
Torrance, CA 90503
213.542.3566
One-stop shopping for party supplies, invitations, balloons, paper supplies, imprinting, machine calligraphy, decorations.

[Continued on next page.]

TIFFANY & CO.
210 N. Rodeo Drive
Beverly Hills, CA 90210
310.273.8880
Michele Sheid

South Coast Plaza
3333 Bristol Street
Costa Mesa, CA 92626
714.540.5330
The finest in engraved invitations, favors, accessories, stationery, bridal registry, fine crystal and china, Tiffany flatware and gifts for all occasions.

VALLEY STATIONERS, INC.
14209 Ventura Blvd.
Sherman Oaks, CA 91423
818.788.0421
Julie Wasmer
Areas served: San Fernando Valley, Beverly Hills, Los Angeles, Santa Clarita Valley, Simi Valley, Santa Monica
All kinds of invitations, announcements and printing. Wedding planner books, guest books, wedding and photo albums, plume pens and a full selection of fine pens.

WILLIAM ERNEST BROWN
South Coast Plaza
3333 S. Bristol Street
Costa Mesa, CA 92626
714.540.2265

The Market Place
6529 E. Pacific Coast Hwy.
Long Beach, CA 90803
310.598.1725
Custom-designed and catalogue invitations, seating charts, accessories, place cards and party supplies for all special events. They also provide calligraphy services. Known for their high quality products and special services. Clients all over the United States and Europe.

WORDSTYLE
714.838.4969
Miriam Prell
Areas served: Southern California
Calligraphy for all occasions. Name tags, custom maps, unique custom invitations, place cards, menu cards, programs, certificates. Staff includes writers, designers and graphic specialists.

LIGHTING, STAGING & SOUND

ACADEMY TENT AND CANVAS, INC.
2910 S. Alameda Street
Los Angeles, CA 90058
213.234.4060
800.228.3687 (inside CA)
800.222.4535 (outside CA)
Maury Rice
Areas served: National
Provide complete facility hospitality equipment for private, commercial, institutional, and corporate hospitality events. Including tents, flooring, ground covering, staging, lighting, heating, air conditioning, and power. Founded 1981.

IMAGES EVENT PRODUCTION
1649 Twelfth Street
Santa Monica, CA 90404
310.392.4240
Jerry Astourian
Areas served: International
Event design, lighting design, set and prop construction. Specializing in Hollywood premiere parties, corporate galas, fundraising events, private affairs. Special Events Magazine Gala Awards: Best Decorated Theme Event, Most Imaginative Use of Lighting & Special Effects (four years), Most Imaginative Use Of A Tent, Most Imaginative Use of Equipment, Special Logistic Award.

LA PARTY RENTS, INC.
7100 Valjean Avenue
Van Nuys, CA 91406
818.989.4300
310.785.0000
Cindy Giordano
Areas served: Southern California, including Palm Springs, Las Vegas, Northern California
Event equipment rentals including: tents, canopies, caterer's service and kitchen equipment, tables, chairs, linen, china, glassware, flatware, lighting, floor coverings. Twenty-four hour emergency service, free one-on-one consultation, two-way radio dispatched trucks. Distinctions include Reagan Library opening, exclusive rental company to Universal Studios

LOS ANGELES

Hollywood, Hugh Hefner's wedding, JFK Premiere, Elizabeth Taylor's birthday at Disneyland, Fantasmic's Grand Opening at Disneyland, Earth Day 1990, Gorbachev's visit to Reagan Library.

PARTY PLANNERS WEST, INC.
4141 Glencoe Avenue
Building C
Marina Del Rey, CA 90292
310.305.1000
Patricia Ryan
Robyn Leuthe
Areas served: National
Full service corporate event planning company providing innovative concept development, in-house production department, set and lighting, design, theme parties, in-house floral department, menu development and coordination with caterers, entertainment bookings, audiovisual coordination, technical and special effects. Customized events to client's specific needs. Named fifteenth largest woman owned business in Los Angeles County by the *Los Angeles Business Journal*. Named in *Inc. Magazine's* Top 500 Private Corporations.

RHYMES AND DESIGNS
1838 S. Robertson Blvd.
Los Angeles, CA 90035
310.838.7755
Sandra Gutterman
Areas served: Greater Los Angeles
Party coordinator, florist, custom-designed and catalogue invitations, calligraphy services, custom escort cards, table numbers, complete room decoration, centerpieces, lighting, etc. Past clients include Michelle Lee, Vidal Sassoon, Kaufman & Broad, Bob Dylan, Falcon Cable, Germaine Jackson.

LIMOUSINE & TRANSPORTATION

BARTON'S HORSE DRAWN WEDDING CARRIAGES
818.447.6693
714.599.0627
Arly and Bill Barton
Areas served: Southern California
Provide beautifully restored vintage carriages pulled by majestic white horses; driver and attendant formally attired; carriage/coach tastefully decorated to bridal colors with silk flowers; two personalized calligraphied "Just Married" signs. Specializing in weddings and any special event. Horses are thoroughly trained for heavy, busy traffic on any public street, except freeways. Props, TV, movies. Awards too numerous to list. Featured on: *AM/LA*; *PM TV Magazine*; *NBC Sunday Today*; *Days of Our Lives* - TV; *Eyewitness News, Ch 7*; *Sunset Magazine*; *Woman's World*; *Los AngelesTimes*; *Modern Bride*; *People Magazine*; Pasadena Tournament of Roses Parade, as well as the Hollywood Christmas Parade. Also featured in many other publications. In business since 1969.

CAREY LIMOUSINE
310.275.4153
800.336.4646
Privately chauffeured sedans, limousines, vans and mini buses in 372 cities.

CHIC COACH LIMOUSINE
10636 Magnolia Blvd.
N. Hollywood, CA 91601
818.980.6000
310.473.0884
John
Areas served: Southern California
Personalized limousine service. Served over one quarter of a million people. In business since 1982.

DAV EL CHAUFFEURED TRANSPORTATION NETWORK
800.328.3526 (outside CA)
800.826.5779 (inside CA)
Areas Served: International
Luxury chauffeured services in over 350 cities worldwide. Centralized reservations and billing. Airport concierge services.

LOS ANGELES

G & F CARRIAGES
5033 Los Coyotes - Diagonal
Long Beach, CA 90815
310.597.5267
Terica Campbell
Areas served: Los Angeles and Orange
County
Horses and carriages for rides, photo
shoots, decor. Pony rides for birthdays and
special events for groups up to twenty.
Transportation for larger groups in party
wagons driven by horses. Driver's attire
customized to the event.

MUSIC EXPRESS
2530 Ontario Street
Burbank, CA 91504
818.845.1502
213.849.2244
Harold Berkman
Areas served: Los Angeles, Orange County,
New York
Limousine and messenger service. Sedans,
limousines, vans, buses. Limousine
Operator Of The Year 1989, 1990, 1991,
National Limousine Association.

SIR MICHAEL'S LIMOUSINE SERVICE
2625 W. Thirty-second Avenue
Los Angeles, CA 90007
213.225.5466
Michael Nogueira Jr.
Areas served: Los Angeles County, Ventura
County and Orange County
Limousine Service. Rolls Royce, Mercedes
Benz, vans, Lincolns, Cadillacs.

Z-VALET PARKING & SHUTTLE
6922 Hollywood Blvd.
Los Angeles, CA 90028
213.871.0222
Kent Simmons
Areas served: Greater Los Angeles, Mid-
Wilshire, Beverly Hills, Santa Monica,
Malibu, Westlake/Agoura, Calabassas, San
Fernando Valley, La Canada/Flintridge &
Pasadena
Professional special event valet parking,
excellent ground transportation for groups
via fifteen-passenger maxi vans. Large, gala
events for museums, movie premieres and
charities. Full scale planning for all
vehicular receptions. Commendation from
Occidental Petroleum, Armand Hammer

Museum, LA County Museum of Art, LA
County Museum of Natural History, Annual
Pediatric Aid and Parkinson.

PET TRANSPORTATION
PET LIMO, INC.
2116 S. Sepulveda Blvd.
Los Angeles, CA 90025
213.651.LIMO
Steven May
Areas served: Beverly Hills, Los Angeles,
Hollywood, Southern California, National
Pet transportation to vets, boarders,
groomers, pet shops, airports, parties,
weddings, inter-state, emergency
transportation, etc. Limo type service,
color TV, stereo, flowers, tinted windows,
air conditioning, imitation fur-lined cages,
stuffed animals, toys, stretchers, emergency
lights, radio-dispatched, cellular phone,
and more. Best Delivery Award by
Domino's Pizza Company, limo used for the
National Morris Awards, People Magazine
quote "Got to get that jet set pet to the vet?"
Media kit available upon request.

LINENS
ABBEY PARTY RENTS
1001 N. La Brea Avenue
Los Angeles, CA 90038
310.652.2760
818.340.2131
Jennifer Austin
Areas served: Los Angeles Basin
Party planning. Rentals: linens, tables,
chairs, china, flatware, tenting. Serving
Los Angeles since 1924.

LA PARTY RENTS, INC.
7100 Valjean Avenue
Van Nuys, CA 91406
818.989.4300
310.785.0000
Cindy Giordano
Areas served: Southern California,
including Palm Springs, Las Vegas,
Northern California
Event equipment rentals including: tents,
canopies, caterer's service and kitchen

equipment, tables, chairs, linen, china, glassware, flatware, lighting, floor coverings. Twenty-four hour emergency service, free one-on-one consultation, two-way radio dispatched trucks. Distinctions include Reagan Library opening, exclusive rental company to Universal Studios Hollywood, Hugh Hefner's wedding, JFK Premiere, Elizabeth Taylor's birthday at Disneyland, Fantasmic's Grand Opening at Disneyland, Earth Day 1990, Gorbachev's visit to Reagan Library.

LADY OF THE CLOTHS
13837 Ventura Blvd.
Suite 6
Sherman Oaks, CA 91423
818.986.2843
Shirley LaBossiere
Areas served: Ship anywhere
Linen rentals.

PICO PARTY RENTS
2537 S. Fiarfax Avenue
Culver City, CA 90232
213.936.8268
800.400.8268
Bill Edwards
Area served: Los Angeles County
Party rentals: tents, canopies, chairs, tables, linen, china, silverware. Specialize in wedding arbor and wedding gazebos.

MUSIC & ENTERTAINMENT
✤ ANIMALS
BARTON'S HORSE DRAWN WEDDING CARRIAGES
818.447.6693
714.599.0627
Arly and Bill Barton
Areas served: Southern California
Provide beautifully restored vintage carriages pulled by majestic white horses; driver and attendant formally attired; carriage/coach tastefully decorated to bridal colors with silk flowers; two personalized calligraphied "Just Married" signs. Specializing in weddings and any special event. Horses are thoroughly trained for heavy, busy traffic on any public street, except freeways. Props, TV, movies.

Awards too numerous to list. Featured on: *AM/LA*; *PM TV Magazine*; *NBC Sunday Today*; *Days of Our Lives* - TV; *Eyewitness News, Ch 7*; *Sunset Magazine*; *Woman's World*; *Los Angeles Times*; *Modern Bride*; *People Magazine*; Pasadena Tournament of Roses Parade, as well as the Hollywood Christmas Parade. Also featured in many other publications. In business since 1969.

G & F CARRIAGES
5033 Los Coyotes - Diagonal
Long Beach, CA 90815
310.597.5267
Terica Campbell
Areas served: Los Angeles and Orange County
Horses and carriages for rides, photo shoots, decor. Pony rides for birthdays and special events for groups up to twenty. Transportation for larger groups in party wagons driven by horses. Driver's attire customized to the event.

LA CIRCUS
7531 S. La Salle Avenue
Los Angeles, CA 90047
216.751.3486
Wini McKay
Areas served: International
Customized circus events for all occasions. Equipment rental, seats, tenting, games, performers, elephant rides and acts, as well as complete set-up. Clients include Disney, Yamaha, Pepsi International and many more.

✤ CARICATURES & DRAWINGS
BARBARA DENNY CARICATURES
714.527.8503
Areas: International
Quick sketch caricatures for all occasions

CARICATURES BY TED JEWELL
P.O. Box 69934
Los Angeles, CA 90069
213.467.4822
Lois Jewell
Areas Served: Los Angeles and will travel
Caricatures as entertainment and custom art work. Work appears on TV. Works with the motion picture industry.

"KING SAUL"
        818.980.6991
Areas: International
Former Walt Disney Animator. Creates
caricatures in full animation using color
pastels.

**QUICK PORTRAIT SKETCHES AND
PAINTINGS BY KALAN BRUNINK**
        West Nine Olvera Street
        Los Angeles, CA 90012
        213.464.8185
        Kalan Brunink
Areas served: International
Quick portrait sketches in charcoal in a few
minutes. Very accurate likenesses produced
artistically. Quick oil portrait paintings of
up to 30 or 40 inches for dramatic content
of the environment or as a gift to a
particular person. Awards/Distinctions:
Who's Who in California. First place
ribbon Beverly Hills Art League Affaire in
the Gardens Exhibit. First place ribbon
Hancock Park Art League. Painting of
Pope John Paul II put on calendar
published in 40 countries and approved by
the Vatican's Commission of Sacred Art.
Has done 20,000 portraits including Bruce
Willis, Ry Cooder, Lawrence Welk,
Anthony Quinn for Anthony Quinn Library.
Appeared on *Two on the Town* and as guest
artist on game show *Break the Bank.*

❧ CELEBRITY LOOK-ALIKES
BOOK-A-LOOK
        324 N. Newport Blvd.
        Newport Beach, CA 92663
        714.642.9887
        Kathy Flores
Areas served: National
Full service entertainment and theatrical
costume facility. Costumes for rent and
custom-created. Makeup, wig room,
alterations and hair styling available. Full
service entertainment agent for celebrity
look-alikes, variety acts, singing telegrams,
children's entertainment, magicians,
clowns, mimes, street performers.

CELEBRITY LOOK & SOUND-A-LIKES
        P.O. Box 244
        Northridge, CA 91828-0244
        818.886.5406
        Moe Thomas
Celebrity doubles for parties, conventions,
TV and film, and all occasions. Written up
in *LA Times, People Magazine.*

"BARBARA BUSH"
        Eve Montaiyre Mgmt.
        805.488.8878

"GEORGE BUSH"
        Archie Kessel
        714.536.4694

"CHARLIE CHAPLIN"
"HARPO MARX"
        J. Schwartz
        213.256.9613

"PRINCE CHARLES"
        Michael Raye
        213.874.1483

"GOVERNOR BILL CLINTON"
        Pat Rick
        714.581.9661
        800.988.5717

"CHER"
        Kay Hiltner
        702.878.7044

"LT. COLUMBO"
        Michael Pasternak
        818.716.5977

"JOAN CRAWFORD"
        Patricia Ramsey
        714.949.2336

**PAUL HOGAN
AKA "CROCODILE DUNDEE"**
        Rob Champion
        714.460.0208

"MADONNA"
        Denise Bella Jlasis
        818.981-4451

LOS ANGELES

"GEORGE MICHAEL"
Dan Gore
805.499.5216
818.410.4356 (pager)

"MARILYN MONROE"
Marilyn Mann
702.871.7533

**CARROL O'CONNER
AKA "ARCHIE BUNKER"**
Lee Coy
702.457.8298

"DOLLY PARTON"
Charlene Vollandry
702.878.7044

"POPE JOHN PAUL II"
Gene Greytrak
714.731.0122

"RONALD REAGAN"
Eve Montaigne Mgmt.
805.488.8878

"JOAN RIVERS"
Cafer Lane
818.363.6756

"KENNY ROGERS"
Gary Kalteich
702.878.7044

"SUSAN SARANDON"
"BETTE DAVIS"
Laurie Sheppard
310.473.7137

"ELIZABETH TAYLOR"
Nancy Casey
310.395.3544

"JOHN WAYNE"
Ernal Williamson
818.781-9195

❧ CIRCUS
LA CIRCUS
7531 S. La Salle Avenue
Los Angeles, CA 90047
216.751.3486
Wini McKay

Areas served: International
Customized circus events for all occasions.
Equipment rental, seats, tenting, games,
performers, elephant rides and acts, as well
as complete set-up. Clients include Disney,
Yamaha, Pepsi International and many more.

❧ COMEDY
BERNICE BERNSTEIN
942 Fourteenth Street
Suite 2
Santa Monica, CA 90403
310.393.9631
Richard Hochberg
Areas served: Los Angeles
Roast. Specialties include: Man dressed as
Jewish lady in the Saturday Night Live
style—-Joan River-ish

ENTERTAINMENT CONTRACTOR
P.O. Box 65151
Los Angeles, CA 90065
213.256.9613
Jan Stuart
Areas served: International
Specially gag: "Fighting Couple", "Tipsy
Waiter", etc.

HUMOR DYNAMICS
P.O. Box 2140
Santa Maria, CA 93457
805.934.3232
John Kinde
Areas served: Nationwide
Comedy and magic programs. Also
humorous programs with a message.
Specialties include: Entertaining programs
with a message on the role of humor in life
for business success and life enrichment.
Also, comedy-magician. Full-time humorist
and professional speaker. Promo kit with
references available.

MICHAEL PASTERNAK AS "LT. COLUMBO"
818.716.5977
Areas served: International
Lt. Columbo at your party to deliver
personalized roast written entirely around
birthday honoree, anniversary couple,
guests or sales force.

PURE POETRY

P.O. Box 3592
Granada Hills, CA 91394
818.360.0583
Gloria Nash
Areas served: San Fernando Valley area
Creates and performs customized roasts and
tributes and lyrics. Vocalist with own
accompaniment. Specialties include: Prose
and original poetry (including Rap), lyrics,
parodies. All occasions. Vocalist:
weddings, banquets.

WEST COAST COMEDY CONTACT

11362 Reagan Street
Los Alamitos, CA 90720
310.431.6122
Mariana Tilton
Areas served: Southern California
Name acts, entertainers, comics, magicians,
clowns, novelty acts for parties, hotels,
roasts, etc.

❧ DJs & KARAOKE

BIG APPLE ENTERTAINMENT

17040 Ventura Blvd.
Encino, CA 91316
818.905.9454
Jack Bielan or Sheri Dubin
Areas served: Los Angeles, Ventura &
Orange Counties
Disc jockeys, master of ceremonies, dance
teams, special effects lighting. Specialties
include: Weddings, Bar Mitzvahs,
corporate events.

CRAIG'S CREW

By Appointment Only
Pasadena, CA
818.398.0559
213.257.1920
Craig T. or Teri Weeks
Areas served: National
Specializing in party staffing and mobile
DJ's. Complete party planning and
catering available. McHammer Dancers
and production for corporate and Bar/Bat
Mitzvahs. New division for kids' parties.
Have connections for box lunches for fund
raisers, picnics, etc. Not expensive and
great food. Featured on TV's *Eye on LA*
and *Entertainment Tonight*.

ENTERTAINMENT CONSULTANTS & EC VIDEO PRODUCTIONS

1633 Westwood Blvd.
Los Angeles, CA 90024

1834 Newport Blvd.
Costa Mesa, CA 92627

801 Washington Street
San Diego, CA 92013
800.273.7221
Areas served: Los Angeles, Orange County,
San Diego, Riverside and `Santa Barbara
Bands, DJs, all types of entertainment and
video services.

ENTERTAINMENT CONTRACTOR

P.O. Box 65151
Los Angeles, CA 90065
213.256.9613
Areas served: International
Laser Karaoke machine complete with 150
watt speakers on stands, wide variety of
music, and two microphones. Audio and/or
video taping of clients with tapes given
away.

HOWLING HOUND PRODUCTIONS

1116 Eighth Street
Suite 252
Manhattan Beach, CA 90266
310.521.6898
Areas served: San Diego to Santa Barbara
Karaoke equipment, KJ(Host), video
taping.

KARAOKE-SING-A-SONG

2929 Arizona Avenue
Suite 10
Santa Monica, CA 90404
310.828.8121
Ronnie Simons
Areas served: Los Angeles & Orange
County
Karoake and dance music, background
music, games. M.C. voted Number One in
Los Angeles Bargain Book.

OFF THE RECORD MOBILE D J SERVICE & ENTERTAINMENT

23715 West Mailbu Road
Suite 254
Malibu, CA 90265
310.456.8342
818.880-6901

Jeff Ames
Areas served: Southern C alifornia
DJs karoake, bands, magicians, etc.
Jeff Ames is Director at Large for NACE
and a director for the Malibu Chamber of
Commerce.

MUSIC BY REQUEST
800.HIT.MIXX
818.713.1313
Clark Chuka
Areas seved: California
Musicians, DJs bands, music for film, T.V.
and advertising. Wide variety of crowds
from small to very large events. Celebrity
clientele.

SONGSTAR KARAOKE
818.980.4360
Denny Gerard
Areas served: Los Angeles and Orange
County
Complete Karaoke style Sing-A-Long
entertainment featuring the best MCs, state
of the art sound systems, lyrics on video
monitors and thousands of songs from laser
disc. Songbooks with complete listings by
song title, artist and first line of song.
Provide singers with costume items, props
and percussion instruments to enhance the
fun if desired. Can provide music for your
dining and dancing pleasure.

❧ DANCE TROUPES

ARGENTINE TANGO WITH ALBERTO TOLEDANO AND LOREEN ARBUS
5221 Bellingham Avenue
Suite 107
North Hollywood, CA 91607
818.506.0780
Alberto Toledano
Areas served: Willing to drive up to a 90
minute distance from North Hollywood, or
be flown to location.
Performs and teaches introductory group
classes in authentic, classical Argentine
Tango. Can provide two to four musicians
or audio cassetes. Media coverage includes
feature stories on *Entertainment Tonight*,
Los Angeles Times, *Movieline*, *Scene At The
Movies* and *Entertainment Today*, etc., and

numerous other television, feature and
commercial credits.

LE MASQUERADE
136 Oak Drive
Syosset, NY 11791
516.496.7260 (New York)
213.383.1191(Los Angeles)
305.936.2446 (Florida)
800.666.7260
Dennis Schussel
Bernard Schussel
Areas served: International
Interactive high energy, costumed and
theatrical entertainment with music and
special effects. Interaction with the guests.
Private and corporate events. Media
awards and distincitons include entertaining
at the White House, National TV and
newspaper coverage. Award for
entertaining all northwest caterers.

THE MUMS
1347 N. Poinsettia Place
Suite 6
Los Angeles, CA 90046
213.874.4268
Roy Johns
Areas served: Los Angeles, Anaheim and
Palm Springs
Juggling, magic, stilt walking, rope dancing,
ball walking and dance. Group known for
spectacular stage presentation and voted
best performance artists by *LA Weekly*.

QUELLES TOMATES! PRODUCTIONS
4605 Fulton Avenue
Suite 3
Sherman Oaks, CA 91423-5125
818.981.4373
Jodi Laine
Pat Tallman
Areas served: National
Music, action, adventure and
entertainment. Also, look-a-likes and other
characters to enhance the atmosphere.
Shows are custom tailored to suite the event
or revue. The entertainment is completely
unique and original - choreography,
costumes - you name it!

[Continued on next page.]

LOS ANGELES

TIARE PRODUCTIONS POLYNESIAN ENTERTAINMENT
8172 Slater Avenue
Huntington Beach, CA 92647
714.847.3910
Pete and Portia Seanoa
Areas served: Los Angeles and Orange County. Have show and will travel anywhere. Fees to be discussed. Audience participation/hula lesson. Fire dancer, pretty Polynesian girls and handsome Polynesian warriors, songs, dances and humor. First place winners, Kiki Raina Tahiti Fete 92 and numerous service and cultural awards for various cities in the southland.

ENTERTAINMENT PRODUCTION & BOOKING

THE DEVROE TALENT AGENCY
3666 Valleybrink Road
Los Angeles, CA 90039
213.666.2666
Billy Devroe
Variety acts for all occasions. Bands, clowns, mariachis, magicians, comedians, pony rides, hypnotists, male dancers, mimes, jugglers, mobile D.J.'s, Hawaiian acts, puppet shows, caricaturists, belly dancers, name entertainers, strippers.

ENTERTAINMENT CONSULTANTS & EC VIDEO PRODUCTIONS
1633 Westwood Blvd.
Los Angeles, CA 90024

1834 Newport Blvd.
Costa Mesa, CA 92627

801 Washington Street
San Diego, CA 92013
800.273.7221
Areas served: Los Angeles, Orange County, San Diego, Riverside and Santa Barbara Bands, DJs, all types of entertainment and video services.

ENTERTAINMENT CONTRACTOR
P.O. Box 65151
Los Angeles, CA 90065
213.256.9613
J. Schwartz

Areas served: International
Entertainment for any occasion. Clowns, mimes, carnival rides, booths, food carts, fighting couples, tipsy waiters, look-alikes, magicians, Santas, laser karaoke, etc.

EXTRAORDINARY EVENTS
13437 Ventura Blvd.
Suite 210
Sherman Oaks, CA 91423
818.783.6112
Andrea Michaels
Areas served: International
Full event planning, destination management, entertainment, decor, location selection. Numerous awards from *Special Event Magazine*: "Best Theatrical Show Production," first and second place awards for best entertainment concept, theme decor, fundraising event and tabletop decor.

KUSHNER AND ASSOCIATES
1104 S. Robertson Blvd.
Los Angeles, CA 90035
310.274.8819
Linda Kushner
Areas served: Southern California
Corporate event, meeting and full service destination management company. Handle transportation, sight seeing, companion programs, sports and special events, music, novelty entertainment, celebrity acquisition, registration and hospitality staff. Theme parties and technical support.

THE LIVE ENTERTAINMENT STORE
17040 Ventura Blvd.
Encino, CA 91316
818.783.9509
Sheri Dubin
Areas served: Los Angeles, Ventura, Orange County
A one stop entertainment boutique providing exceptional entertainment. Weddings, Bar Mitzvahs, private parties, corporate events. Bands, disc jockey's, dance teams, klesmer, mariachi, classical groups.

MIKE VACCARO PRODUCTIONS, INC.
3848-A Atlantic Avenue
Suite 4
Long Beach, CA 90807

310.424.4958
Mike Vaccaro
Areas served: International
Music, entertainment, theme parties, party planning, site selection, celebrity entertainment, etc.

MUSIC BY REQUEST
800.HIT.MIXX
818.713.1313
Clark Chuka
Areas seved: California
Musicians, D.J.'s, bands, music for film, T.V. and advertising. Wide variety of crowds from small to very large events. Celebrity clientele.

OFF THE RECORD MOBILE DJ SERVICE & ENTERTAINMENT
23715 West Mailbu Road
Suite 254
Malibu, CA 90265
310.456.8342
818.880-6901
Jeff Ames
Areas served: Southern California
DJs karaoke, bands, magicians, etc. Jeff Ames is Director at Large for NACE and a director for the Malibu Chamber of Commerce.

OMNI ENTERTAINMENT & SERVICES
18618 Collins Street
Suite 203
Tarzana, CA 91356
818.345-8399
Bill Malinsky
Areas served: Los Angeles, Ventura and Orange County
Musical entertainment - jazz, classical and popular selections. Specializing in vocal entertainment such as holiday ensembles and Christmas carolers with English handbells and Dicken's costumes.
Theatrical theme parties and costumed acts, Halloween characters and hauntings with special props/haunted graveyard. Fifteen years of experience in the entertainment field. Grammy nominated vocalists and studio quality musicians with National TV experience.

PARTY PLANNERS WEST, INC.
4141 Glencoe Avenue

Building C
Marina Del Rey, CA 90292
310.305.1000
Patricia Ryan
Robyn Leuthe
Areas served: National
Full service corporate event planning company providing innovative concept development, in-house production department, set and lighting, design, theme parties, in-house floral department, menu development and coordination with caterers, entertainment bookings, audiovisual coordination, technical and special effects. Customized events to client's specific needs. Named fifteenth largest woman owned business in Los Angeles County by the Los Angeles Business Journal. Named in Inc. Magazine's Top 500 Private Corporations.

SOUTHERN CALIFORNIA ENTERTAINMENT & MUSICAL CONCEPTS (SCEML)
16123 Orsa Drive
La Mirada, CA 90638
714.994.5798
Thomas Axworthy
Areas served: Southern California
Provide specialty, costumed, ethnic, classical music and related actors, dancers, etc.

WEST COAST COMEDY CONTACT
11362 Reagan Street
Los Alamitos, CA 90720
310.431.6122
Mariana Tilton
Areas served: Southern California
Top notch entertainers, name and novelty acts, comics, magicians and clowns for parties, hotels and roasts.

[Continued on next page.]

LOS ANGELES

♣ MAGIC, HYPNOSIS & PSYCHICS

AMAZING TOM SILVER HYPNOTIST
    8049 Mammoth Avenue
    Van Nuys, CA 91402
    818.780.4974
    Tom Silver
Areas served: Southern California, Orange
County, Ventura County and Santa Barbara
Hypnosis show that includes music and
sound effects. Show time is approximately
one hour. Great fun for company, private
parties and holidays. Performances
designed for specific age and party groups.
Hidden talents include amazing mental
powers and spontaneous comedy that are
part of the show. Performance as The
KROQ Hypnotist on *The Kevin and Bean
Morning Show.*

BODINE BALASCO AND COMPANY
    6664 Wilknson Avenue
    Suite 3
    North Hollywood, CA 91606
    818.777.6642
    800.503.9813
    Bodine Balasco
Areas served: National
Magic entertainment for all occasions.
Stand-up-comedy, magic, strolling sleight of
hand magic for after dinner performances,
private parties and hospitality suites.
Bodine Balasco has appeared on both *The
Phil Donahue* and *The Johnny Carson
Show* and his clients include Texaco,
Motorola, SCE, the California State
Government and ARCO.

CELESTE "MAGICALLY UNIQUE"
    21724 Ventura Blvd.
    Suite 293
    Woodland Hills, CA 91364
    818.705.8628
    Celeste Mills
Areas served: International
Magic and psychic entertainment provided,
palm, tarot readings and hypnosis show.
Two awards presented from the American
Council of Hypnotist Examiners and the
American Cancer Society Award for
outstanding public speaking.

DAVID AVADON
    P.O. Box 3222
    Santa Monica, CA 90408
    310.397.5539
    David Avadon
Marvelous magical entertainment that
includes elegant strolling sleight of hand
magic and a stage show featuring outrageous
humor and daring pick pocketing. David
Avadon has many national television
appearances and often serves as a technical
advisor in the film and television industry.

HOWARD JAY "MAGICIAN"
    1709 North Fuller Avenue
    Suite 22
    Hollywood, CA 90046
    213.851.4773
    Howard Jay
Areas served: International
Unique comedy magic entertainment for
private parties, banquets, corporate and
sales presentations customized to serve your
needs. Providing close-up comedy magic,
stage performance and awards ceremonies.
Howard Jay is a star performer at *The
Magic Castle.* He has more than eighteen
years of experience as a magician.

HUMOR DYNAMICS
    P.O. Box 2140
    Santa Maria, CA 93457
    805.934.3232
    John Kinde
Areas served: National
John Kinde is a full-time humorist and
professional speaker. Comedy or magic
programs provided. An emphasis on
programs that have a message of humor for
success and life enrichment.

"PSYCHICS TO THE STARS"
    18643 Burbank Blvd.
    Tarzana, CA 91356
    818.343.1565
    Valerie Stone
Areas served: National
Psychic entertainment provided with
Jamaican bones, tarot cards, palmistry
readings, handwriting analysis and crystal
ball gazing.

SICARD & MCKAY
7531 S. La Salle Avenue
Los Angeles, CA 90047
213.751.3486
310.445.5667
Cheri
Wini

State-of-the-art magic, side show
entertainment, fortune telling and hypnosis
provided. This group is a *Magic Castle*
member with years of corporate experience.

♪ MUSIC

AMBIENCE MUSIC CO.
11362 Reagan Street
Los Alamitos, CA 90720
310.594.9711
Richard Hastings

Areas served: Southern California
All styles of music provided such as Latin,
Caribbean and popular. Popular group
entertainers as well as small classical and
jazz ensembles are available.

BRYAN MANN & COMPANY
4716 Park Granada
Suite 200
Calabasas, CA 91302
818.591.1984
Bryan Mann

Areas served: Los Angeles, Valley, Westlake
Musical entertainment. World class studio
musicians, duos, trios, dance band, strings.
Featured in *Los Angeles* magazine
"Peoplescape", November 1991.

"BY REQUEST" STROLLING MUSICIANS
11362 Reagan Street
Los Alamitos, CA 90720
310.594.9711
Richard Hastings

Areas served: Southern California
All types of strolling musicians that include
flutists, guitarists and violinists who
provided a diverse repertoire from Bach to
the Beatles.

FIFTH AVENUE ORCHESTRAS
17040 Ventura Blvd.
Encino, CA 91316
818.783.9509

Jack Bielan
Sheri Dubin

Areas served: Los Angeles, Ventura and
Orange Counties
Musical groups provide Latin, big band,
fifties, sixties through the current top forty
and classical selections.

FLUTES UNLIMITED
1309 N. Linwood Avenue
Santa Ana, CA 92701
714.835.7293
Karen Steven

Areas served: Los Angeles and Orange
Counties
Flute and voice along with the piano and
string instruments such as the harp and
guitar provide elegant combinations to
enhance any special occasion. Call for a
complementary demo tape and brochure.

GOODE COMPANY
P.O. Box 1961
Wrightwood, CA 92397
619.249.3180
818.985.6982
Laura Kelly
S. Sellin

Areas served: San Diego to Santa Barbara
Entertaining performances of Christmas
carols or Renaissance madrigals in
elaborate, authentic costumes – either
Dickens or Elizabethan costumes. Strolling
carolers for all occasions. Won several first
place awards for best musical performance
at Southern California Renaissance
Pleasure Faire.

HARP AND CHAMBER MUSIC
P.O. Box 9672
North Hollywood, CA 91609
818.985.6982
Shawna Lynn Sellin

Areas served: Los Angeles
All varieties of classical and Celtic harp
music provided. Folk and chamber
ensembles available. Irish and classical
music are copyright free. Original and
improvisational work for sound tracks are
available. Shawna Lynne Sellin is an
experienced studio musician and 1984 All
Ireland Champion. She is a published
author of harp music and instructional
materials.

LOS ANGELES

ISLANDS OF TIME
310.470.8188
Rebecca Bonney
Areas served: Los Angeles
A Latin jazz trio specializing in bossa nova, sambas and jazz.

KEITH WILLIAMS ORCHESTRAS - ENTERTAINMENT
P.O. Box 6
Pacific Palisades, CA 90272

108 Foxtail Drive
Santa Monica, CA 90402
310.454.4000
Keith Williams
Areas served: California, Southwestern states, Midwest, Miami, Caribbean Cruise Lines
Featuring: The Westside Trio, Westside Quartet, and The Famous Keith Williams Big Band. Live music of all types and styles. Emphasis on jazz and traditional dance music, "name" musical artists, concerts. Awards include Grammy Award for Number One Instrumental Arranger for motion picture, *Last Of The One Night Stands,* winner of five national awards as Best Documentary Film, 1986.

KIM THE SONGWRITER
1219 E. Adams Avenue
Orange, CA 92667
310.288.1611
714.633.7513
Kim Olson
Areas served: International
Unique entertainment. Creates humorous songs instantly. Warm, personable and funny, creating on the spot songs and writing, producing theme songs for companies. Host for variety of club telethons. Dream Pin Winner of Quarter, highest award a cast member can achieve. Call or write for information.

NOUVELLE MUSIQUE
818.789.2931
Areas served: Southern California
Jazz combo's, chamber music and strolling musicians for all occasions. Formal attire. Call for complementary demo tape.

PAM AND BILLY KAY
10322 Mary Bell Avenue
Sunland, CA 91040
818.352.9774
Pam & Billy Kay
Areas served: International
Musical and comedy entertainment is provided.

THE PERINES
942 Fourteenth Street
Suite 2
Santa Monica, CA 90403
310.393.9631
Richard Hochberg
Areas served: Los Angeles and vicinity, will travel
1960's musical group, two women and one man spoofing the '60's. Comedy, big hair, great harmonies, perfect for private parties. Distinctions include commercials (McDonald's), *The Late Show, 2 Hip for TV, Rick Dees Comedy Show.*

ROY PHILLIPPE
8145 Redlands Street
Suite 204
Playa Del Rey, CA 90293
310.306.2410
Roy Phillippe
Areas served: Los Angeles area, will travel
Pianist, acoustic and electric, composer and arranger. Specialize in standards (Gershwin, Porter, etc.), show tunes, film themes.

THREE P PRODUCTIONS
P.O. Box 691689
Los Angeles, CA 90069
310.657.3092
Jere Ring
Areas served: Los Angeles, Southern California and worldwide
Provide: master of ceremony, piano/singer/entertainer, variety show, and piano combo (three to four piece). Distinctions include television specials, benefit concerts, featured entertainer.

LOS ANGELES

❧ NOVELTY

CASANOVA ROBOTS
> P.O. Box 4982
> West Hills, CA 91308-4982
> **818.716.9088**

David Leventhal
Areas served: Southern California and
Las Vegas
Robot entertainment.

CASINO DE PARIS, INC.
9636 Long Beach Blvd.
> South Gate, CA 90280
> **213.566.1001**
> **714.549.3396**

Areas served: Southern California
Las Vegas style casino equipment and
dealers. In business for thirty-two years.

**VIDA MCGAUGHEY, HANDWRITING
ANALYST EXTRAORDINAIRE**
> 3389 Charleston Way
> Hollywood, CA 90068
> **213.851.3762**
> Vida

Areas served: Southern California
Funtastic handwriting analysis for parties.
Fast, fun and very entertaining. Specialize
in private, corporate events, and Bar
Mitzvahs.

**WESTERN SQUARE DANCING
& COUNTRY LINE DANCING**
> 10746 Francis Place
> Suite 240
> Los Angeles, CA 90034
> **310.837.2880**
> Ronald Black

Areas served: Greater Southern California
Provide own sound equipment at all
outdoor or indoor events. Teaches and calls
square dancing. Reasonably priced.

PARTY SITES
❧ BEACHFRONT

415 P.C.H.
> 415 Pacific Coast Hwy.
> Santa Monica, CA 90402
> **310.458.2296**
> Annie Laskey

Beach front property with the look of a
1940's beach club. Complete with banquet
hall and small reception rooms. On the
water, complete with locker rooms and
showers. Started as an estate, turned into a
luxury beach hotel, then it became a beach
club with no hotels, now it's a public
recreation facility. Open to public daily.
Events available after 5 pm. Kitchen
attached and contains a raised bar area.
Receptions: 3 - 400 people. Inside: 200
people. Outside: 2000 people. 110 parking
spaces available.

CARVIN BEACH PROPERTY
> **310.453.7004**
> Ambrosia Caterers

Private beach property in Malibu.
Receptions and sit down: 1000 people.

GLADSTONE'S 4 FISH
> 17300 Pacific Coast Hwy.
> Pacific Palisades, CA 90272
> **310.573.0212**
> Steve Herbert

An LA institution on the ocean. Parties can
be held right on the beach for breakfast,
lunch, dinner and anytime. Seafood is their
specialty, but Mexican, Chinese, or
anything can be prepared. Full service
catering facility as well. Small dining room
seats twenty-five people. Beach available
for any size party.

❧ CONVENTION CENTERS

LA CONVENTION CENTER
> 1201 S. Figueroa Street
> Los Angeles, CA 90015
> **213.741.1151**
> Marketing Department

Seating capacity of 17,000. Parking
available for 3000. Will double exhibit
space and triple meeting room space by end
of 1993. Expansion includes huge atrium
lobbies, ideal for private events.

[Continued on next page.]

LOS ANGELES

❧ GALLERIES

BORITZER/GRAY GALLERY
903 Colorado Avenue
Santa Monica, CA 90401
310.394.6652
Etan Boritzer
1,700 square feet of space for events in a
contemporary fine arts setting.

DANIEL SAXON GALLERY
7525 Beverly Blvd.
Los Angeles, CA 90036
213.933.5282
Daniel Saxon
Art gallery with gallery space and an
outdoor patio for private events. 4200
square feet. Receptions: 300 people. Sit
down: 125 people.

FRED HOFFMAN GALLERY
912 Colorado Avenue
Santa Monica, CA 90401
310.394.4199
Contemporary gallery with skylights, high
ceilings, avant-garde art. 10,000 square
feet. Parking available.

ROY BOYD GALLERY
1547 Tenth Street
Santa Monica, CA 90401
310.394.1210
Richard Telles
Contemporary art gallery with concrete
floors, white walls, skylights. 2400 square
feet. Receptions: 50 people. Sit down: 30
people.

SCULPTURE GARDENS GALLERY
1031 Abbott Kinney Blvd.
Venice, CA 90291
310.476.6618
Sam Mowery
Indoor and garden setting featuring local
artists, photographers and sculptures.
Pond, waterfall, water lilies and beautiful
plants. Limited availability. Receptions:
125 people. Sit down: 75 people.

❧ HOTELS

THE BILTMORE HOTEL
506 S. Grand Avenue
Los Angeles, CA 90071
213.624.1011
Randy Villareal
Cooking classes, banquet rooms, catering
services, children's etiquette classes. Four
star hotel and Bernard's restaurant.

CALABASAS INN
23500 Park Sorrento
Calabasas, CA 91302
818.222.8870
Victoria Binetti
A picturesque backdrop of the Calabasas
Inn gardens and waterfall, perfect for
couples to exchange wedding vows outdoors.
Two indoor reception rooms, The California
Room and The Parkview Room. Both
rooms have two walls of ceiling to floor
windows. The Parkview Room overlooks
the ceremony area and The California
Room has an adjoining patio. 2400 square
feet in The California Room and 4200
square feet in The Parkview Room. The
ceremony site will accommodate more than
300 people. The California Room
accommodates 200 people. The Parkview
Room accommodates 300 people.

CENTURY PLAZA HOTEL AND TOWER
2025 Avenue of the Stars
Los Angeles, CA 90067
310.277.2000 x2598
Catering Department
Full service banquets and catering, theme
party planning, specialized menus. Over
100,000 square feet of meeting space,
including the Los Angeles Ballroom which
accommodates up to 3000 people. Four
Diamonds from AAA, Four Stars from
Mobil, Gold Key Award from *Meetings and
Conventions Magazine*, Pinnacle Award
from *Successful Meetings Magazine*, Award
of Excellence from *Incentive Travel
Magazine*, and Top Five Hotels in North
America from Nikkei Business.

FOUR SEASONS HOTEL AT BEVERLY HILLS
300 S. Doheny Drive
Los Angeles, CA 90048
310.273.2222
Judy Jamos

LOS ANGELES

The sixteen-story hotel is like a grand residence, bringing an East Coast and European flavor to the city. The residential size and style of the hotel caters to smaller and mid-sized groups in assorted salons and meeting rooms. The largest of the hotel's function areas are the ballroom and nearby Wetherly Garden. The latter, a beautifully landscaped court of white camellias and bougainvillea, is popular for outdoor social events, i.e., weddings. 9650 square feet of ten meeting rooms and a ballroom. Receptions: 500 people in ballroom. Sit down: 280 people dining in ballroom and 400 people theatre style in ballroom. Mobil Five Star 1991-1992, AAA Four Diamond 1990-92, California Restaurant Writers Association Four Star 1990-092, Calibre Award for Excellence in Design 1988, LA Beautiful Award for Landscaping in 1988.

LOEWS SANTA MONICA BEACH HOTEL
1700 Ocean Avenue
Santa Monica, CA 90401
310.458.6700
Misti Kerns

Full service, meetings, conventions, banquets, small lunches, dinners, receptions and weddings. Kosher catering available. The only luxury beach front hotel in Los Angeles.

THE NEW OTANI HOTEL AND GARDEN
120 S. Los Angeles Street
Los Angeles, CA 90012
213.629.1200

Banquet and garden facilities. Half acre garden with waterfall. Traditional Japanese style weddings as well as regular weddings. Garden receptions: 200 people. Garden wedding ceremonies: 150 people. Garden sit down: 100 people. Receptions: 800 people.

THE RITZ
880 Newport Center Drive
Newport Beach, CA 92660
714.720.1800
Nancy Rasoletti

Understated elegance and tradition combined with classic European fare. Parties, meetings, and event facilities. Epicurean Wine Cellar: 32 people. Vintage Room: 70 people. Escoffier Room (not available Friday & Saturday): 125 people. Entire restaurant (Sunday only): 100 people.

THE RITZ-CARLTON, MARINA DEL REY
4375 Admiralty Way
Marina Del Rey, CA 90292
310.823.1700
Jackie Geiger

Complete range of special events. Weddings, anniversaries, receptions, Bar/Bat Mitzvahs, retirement parties, birthday celebrations, reunions, fundraisers, catering, yacht chartering. Additional services include: decorations, transportation, floral creations, entertainment, gourmet cuisine, tuxedos. Ballroom has 7911 square feet. Five conference rooms and a dedicated conference concierge. Beautiful English gardens. Voted Best New Hotel on the West Coast and Hawaii by *Prestige Magazine*. Recipient of Mobil's Four Star Award and AAA's Four Diamond Award.

UNIVERSAL CITY HILTON AND TOWERS
555 Universal Terrace Pkwy.
Universal City, CA 91608
818.506.2500
800.727.7110
Juan Aquinde

Twenty-four story glass tower situated high atop the Hollywood Hills, The Universal City Hilton and Towers is located in the heart of the Entertainment District and at the very entrance to Universal Studios Hollywood, The Universal Amphitheater and CityWalk. Centrally located to downtown Los Angeles, Hollywood, Beverly Hills, The San Fernando Valley and to all airports and freeways. Conference and banquet facilities have 27,000 square feet of multi-use function space. Grand Ballroom has 16,000 square feet. Receptions: 1500 people. Sit down: 2000 theater style. 1991 Lasnier Award for excellence in food and beverage quality, creativity, and presentation.

THE WESTIN BONAVENTURE
404 S. Figueroa Street
Los Angeles, CA 90071
213.624.1000 x4808
Jorge Ber

Continental cuisine serving all social and corporate needs as well as theme parties, weddings, and fundraisers. Banquets and catering facilities from 10 - 3000. Largest ballroom in Los Angeles.

WESTWOOD MARQUIS HOTEL AND GARDENS
930 Hilgard Avenue
Los Angeles, CA 90024-3025
310.208.8765
Terri Tolliver

Marquis Pool & Gardens, Garden Terrace Restaurant, Erte Room, 5 banquet rooms. Mobil Four Star Award, AAA Four Diamond Award, Award of Distinction from International Food, Wine & Travel Writers Association, Circle of Fame and Four Star Wine Cellar Award from California Restaurant Writers Association, Five Star Award for Excellence from KABC's "The Food Show", and the Travel Holiday Award for Dining Distinction.

LOCATION BUREAUS

MARQUIS EVENTS
3007 Washington Blvd.
Suite 225
Marina Del Rey, CA 90292
310.574.6611

Full service event planning company with exclusive locations including elegant custom yachts, private homes, castles, mansions, and estates. Events at land and sea.

MANSIONS & GARDEN SETTINGS

THE ADAMSON HOUSE
23200 Pacific Coast Hwy.
Malibu, CA 90265
818.706.8809
Terry Brann

A national historic sight as well as a California landmark. Former home of Adamson family, heirs to last original Spanish land grants. 1929 Moorish Spanish Colonial revival style residence. Events held on grounds. Maximum of 200 people for event. Overlooks the ocean one quarter mile form Malibu Pier. Available seven days a week with some restrictions.

CALAMIGOS RANCH
327 S. Latigo Canyon
Malibu, CA 90265
818.889.6280
Mon-Li

A variety of romantic settings including a beautiful lawn and patio area, complete with a wedding terrace and waterfalls. Banquet rooms, featuring dramatic flagstone fireplaces and mountain vistas adjoin the patio area. Additional banquet facilities are available at other locations on the ranch with complete on-site catering. Receptions and sit down: 350 people and can be expanded with the use of a tent.

THE HISTORIC GRABER OLIVE HOUSE
315 E. Fourth Street
Ontario, CA 91764
714.983.1761
Clifford Graber

The grounds are frequently used for art festivals, political and civic organization dinner/parties, local community organization functions. Free tours of the historic cannery, small museum, picnic area, gourmet food/kitchen shop and gift shop, featuring Graber Tree-ripened olives and other Graber of California delicacies.

LA VENTA INN
796 Via Del Monte
Palos Verdes Estates, CA 90274
310.372.0737
310.373.0123
Jim Wharton

Historic home built in 1924 graces a lush garden setting with a panoramic view of Palos Verdes Peninsula, Santa Monica Bay and city lights. Enjoy the nostalgia of days past in this graceful setting. Wedding ceremonies, receptions and special events produced by The New York Food company, the South Bays premier catering company. Approximately 3000 square foot indoor facility located on three private acres. Receptions: 250 people. Sit down: 175 people.

NEW YORK FOOD COMPANY'S CATALINA ROOM
6610 Palos Verdes Drive South
Rancho Palos Verdes, CA 90274
310.544.4971

LOS ANGELES

310.376.6929
Jim Wharton
Keith Levine
Breathtaking garden setting in Palos Verdes for creative ocean front weddings, receptions and special events to 500 guests. Customized menu design and event production by the New York Food Company. Cliff side, terraced gardens, romantic sunsets, amazing views, one event per day, secluded on 150 acres, provide your own alcoholic and nonalcoholic beverages.

PADDISON FARM/VICTORIAN FARM HOUSE
11951 Imperial Hwy.
Norwalk, CA 90650
310.863.4567
Margaret
Six acres of manicured lawns and gardens. Garden weddings in garden gazebo or on Victorian porch. Receptions on spacious lawns surround Victorian Farm House. Patio dance area, patio bar and buffet area. Outside catering is allowed but can provide on-site catering.

THATCHER MANOR
22220 Gavilan Road
Gavila Hills, CA 92570
714.780.1742
Joyce Thatcher
All garden facility. Five acres of lawns and gardens available for private events. Dance pavillion, outdoor party, formal garden with gazebo. Canopied area for seating available for weddings and private events. Receptions and sit down: 350 people.

WATTLES MANSION
1824 N. Curson Avenue
Hollywood, CA 90046
213.874.4005
Steve Sylvester
Both mansion and grounds available for events. 1905 Mission Revival residence. Large lawn and formal garden. Receptions and sit down: 150 people. 9 p.m. curfew for evening events.

❧ MUSEUMS

GENE AUTRY WESTERN HERITAGE MUSEUM
4700 Western Heritage Way
Los Angeles, CA 90027-1462
213.667.2000
Janis Dinwiddie
Situated on thirteen acres in Griffith Park in Los Angeles, the Gene Autry Western Heritage Museum is a cultural and educational institution which exhibits art and artifacts related to the history of the American West. The museum makes its facilities available for limited use by selected corporate and non-profit organizations for private events. Entire museum complex is 148,000 square feet. Receptions: entire museum and outdoor plaza - 2000+, Parkland - 4000 +(suitable for outdoor fairs, festivals, concerts). Sit down: Heritage Court (indoors) - 225 people, main plaza (outdoors) - 450 people, Parkland (tent/outdoors) - 2000 people. Blue Ribbon Award of Merit, Society of American Registered Architects, 1991. New Public Projects Award, Los Angeles Business Council, 1989.

KIDSPACE MUSEUM
390 S. El Molino Avenue
Pasadena, CA 91101
818.449.9144
Lindi
Children's museum offering deluxe theme parties, private parties, semi-private parties, public hour parties. Museum is 6000 square feet. Sit down: 30 people in party room.

LONG BEACH MUSEUM OF ART
2300 E. Ocean Blvd.
Long Beach, CA 90803
310.439.2119
Karen Kent
Outdoor sculpture garden situated on bluff overlooking ocean. Receptions: 400 people. Sit down: 400 people. Grounds available from 5:00 pm through evening. Set-up can begin as early as 2:00 pm.

[Continued on next page.]

LOS ANGELES

LOS ANGELES CHILDREN'S MUSEUM
310 N. Main Street
Los Angeles, CA 90012
213.687.8801
Frank Pittarese

Interactive, hands-on museum. Designed as an educational play space for children, but lends itself to special events and parties that fun loving adults can also enjoy. Nineteen interactive exhibits include Recording Studio, Television Studio, Art Workshop, Performance Theatre, Velcro Room and much more. A unique location for a special event where everyone is encouraged to be a child, explore and play. 17,000 square feet. Receptions: 350 people. Sit down: 25 people, but not very practical, buffets are recommended.

MUSEUM OF CONTEMPORARY ART
250 S. Grand Avenue
Los Angeles, CA 90012
213.621.2766
Kay Carrillo

Event facilities for corporate and non-profit professional events. Exhibition viewing available during events. Variety of spaces available. Interior spaces can accommodate up to 150 people. Exterior receptions: 2000 people.

MUSEUM OF FLYING
2772 Donald Douglas Loop North
Santa Monica, CA 90405
310.392.8822
Debbie Schaak

Ultra-modern space with displays of vintage aircraft. Large board room, fully equipped screening room. Historic space providing both intimate and expansive space. 35,000 square feet covering three floors. Receptions: 1500 people. Sit down: 850 people.

NEWPORT HARBOR ART MUSEUM
850 San Clemente Drive
Newport Beach, CA 92660
714.759.1122
Marilyn Kaun

Contemporary art museum internationally recognized for the scope and quality of exhibition programs, outreach programming and growing regional collection of post-1945 California art.

23,000 square feet. Receptions: 500 people. Sit down: 500 people for weddings, 800 people for cocktail parties.

SANTA MONICA HERITAGE MUSEUM
2612 Main Street
Santa Monica, CA 90405
310.392.8537
Tobi Smith

1894 historic landmark house. Two floors, patios and outdoor grounds available to rent. First floor has period rooms and second floor has open galleries with rotating exhibitions. Free parking for 100+ cars. Victorian furnishings, living room, dining room, 1930's kitchen, pantry. Receptions: 150 people indoor only and 300 people inside and outside areas. Sit down: 100 people indoor only - formal dining and 300 people inside and outdoor areas.

SOUTHWEST MUSEUM
234 Museum Drive
Los Angeles, CA 90065
213.221.2164 x234

Available to non-profit groups, corporate members, and private individuals who join the museum at the $1,250 level, for the purpose of meetings, receptions, and parties. Events must be held outside of museum hours. Please call at least sixty days in advance for fee and scheduling information. Auditorium: 2240 square feet, California Hall: 3008 square feet, Lower lobby: 506 square feet, Plains Hall: 1600 square feet, Temporary Gallery: 1232 square feet. Receptions: 300 people if alternate parking arrangements are made (parking lot can only accommodate about 100 vehicles). Sit down: 100 - 150, unless the group can be split into two rooms.

❧ NOVELTY

CHAYA BRASSEREE'S ANNEX "PLACE SAZABY"
110 N. Robertson Blvd.
Los Angeles, CA 90048
310.859.0996
Chikako DeZonia

Glassed front and beautiful brand new space with two big palm trees in the center. 4000 square feet plus terrace of 700 square feet. Receptions: 250 people. Sit down: 150 people.

HAUNTED STUDIOS
6419 Hollywood Blvd.
Hollywood, CA 90028
213.465.3372
Greg

Cabaret coffee house atmosphere that holds up to fifty people. A haunted spirit atmosphere prevails. Can provide both theatre and reception facilities for events. In addition to the event site they also have a full costume rental department complete with a wig and makeup room.

ICE CAPADE CHALET ICE ARENA
6100 Laurel Canyon Blvd.
N. Hollywood, CA 91606
818.985.5555
Pat Ferrick

Private party room for rent adjacent to ice rink. Catering available. A great idea for $25.00 an hour, a minimum of ten or more. Rental of entire ice rink available after public hours at $225.00 an hour.

LOS ANGELES UNION STATION
"The Last Great Train Station"
800 N. Alameda Street
Los Angeles, CA 90012
213.625.5865

Two indoor areas: 1. Main Concourse - 10,000 square feet. Receptions: 1000 people. Sit down: 600 for dinner or concert. 2. Former Fred Harvey Restaurant - 4000 square feet. Receptions: 200 people plus additional 300 people with use of adjoining south patio. Sit down: 100 people for dinner.

MARQUIS EVENTS
3007 Washington Blvd.
Suite 225
Marina Del Rey, CA 90292
310.574.6611

Full service event planning company with exclusive locations including elegant custom yachts, private homes, castles, mansions, and estates. Events at land and sea.

MONTANA MERCANTILE
1500 Montana Avenue
Santa Monica, CA 90403

310.451.1418
Rachel Dourec

Spacious, modern kitchen with a 20 foot granite countertop, an ideal and innovative space for any type of special occasion. Seating for as many as thirty people for a cooking class or up to fifty for an informal wine tasting. Ample outdoor patio and grill with seating capacity for approximately forty. The patio also serves as a pre-function space.

MOONLIGHT ROLLERWAY ROLLER SKATING CENTER
5110 San Fernando Road
Glendale, CA 91204
818.241.3630
Dominic Cangelosi
Barbara Peters

For roller skating parties only, i.e., private birthday parties. Private fundraising roller skating parties for churches, schools, organizations. Private roller skating for day care center, YMCA, YWCA, day camps or any organization or group. A complete snack bar operates within the facility. 21,000 square foot building and 12,000 square foot skating surface - hardwood maple floor. Carpeted lobby with lockers. Maximum capacity is 1000 people.

MORE THAN A MOUTHFUL, CATERING INC.
743 S. Lucerne Blvd.
Los Angeles, CA 90005
213.937.6345
Barry Colman

Areas served: Southern California, travel to Northern California, Nevada, East Coast

Full service event planners including food, decor , rentals, entertainment, banquet facilities for 1000 guests. Specialize in over-abundance of food, mind boggling displays, into the visuals, catering to fantasies. All graduates of the Culinary Institute of America.

THE PALACE
1735 N. Vine
Hollywood, CA 90028
213.462.6031
213.462.3000
Dennis Lidtke

LOS ANGELES

Complete multi-media facility. Entertainment complex/night club including on-site catering and full event production. Festivals: 1200 people. Sit down: 500 people. Lasers, large screen video projection, sound concert PA and stage lights. The Palace Court, located upstairs, is complete with a dance floor and accommodates from 100 - 200 people.

PARAMOUNT PICTURES STUDIO
5555 Melrose Avenue
Los Angeles, CA 90038-3197
213.956.5100
Reece Thomson

Outdoor plazas, parks, stages, dining rooms, banquet facilities. 3000 to 18,000 square feet. Receptions: 4000 people. Sit down: 1000 people. Awarded three and one half stars by *People Magazine*, hosted People's Choice Awards, Celebrity Outreach Awards, etc.

ROBERT MONDAVI WINE & FOOD CENTER
1570 Scenic Avenue
Costa Mesa, CA 92626
714.979.4510
Joyce Barela
Harriet Lewis

Special event lunches, dinners, seminars and receptions with a focus on wine and food. World-class cuisine paired with the fine wines of the Robert Mondavi family. Best Meal of 1989 by Max Jacobson of Los Angeles Times. Orange County Leading Woman Chef to Rosanne Ruiz by Ruth Reichl, *Los Angeles Times*.

YANKEE DOODLE'S (BILLIARD CLUB/RESTAURANT)
1410 Third Street Promenade
Santa Monica, CA 90401
310.394.4632
Irene Astrow

14,000 square feet on two levels, twenty-nine pool tables, two private rooms, foozball, pin ball, games, etc. Must be seen to be appreciated. Have held many film industry wrap parties for up to 400 people. 500 maximum capacity, approximately 200 chairs.

❧ PRIVATE CLUBS

LOS VERDES COUNTRY CLUB
7000 W. Los Verdes Drive
Rancho Palos Verdes, CA 90274
310.377.7888

Breath taking view of the Pacific Ocean and Catalina Island. Overlooks the beautifully landscaped golf course. Club features have recently been redecorated. Outdoor patio available for weddings and cocktail receptions. 5000 square feet. Receptions: 400 people. Sit down: 400 people.

THE LOS ANGELES ATHLETIC CLUB
431 W. Seventh Street
Los Angeles, CA 90014
213.625.2211 x300
Paul Steen
Marlene Tolentino

Traditional club setting with private meeting rooms and ballroom. Rich tradition of servicing club members and guests since 1880. Twelve story facility, seventy-two hotel rooms, four restaurants, secure parking, private meeting rooms. Receptions: (ballroom) 350 - 400 people depending upon set-up. Sit down: (ballroom) 250 people with dance floor.

ST. JAMES HOTEL & CLUB
8358 Sunset Blvd.
Los Angeles, CA 90069
213.656.7100
Gary Clauson

Art Deco decor. 2000 square feet. Receptions: 300 people. Sit down: 120 people.

❧ RESTAURANTS

AL AMIR
Wilshire Courtyard
5750 Wilshire Blvd.
Suite 195
Los Angeles, CA 90036
213.931.8740
John & Natalie Sabga

Lebanese/Middle Eastern restaurant. Upscale ambiance and decor. 5121 square feet. Receptions: 148 people. Sit down: 148 people. CRWA Three Stars 89, 90, 91. Voted Top Three Specialty Restaurants in Los Angeles by *Money Magazine*.

LOS ANGELES

ANTONELLO RISTORANTE
1611 Sunflower Avenue
Santa Ana, CA 92704
714.751.7153
Gilda Boswell
Northern Italian lunch and dinner banquets
and catering. Closed Sundays. Receptions:
125 people. Sit down: 125 people.
Southern California Restaurant Writers,
Golden Sceptre Award for Restaurateur
of the Year.

**ASSISTANCE LEAGUE
OF SOUTHERN CALIFORNIA®**
Fountain Court Restaurant
1370 N. St. Andrews Place
Los Angeles, CA 90028
213.469.1973
Nora Abbott
Traditional old Hollywood styled mansion,
marble foyer with grand staircase, outdoor
patio with fountain. Oval banquet room
with French patio doors. 3000 square feet.
Receptions: 300 people. Sit down: 300
people. Designed by Paul Williams.

THE BISTRO GARDEN AT COLDWATER
12950 Ventura Blvd.
Studio City, CA 91604
818.501.0202
7500 square feet. Receptions: 275 people.
Sit down: 250 people.

CAMELIONS RESTAURANT
246 Twenty-sixth Street
Santa Monica, CA 90402
310.395.0746
Steven Gomberg
Three private rooms and two patios.
Receptions: 50 people. Sit down: 35, 45,
60, also seating on front and back patios.

THE CELLAR
305 N. Harbor Blvd.
Fullerton, CA 92632
714.525.5682
Ernest Zingg
Sean Lewis
Romantic dining experience. Restaurant
was built by the trades people from
Disneyland. Approximately 2500 square
feet. Fully licensed. Receptions: 150
people. Sit down: 100 people in main

dining, 20 people in Wine Cellar Room.
AAA Four Diamond Award, Americas Fifty
Best French Restaurant Award, Epicurean
Rendezvous Award, Golden Sceptre, and
Golden Bacchus Award from Southern
California Restaurant Writers, The Wine
Spectators, Best Award of Excellence.

CHASEN'S
9039 Beverly Blvd.
W. Hollywood, CA 90048
310.271.2168
Ralph Woodworth
Serving only the finest cuisine for over fifty-
six years. Luncheon, Tuesday - Friday,
11:30 am - 3:00 pm. Dinner, Tuesday -
Sunday, 6:00 pm - 1:00 am. Holiday Award
from DRNA. Restaurant Writers Award.

CHEZ MELANGE
1716 Pacific Coast Hwy.
Redondo Beach, CA 90277
310.540.1222
Michael Franks
Areas served: South Bay, Orange County,
Los Angeles County
Banquet rooms, off-premise catering, full
service event management. Specialize in
gourmet wine dinners, ethnic menus, first
class service. Distinctions include Top 100
Restaurant by *Epicurean Rendezvous*, Top
50 Restaurant in *Zagat Guide*. Owners
voted South Bay Citizens of the Year.

CHIN CHIN
13455 Maxella Avenue
Marina Del Rey, CA 90292
310.823.6948
Judy Caspe
Areas served: Los Angeles
Full service catering and banquet facility.
Four locations throughout LA. Chinese
food prepared fresh and healthful. Dim
Sum, tabletop wok cooking, chocolate
dipped fortune cookies with personalized
messages.

CITRUS RESTAURANT
6703 Melrose Avenue
Los Angeles, CA 90038
213.857.0034
Jean Jacques Retourne
[Continued on next page.]

LOS ANGELES

French/California cuisine. Private inside room for up to 65, full bar, outside patio with flowers and large umbrellas, seats to 150. 800 square feet inside, 2200 square feet outside patio. Receptions: 450 people. Sit down: 215 people.

DC3 RESTAURANT
2800 Donald Douglas Loop North
Santa Monica, CA 90405
310.314.3654
Stephanie Edens
Unique restaurant at Santa Monica Airport. Private rooms for groups of 10 - 250. All rooms have stunning views and patios. 7000 square feet. Awards for Restaurant Design. Receptions: 500 people. Sit down: 250 people.

THE DEPOT
1250 Cabrillo Avenue
Torrance, CA 90501
310.787.7501
Michael Shafer
Areas served: South Bay, Los Angeles, Orange County
Banquet facilities and catering. Wide selection of micro-brewery beers. Amazingly creative menu.

FENNEL RESTAURANT
755 N. La Cienega Blvd.
Los Angeles, CA 90069
310.657.8787
Andre Bodisco
Jean-Christophe Le-Varrat
Maureen Murphy
An authentic French Bistro headed by chef Laurent Grangien, who, immediately prior to taking over as the Head Chef at Fennel, was the chef at Restaurant Michel Rostang and Bistrot da Cote, both in Paris. Sit down: 65 people. American Writers Association, Epicurean Rendezvous Award, Wine Spectator Award, several others.

GLADSTONE'S 4 FISH
17300 Pacific Coast Hwy.
Pacific Palisades, CA 90272
310.573.0212
Steve Herbert
An LA institution on the ocean. Parties can be held right on the beach for breakfast, lunch, dinner and anytime. Seafood is their specialty, but Mexican, Chinese, or

anything can be prepared. Full service catering facility as well. Small dining room seats twenty-five people. Beach available for any size party.

THE GOLDEN TRUFFLE
1767 Newport Blvd.
Costa Mesa, CA 92627
714.645.9858
Alan Greeley
Bistro restaurant. 500 square feet. Receptions: 60 people. Sit down: 60 people. Epicurean Rendezvous 1988-1991, Southern California Restaurant Writers Gold 1987-1991.

THE HOLLYWOOD YACHT CLUB
7021 Hollywood Blvd.
Hollywood Galaxy
213.465.8916
John Laney
A fun, high energy, casual restaurant with fun decor of old Hollywood and a surf theme with nine small monitors and two wide screens. LA's best sound system. Four pool tables, black jack, darts. Perfect for premiers, openings, record release parties. Lots of secured well lit parking. 11,250 square feet with a 750 square foot dance floor. Receptions: 550 people. Sit down: 275+ people.

INN OF THE SEVENTH RAY
128 Old Topanga Canyon Road
Malibu, CA 90290
310.455.1311
Kelly Hancock
Shirley Vernale
Creekside setting under the sycamores with lovely, soft, mountain air. When day ends, the sun bows out gracefully to an evening of romantic candlelight dining beneath the stars. Good food and good wine. A special place for your magical wedding. Open seven days for lunch and dinner. Sunday brunch. 3000 square feet. Receptions: 175 people. Voted by *People Magazine*, Los Angeles' Most Romantic Restaurant.

LE DOME RESTAURANT
8720 Sunset Blvd.
Los Angeles, CA 90069
310.659.6919
Eddie Kerkhofs

French-continental dining. Various banquet rooms for maximum of 100 people. Can reserve entire restaurant for private parties. Sit down: 275 people. Travel Holiday Dining Distinction, The Food Show Award of Excellence, California Restaurant Writers Association, Epicurean Rendezvous, Distinguished Restaurants of North America, Dining Professionals.

MICHAEL'S
1147 Third Street
Santa Monica, CA 90403
310.451.0843

Located three blocks from the Pacific Ocean. Known for its beautiful decor and prized modern art (American) collection. Indoor rooms, upstairs, terrace and gardens outside. Sit down: 120 people.

ORLEANS RESTAURANT
11705 National Blvd.
W. Los Angeles, CA 90064
310.479.4187
Mary Atkinson
Ronald Wallace

Fine Southern cooking, spicy or not, in a casual elegant setting. 5000 square feet. Receptions: 350 people up and down. Sit down: main dining, 165 people. private room, 80 people. Three stars from CRA, Paul Wallach Award of Excellence, Epicurean Rendezvous Award. Open since 1984.

PAZZIA RESTAURANT
755 N. La Cienega Blvd.
Los Angeles, CA 90069
310.657.9271
Maureen Murphy
Andre Bodisco

Italian restaurant. The food is brilliantly prepared and the pasta is always perfect. A big, sparsely modern furnished place. Has become a favored spot for celebs and entertainment industry honchos.

REBECCA'S
2025 Pacific Avenue
Venice, CA 90291
310.306.6266
Carolyn or Robert

Room is designed by Frank Gehry. A giant crystal octopus chandelier hangs above the entire room. 2000 square feet. Receptions and Sit down: 35 people. Awarded by *Epicurean*, California Writers Association, Great Chefs of Los Angeles, and *Life Styles of The Rich and Famous*.

SAGEBRUCH CANTINA
9523 Culver Blvd.
Culver City, CA 90230
310.836.5321
Penny Burton

Square room with bar in the middle between dining room and bar room. All tables have glass tops with linens. Colors are seafoam green and mauves. Can either be casual or formal. Receptions: 250 people. Sit down: 200 people.

SPORTSMEN'S LODGE RESTAURANT
12833 Ventura Blvd.
Studio City, CA 90405
818.984.0202
213.396.6953

Nine large banquet rooms and luxurious garden setting. Rooms from 600 square feet to 10,000 square feet. Receptions: 1200 people. Sit down: 1000 people. Forth-six years of distinguished service. Newly refurbished.

TREES RESTAURANT
440 Heliotrope Avenue
Corona Del Mar, CA 92625
714.673.0910
Russell Armstrong
Richard Barnes

100 seat restaurant with thirty-five seat piano lounge, and private party room. Full or limited service catering. Approximately 3000 square feet. Receptions: 125 people. Sit down: 100 people. Off premise location for 500 available. Southern California Restaurant Writers Gold Award. Paul Wallach Three Star designation, *Epicurean Rendezvous* "100 Best" Award, KABC Food Show Award of Excellence.

WEST BEACH CAFE
60 N. Venice Blvd.
Venice, CA 90291
310.823.5396
Patrick McMahon

California Bistro with French influence. Also functions as an art gallery. No private rooms available, but the restaurant can be booked for private affairs. 1750 square feet. Receptions and sit down: 88 people for whole restaurant. An award winning wine list, including awards form Epicurean, Southern California Writers Association, and Cordon Bleu.

YAMASHIROS
1999 N. Sycamore Avenue
Hollywood, CA 90068
213.466.5125
Nestled in the Hollywood Hills. Panoramic view of Hollywood and the LA Basin. Spectacular Mountain Palace. Unique setting for weddings, receptions, and special events. Authentic Japanese and Continental cuisines. 14,250 square feet. Receptions: 700 people. Sit down: 500 people.

❧ THEATRES & AUDITORIUMS
SANTA MONICA CIVIC AUDITORIUM
1855 Main Street
Santa Monica, CA 90401
310.458.8551
Carole Curtin
Ellen French
3000 seat auditorium with 12,000 square feet hydraulically operated slab floor. Stage proscenium 65 feet wide and 31 feet high. 41 sets of lines. I.A.T.S.E., Local 33 stagehands. Eleven dressing rooms. Has been serving Los Angeles for over thirty years hosting a variety of events including the Academy Awards, People's Choice Awards and Rock'n Roll to Symphony concerts. Exhibit shows include antique shows, International Gem & Jewelry Show and Crafts Market. 27,000 square feet of exhibit space includes lobby, stage, main floor, and east wing. Receptions and sit down: 3,000 theatre seating, 3500 - 4250 festival seating, 810 people for banquets.

THE WILTERN THEATRE
3790 Wilshire Blvd.
Los Angeles, CA 90010
213.388.1400
Candy Croteau
Historical landmark located in Mid-Wilshire

District. Beautifully refurbished Art Deco Building. Theatre style venue offering. Receptions: 750 people. Sit down: 450 people. Theatre: 2200 people. Parking lot adjacent to theatre.

❧ ZOOS & THEME PARKS
GREATER LOS ANGELES ZOO ASSOCIATION
5333 Zoo Drive
Los Angeles, CA 90027-1498
213.664.1100
Debbie Dendrinos
Special event locations for groups of 50 to 5000. Full range of services. Unique dining opportunities amongst a highly acclaimed collection of animals and exotic botanical gardens. Numerous awards for successful propagation of endangered species. Significant achievement awards in the field of education.

KNOTTS BERRY FARM
8039 Beach Blvd.
Buena Park, CA 90620
714.220.5074
Barbara Kranz
Parties from 20 - 20,000. Two picnic centers, themed events inside park. 165 attractions to chose from. Full service catering. Weddings in Historic Church of Reflections, private parties, special theme events and company picnics.

PARTY SUPPLIES
AAH's
1083-1087 Broxton Avenue
Westwood, CA 90024
310.824.1688

3223 Wilshire Blvd.
Santa Monica, CA 90403
310.829.1807

14548 Ventura Blvd.
Sherman Oaks, CA 91403
818.907.0300
Jack Sing

LOS ANGELES

Lesley Chapman
Party supplies, gift wrap, balloons,
novelties, unusual gifts.

THE BAG LADIES
4214 Glencoe Avenue
Marina Del Rey, CA 90292
310.822.1706
800.359.BAGS
Linda Hollander
Custom-printing on paper and plastic bags,
also carry festive gift bags, shred and tissue.
Metallic foil printing and bags are available
at an additional charge.

BALLOONS BY MAGIC WORLD
10122 Topanga Canyon Blvd.
Chatsworth, CA 91311
818.700.8100
Areas served: Greater Los Angeles area
Balloons, helium tank rentals, paper
supplies, balloon decorating (small & large),
costumes, magic themes. Twenty years in
business. Duplicated Brooklyn Bridge for
Paramount Studios with balloons.

CAMPBELL-TOLSTAD STATIONERS
1022 Westwood Blvd.
Los Angeles, CA 90024
310.208.4322

23823 W. Malibu Road
Malibu, CA 90265
310.456.9838
Jeanne Judin
Areas served: Westwood, W. Los Angeles,
Beverly Hills, Los Angeles
Stationery (including Crane's), printing,
party goods, fine gifts, novelties, office
supplies, furniture, pens, etc. Extensive
catalogue available. Free delivery, free gift
wrapping, assistance with special events
planning. Westwood branch in business
since 1924.

GIFT ALBUMS
818.580.7803
818.447.6693
Arlowyn Barton
Carolyn Boyd
Areas served: Southern California
Twenty different gift albums featuring
quality name brands. Selective gifts for
exceptional people.

LEHR AND BLACK, INC.
3542 Hayden Avenue
Culver City, CA 90230
310.839.0990
Sol Lehr
Ellen Black
Areas served: National
Custom invitations, table favors,
centerpieces, escort cards, escort boards,
napkins, decorations, party consultation.
Specializing in weddings, Bar Mitzvahs,
theme parties, birthdays, holiday parties.
Received Beverly Hills Chamber of
Commerce First Place Award 1988, 1989,
1990 and 1991 for Christmas decorations.

PARTY MANIA
818.609.8633
Linda Drew
Areas served: Los Angeles
Custom decorations to fit any event.
Balloon decorations, sculptures, arches,
prop centerpieces, theme related prop
rental, gift deliveries, costume deliveries,
invitations. Balloon decorations to fit any
budget. Member of the National
Association of Balloon Artists for five years.

PARTY WORLD
19450 Business Center Drive
Northridge, CA 91324
818.993.3033

2011 Hollywood Way
Burbank, CA 91505
818.846.6202

1754 Moorpark Road
Thousand Oaks, CA 91360
805.496.6611

19816 Ventura Blvd.
Woodland Hills, CA 91364
818.716.1266

11910 W. Pico Blvd.
West Los Angeles, CA 90064
310.473.8822

17843 Colima Road
City of Industry, CA 91748
818.810.8877

[Continued on next page.]

LOS ANGELES

PARTY WORLD (CONTINUED)

18681 Main Street
Huntington Beach, CA 92648
714.841.2999

25375 Crenshaw Blvd.
Torrance, CA 90505
310.530.0566

5509 Woodruff Avenue
Lakewood, CA 90713
310.925.9777

1521 S. Harbor Blvd.
Fullterton, CA 92632
714.526.3855

25410 Marguerite Pkwy.
Mission Viejo, CA 92691
714.768.3850

1026 W. Covina Pkwy.
West Covina, CA 91790
818.813.0039

1060 Commerce Center Drive
Lancaster, CA 93534
805.940.7079

5840 Sepulveda Blvd.
Van Nuys, CA 91411
818.909.0799

500 W. Broadway
Glendale, CA 91204
818.241.6464

3404 E. Chapman
Orange, CA 92669
714.633.6693

2011 Via del Norte
Oxnard, CA 93030
805.485.0714

349 S. Mountain
Upland CA 91786
714.946.8090

3675 E. Colorado Blvd.
Pasadena, CA 91107
818.796.8022

3480 La Sierra
Riverside, CA 92503
714.687.7734
Stanley Tauber
One-stop center for all your party needs at
20 - 50% discount.

STREAMERS

North County Fair
272 E. Via Rancho Pkwy.
Suite 463
Escondido, CA 92025
619.737.8408

Main Place
2800 N. Main Street
Space 284
Santa Ana, CA 92701
714.647.1356

Sherman Oaks Fashion Square
14006 Riverside Drive
Space 116
Sherman Oaks, CA 91423
818.784.8724

284 Del Amo Fashion Center
Torrance, CA 90503
213.542.3566
One-stop shopping for party supplies,
invitations, balloons, paper supplies,
imprinting, machine calligraphy,
decorations.

WILLIAM ERNEST BROWN

South Coast Plaza
3333 S. Bristol Street
Costa Mesa, CA 92626
714.540.2265

The Market Place
6529 E. Pacific Coast Hwy.
Long Beach, CA 90803
310.598.1725
Custom-designed and catalogue invitations,
seating charts, accessories, place cards and
party supplies for all special events. They
also provide calligraphy services. Known
for their high quality products and special
services. Clients all over the United States
and Europe.

PERSONNEL & STAFFING

BLACK TIE EVENT SERVICES
1454 Third Street Promenade
Suite 212
Santa Monica, CA 90401
310.576.1800
Stephen Plache
Areas served: Southern California
Bar catering coordination and event staffing
services to both industry and private
clients, from the informal to the very formal
special event. Receptions, premieres,
holiday celebrations, weddings, fundraisers,
birthdays and much more.

CRAIG'S CREW
By Appointment Only
Pasadena, CA
818.398.0559
213.257.1920
Craig T. or Teri Weeks
Areas served: National
Specializing in party staffing and mobile
DJ's. Complete party planning and
catering available. McHammer Dancers
and production for corporate and Bar/Bat
Mitzvahs. New division for kids' parties.
Have connections for box lunches for fund
raisers, picnics, etc. Not expensive and
great food. Featured on TV's Eye on LA
and Entertainment Tonight.

HOST HELPERS
1633 Westwood Blvd.
Suite 120
Los Angeles, CA 90024
310.478.7799
Patricia Moore
Areas served: Southern California
Waiters, waitresses, bussers, bartenders,
chefs, chef assistants, clean-up crew.
Featured in *Los Angeles Times*, *Los Angeles
Magazine*, *Entrepreneur*, *Home & Garden*,
LA Style.

PHOTOGRAPHY & VIDEO

A VIDEO AFFAIR
1538 Franklin Street
Suite L
Santa Monica, CA 90404
310.828.1557
Jim or Kim Wooden
Areas served: Los Angeles, Santa Barbara,
San Diego.
Specialize in capturing celebrations on
video. Shoots in London, Saudi Arabia,
Sweden... Personal videographer for many
celebrities.

ADVANCED VIDEO SERVICES
714.897.5387
Phil Barton
Areas served: Southern California
State of the art video. One or two cameras.
Professional editing with music.

BILL ENGLEMAN PHOTOGRAPHY
19137 Haynes Street
Reseda, CA 91335
818.881.0397
Bill Engleman
Areas served: Beverly Hills and San
Fernando Valley
Exclusive and personal photography.
Weddings, Bar Mitzvahs, anniversaries.
Photographed Goldie Hawn's sister 's
wedding. Photographer for social events,
motion picture industry and National
Association of Women Executives, Los
Angeles.

BOULEVARD VIDEO PRODUCTIONS
15016 Ventura Blvd.
Suite 4
Sherman Oaks, CA 91403
818.501.7369
David Robin
Jay Stein
Areas served: National
Complete video production. Charter
member, founder and president of the
American Videographers Association.

BROOKE VIDEO
15946 Sherman Way
Suite 4
Van Nuys, CA 91406
818.786.4671
Sandy Brooke

LOS ANGELES

Areas served: Los Angeles, Orange County
Special event videography. All
videographers dress in tuxedos. Many
awards for video work.

CHRIS HUNTER
8917 Dorrington Avenue
W. Hollywood, CA 90048
310.273.8311
Chris Hunter
Areas served: International
Provide photography and video services for
all special events. Specializing in public
relations and interior design photos.
Clients include special event decor
companies.

**CHRISTOPHER BARR
PHOTOGRAPHY & VIDEO**
1642 N. Wilcox Avenue
Hollywood, CA 90028
213.962.8602
Christopher Barr
Areas served: Beverly Hills, Newport
Beach, Los Angeles County, Orange County
Photography and video coverage for all
events. Specializing in publicity, editorial
coverage and fast turn around. Photos are
internationally syndicated. Shoot the cover
photos for *The Beverly Hills (213)
Magazine* and *Newport Beach (714)
Magazine.*

DAVID KESSLER PHOTOGRAPHICS
5505 Laurel Canyon Blvd.
Suite C
Valley Village, CA 91607-4202
818.766.1676
David Kessler
Areas served: U.S.A., Canada, Mexico
and Europe
Special event photography to include
company parties, weddings, Bar Mitzvahs,
corporate events, room decor photography.
Presidents award of Toastmasters
International, distinguished Best of Show
as Special Event Photographer, APALA.

EICHEN IMAGINE PHOTOGRAPHY
1726 Marvin Avenue
Los Angeles, CA 90019
213.937.3395
Jeff Eichen

Areas served: International
Complete photographic services for special
events, architecture, products, celebrity
portraiture and fine art. Specializes in a
unique party service - "Mr. Polaroid,"
where he transforms Polaroid's of guests
into avant garde art using etching tools and
design techniques.

**ENTERTAINMENT CONSULTANTS
& EC VIDEO PRODUCTIONS**
1633 Westwood Blvd.
Los Angeles, CA 90024

1834 Newport Blvd.
Costa Mesa, CA 92627

801 Washington Street
San Diego, CA 92013
800.273.7221
Areas served: Los Angeles, Orange County,
San Diego, Riverside and Santa Barbara
Bands, DJs, all types of entertainment and
video services.

HELEN P. CHERRY PHOTOGRAPHY, INC.
7956 Beverly Blvd.
W. Hollywood, CA 90048
213.653.1966
800.585.CHERRY
Helen Cherry
Areas served: Los Angeles, San Fernando
Valley, and Orange County
Romantic wedding photography, sensuous
bridal boudoir portraits, casual outdoor
portrait sessions, beach photo sessions,
black and white photography and coverage
which includes hundreds of candid
photographs of each wedding. "Reflections
Presentation" slide show to be shown at
your wedding. Casual romantic portraits,
lots of humor in photographs. Two
photographers cover each event and feature
electronic video proofs. All proofs may be
watched at home on your TV screen and
kept for future reference. Member of
Wedding Photographers International,
Professional Photographers of America,
listed in Who's Who in California. Taught
other wedding photographers her special
techniques at national conventions and local
seminars.

LOS ANGELES

JEWELL VIDEO SERVICES
10568 1/2 Ayres Avenue
Los Angeles, CA 90064
310.558.4938
Dan or Karen
Areas served: Los Angeles and Orange
Counties
Video parties, Bat Mitzvahs, weddings,
picture montage, lifetime tributes.
Featured as one of Twelve Best
Videographers in Nation by *Forbes
Magazine*.

JUDY LAWNE PHOTOGRAPHER
2122 Lemoyne Street
Los Angeles, CA 90026
213.660.0960
Judy Lawne
Areas served: Los Angeles & New York
Provide photography services for
corporate, special events, parties, portraits.
Kodak funding for "Portraits of Dance"
1986-87 Best Black & White Advertising at
the Rockefeller Center.

MOTION IMAGES
22011 Ventura Blvd.
Suite 103
Woodland Hills, CA 91364
818.713.8433
David Rozzen
Video production services and post-
production. Weddings, Bar/Bat Mitzvah,
parties, anniversaries, etc. Industrial and
Broadcast.

RICHARD BRADLEY GLENN
4069 E. Boulevard
Los Angeles, CA 90066
310.398.9897
Richard Bradley Glenn
Areas served: California
Photography, prints, frames.

TRAUDE WINIK PHOTOGRAPHY
P.O. Box 49206
Los Angeles, CA 90049
310.476.6164
Traude Winik
Areas served: Santa Monica, Brentwood,
W. Los Angeles, Bel Air, Beverly Hills, N.
Hollywood, San Fernando Valley, Pasadena
Photography for charities, balls, openings

and private parties. Received
Humanitarian and Contributors Awards for
her work from SCMPC, Thalians and The
Jeffrey Foundations

PLANT RENTALS

**RUBIN/JOSEPH ENVIRONMENTAL
DESIGN, INC.**
11710 Barrington Court
Los Angeles, CA 90049
310.471.3885
Edward Joseph
Areas served: Southern California
Complete party planning and floral design
services. Movie premiers, corporate
parties, large and small events. Wide range
of fresh florals, silks and dried materials.

PROPS & DECOR

BALLONS BY TIC-TOCK
1601-1/2 N. La Brea Avenue
Los Angeles, CA 90028
213.874.3034
Eddie Zaratsian
Areas served: National
Specializing in original centerpiece
creations for weddings, Bar/Bat Mitzvahs,
corporate marketing, charities, major
events and parties. Winner of several
awards including Best Centerpiece - 1991.

**BARTON'S HORSE DRAWN
WEDDING CARRIAGES**
818.447.6693
714.599.0627
Arly and Bill Barton
Areas served: Southern California
Provide beautifully restored vintage
carriages pulled by majestic white horses;
driver and attendant formally attired;
carriage/coach tastefully decorated to bridal
colors with silk flowers; two personalized
calligraphied "Just Married" signs.
Specializing in weddings and any special
event. Horses are thoroughly trained for
heavy, busy traffic on any public street,
except freeways. Props, TV, movies.
Awards too numerous to list. Featured on:

LOS ANGELES

AM/LA; PM TV Magazine; NBC Sunday Today; Days of Our Lives - TV; Eyewitness News, Ch 7; *Sunset Magazine; Woman's World; Los AngelesTimes; Modern Bride: People Magazine*: Pasadena Tournament of Roses Parade, as well as the Hollywood Christmas Parade. Also featured in many other publications. In business since 1969.

EXTRAORDINARY EVENTS
13437 Ventura Blvd.
Suite 210
Sherman Oaks, CA 91423
818.783.6112
Andrea Michaels
Areas served: International
Full event planning, destination management, entertainment, decor, location selection. Numerous awards from *Special Events Magazine*: "Best Theatrical Show Production," first and second place awards for best entertainment concept, theme decor, fundraising event and tabletop decor.

G & F CARRIAGES
5033 Los Coyotes - Diagonal
Long Beach, CA 90815
310.597.5267
Terica Campbell
Areas served: Los Angeles and Orange County
Horses and carriages for rides, photo shoots, decor. Pony rides for birthdays and special events for groups up to twenty. Transportation for larger groups in party wagons driven by horses. Driver's attire customized to the event.

IMAGES EVENT PRODUCTION
1649 Twelfth Street
Santa Monica, CA 90404
310.392.4240
Jerry Astourian
Areas served: International
Event design, lighting design, set and prop construction. Specializing in Hollywood premiere parties, corporate galas, fundraising events, private affairs. *Special Events Magazine* Gala Awards: Best Decorated Theme Event, Most Imaginative Use of Lighting & Special Effects (four years), Most Imaginative Use Of A Tent, Most Imaginative Use of Equipment, Special Logistic Award.

IT'S THE MAIN EVENT, INC.
29399 Agoura Road
Suite 105
Agoura Hills, CA 91301
818.706.0340
Cheryl Fish
Areas served: Western States
Full event production company specializing in corporate and social events. In-house prop production, graphic arts department and high styled floral department. Seven time recipient of *Special Event Magazine* Gala Awards. Best Floral, three years in a row, Best Corporate Event Over $30,000, Best Event Done On A Shoestring Under $5,000, Most Imaginative Invitation, two years in a row.

JOHN DALY INC.
2210 Wilshire Blvd.
Suite 886
Santa Monica, CA 90403
310.459.0586
John Daly
Areas served: International
Design and decor for all events. Gala Awards from The Special Event, Best Table Top, Best Floral, Best Use of Equipment, nominated six years in a row. Twenty-seven years experience in the industry.

LA CIRCUS
7531 S. La Salle Avenue
Los Angeles, CA 90047
216.751.3486
Wini McKay
Areas served: International
Customized circus events for all occasions. Equipment rental, seats, tenting, games, performers, elephant rides and acts, as well as complete set-up. Clients include Disney, Yamaha, Pepsi International and many more.

LOS ANGELES PARTY DESIGNS, INC.
3368 S. Robertson
Los Angeles, CA 90024
310.836.5273
Debra Stevenson
Areas served: National
Event production, decor and floral design. Gala Award Best Floral Design, Blooming Inspirations Exhibitor, LA Top 100 Women Owned Business.

MASTROIANNI'S/JAY'S CATERING
10581 Garden Grove Blvd.
Garden Grove, CA 92643
714.636.6045
800.585.6045
Norman Meyer
Areas served: Los Angeles, Orange, San Diego, Riverside, Santa Barbara Counties
Catering, full scale props, rentals, flowers, bakery, linens, entertainment.

PAGEANTRY PRODUCTIONS
11122 Wright Road
Lynwood, CA 90262
310.632.5600
Jakki Hill
Areas served: California, Arizona and Nevada
Specializing in Christmas decor. Provides studios with designs for Christmas movies such as: *The Story Lady, All I Want for Christmas, Roseann Barr's X-Mass Show*, etc.

PARTY PLANNERS WEST, INC.
4141 Glencoe Avenue
Building C
Marina Del Rey, CA 90292
310.305.1000
Patricia Ryan
Robyn Leuthe
Areas served: National
Full service corporate event planning company providing innovative concept development, in-house production department, set and lighting, design, theme parties, in-house floral department, menu development and coordination with caterers, entertainment bookings, audiovisual coordination, technical and special effects. Customized events to client's specific needs. Named fifteenth largest woman owned business in Los Angeles County by the *Los Angeles Business Journal*. Named in *Inc. Magazine's* Top 500 Private Corporations.

RC VINTAGE STUDIO RENTALS, INC.
1644 N. Cherokee Avenue
Hollywood, CA 90028
213.462.4510
Bill Carter
Chris Phillips
Areas served: Southern California

Forties through the sixties props such as: Diners, gas stations, streets, neon signs, jukeboxes, pinball machines, furniture and light fixtures. Distinctive props for mood parties such as: Rolling Stones, U2, Dick Tracy and Back to the Future 3.

RHYMES AND DESIGNS
1838 S. Robertson Blvd.
Los Angeles, CA 90035
310.838.7755
Sandra Gutterman
Areas served: Greater Los Angeles
Party coordinator, florist, custom-designed and catalogue invitations, calligraphy services, custom escort cards, table numbers, complete room decoration, centerpieces, lighting, etc. Past clients include Michelle Lee, Vidal Sassoon, Kaufman & Broad, Bob Dylan, Falcon Cable, Germaine Jackson.

ROSCHU, INC.
7100 Fair Avenue
N. Hollywood, CA 91605
818.503.9392
Bill Coffey
Unique prop rentals for special occasions: African, Arabian (Mid East), Egyptian, French, Hawaiian, Italian, Mexican, Oriental, Roman, Patriotic, Art Deco, garden decor, Hollywood movies, westerns, space, monsters (Halloween, etc.), toys, Christmas, underwater, serving carts, lighting (street lights) lightweight chandeliers, candelabras, serving carts.

S & R ORIGINALS
18344 Oxnard Street
Suite 106
Tarzana, CA 91356
818.705.1778
Cindy Symans-Hassel
Areas served: Southern California
Event planning for all occasions. Flowers, props, invitations, decor, entertainment, locations and food. Specialize in floral design and event decor. Props produced in-house.

[Continued on next page.]

LOS ANGELES

STREAMERS

North County Fair
272 E. Via Rancho Pkwy.
Suite 463
Escondido, CA 92025
619.737.8408

Main Place
2800 N. Main Street
Space 284
Santa Ana, CA 92701
714.647.1356

Sherman Oaks Fashion Square
14006 Riverside Drive
Space 116
Sherman Oaks, CA 91423
818.784.8724

284 Del Amo Fashion Center
Torrance, CA 90503
213.542.3566

One-stop shopping for party supplies,
invitations, balloons, paper supplies,
imprinting, machine calligraphy, decorations.

PUBLIC RELATIONS

MICHELLE & MICHEL

818.545.0356
805.269.4162
Michelle Lawrence
Carrie St. Michel
Areas served: National
Comprehensive public relations capabilities
including media relations and editorial
services. Specialize in corporate publicity,
special event publicity, and product
publicity.

SECURITY

EXCLUSIVE PROTECTION, INC.

331 N. Rodeo Drive
Suite 3
Beverly Hills, CA 90210
310.859.8248
Jackie Fox
Areas served: Los Angeles
Armed and unarmed uniformed or
plainclothes security officers.

SIGNAGE

SANTA MONICA SIGNS

819 Wilshire Blvd.
Santa Monica, CA 90401
310.393.7404
Phyllis
Lou Anne
Areas served: Santa Monica, Malibu, W.
Los Angeles, Hollywood, Marina
Festive party banners and signs.

SPEAKERS

BODINE BALASCO AND COMPANY

6664 Wilkinson Avenue
Suite 3
North Hollywood, CA 91606
818.503.9813
800.777.6642
Bodine Balasco
Areas served: National
After dinner speaker and conference key-
note speaker. Topics include:
Championship Secrets of Self Motivation
and Prosperity Principles of Quality
Customer Service. Has degrees in Speech
Communications and Social Psychology
from UCLA and his clients are: Texaco,
Motorola, SCE, the California State
Government and ARCO.

**CALIFORNIA LEISURE CONSULTANTS
OF LOS ANGELES**

3605 Long Beach Blvd.
Suite 201
Long Beach, CA 90807-4013
310.427.0414
Ilene Reinhart
Creative approach to total destination
management services. Specialize in
innovative theme party productions,
customized tour coordination, sporting
events, speakers, entertainment, specialty
gift items and expert service for corporate,
association and incentive meetings and
conventions.

DAMON BROOKS ASSOCIATES

1680 N. Vine Street
Suite 910
Hollywood, CA 90028

LOS ANGELES

213.465.3400
Marc Goldman
Areas served: National
Coordination of celebrity involvement with special events. Tennis, golf, and related sporting events. Speaking, entertainment and personal appearances. Recognized by California Meetings, Western Association News, Affordable Meetings, International Festivals Association, American Society of Association Executives.

DUKE OF BOURBON
20908 Roscoe Blvd.
Canoga Park, CA 91304
818.341.1234
David Breitstein
Ron Breitstein
Areas served: San Fernando Valley, Beverly Hills, West Los Angeles, Malibu, Westlake Village, Thousand Oaks, Agoura
Wine tasting seminars, executive wine seminars, party and event planning with delivery of wine, spirits, beer, wine collecting consultation, speakers, gift baskets, newsletter. Specialize in personalized service. Commendations from City and County of Los Angeles for twenty-five years of successful business. Chosen by *The Wine Spectator* and *Market Watch* as one of top twelve wine and spirits shops in America for 1990. *Beverage Dynamics* Retailer of the Year 1991.

HUMOR DYNAMICS
P.O. Box 2140
Santa Maria, CA 93457
805.934.3232
John Kinde
Areas served: National
John Kinde is a full-time humorist and professional speaker. Comedy or magic programs provided. An emphasis on programs that have a message of humor for success and life enrichment.

WALTERS INTERNATIONAL SPEAKERS BUREAU
P.O. Box 1120
Glendora, CA 91740
818.335.8069
Lilley Walters
Areas served: International
Humorists, motivational speakers, magicians.

TABLETOP ACCESSORIES & KITCHENWARE

THE BREWERY COFFEE & TEA CO.
263 Santa Monica Place
Santa Monica, CA 90401
310.393.7793
Robert Myers
Dale Myers
John Heinz
Areas served: Santa Monica, Marina Del Rey, Palisades, Malibu, W. Los Angeles, Brentwood, Beverly Hills
Gourmet coffee beans, loose and packaged tea, coffee makers, espresso machines, replacement parts, coffee and tea accessories, collector tea pots, large selection of mugs, cappuccino cups. Espresso bar with fresh brewed coffee, muffins, chocolate truffles. Gift baskets. UPS or local free delivery with minimum purchase. Serving Santa Monica and the West Side since 1980.

BRISTOL FARMS COOK'N'THINGS GOURMET COOKWARE STORE
606 Fair Oaks Avenue
South Pasadena, CA 91030
818.441.5588
David Gronsky
Areas served: San Gabriel Valley, Los Angeles County, San Fernando Valley
Complete selection of the finest gourmet cookware and accessories, fine china and stemware, linens, cookbook library. On-going demonstrations of the latest in gourmet cookware, guest appearances of cookbook authors professional cooking school on premise.

BY DESIGN
131 N. La Cienega Blvd.
Suite 765
Los Angeles, CA 90048
310.652.9230
Bridal registry and contemporary home furnishings.

CRATE & BARREL
Century City Shopping Center
Los Angeles, CA 90067
310.551.1100
Full line of unique contemporary home furnishings and accessories featuring tabletop accessories and gourmet kitchenware.

LOS ANGELES

FIORI
448 South Coast Hwy.
Suite A
Laguna Beach, CA 92651
714.494.9954
800.373.9853
Bonnie Wolin
Areas served: National and International
Specializing in fine quality Italian and
Greek handpainted ceramics known as
Majolica. Pieces have been featured in the
following publications: *Gourmet,
Metropolitan Home, China Glass &
Tabletop and Laguna Magazine.* Selected
by the *Los Angeles Times* as one of the Best
in Southern California in the November
1990 edition.

MONTANA MERCANTILE
1500 Montana Avenue
Santa Monica, CA 90403
310.451.1418
Rachel Dourec
Store is stocked with a full range of high
quality cooking equipment and specialty
foods as well as fine gifts, tabletop
accessories and hand-crafted items.

MUFFINS, ETC.
12634 Ventura Blvd.
Studio City, CA 91604
818.762.6343
Janet Acquaro
Areas served: Local and UPS shipping
Meal size and mini muffins baked daily on
premises, gourmet coffee, gift baskets.
Sugar free and sugar/fat free muffins a
specialty. Awarded Studio City Business of
the Month.

POTTERY BARN
10914 Kinross Avenue
Los Angeles, CA 90024
213.208.1752
Chester Mcintosh

Beverly Center
131 N. La Cienega Blvd.
Los Angeles, CA 90048
310.657.7505

Century Square Mall
10250 Santa Monica Blvd.
Los Angeles, CA 90067
213.552.0170

2148 Glendale Galleria
Glendale, CA 91201
818.241.6056

Fashion Island Center
1071 Newport Center Drive
Newport Beach, CA 92660
714.664.2406

Galleria at South Bay
1815 Hawthorne Blvd.
Suite 250
213.370.7737

Mainplace Santa Ana
2800 N. Main Street
Suite 832
Santa Ana, CA 92701
714.479.0922

La Cumbre Place
110 S. Hope Avenue
Suite 51C
Santa Barbara, CA 90024
805.687.6707

114 Santa Monica Blvd.
Santa Monica, CA 90401
213.393.1471

14006 Riverside Drive
Suite 64
Sherman Oaks, CA 91423
818.907.5877

6100 Topanga Canyon Blvd.
Woodland Hills, CA 91367
213.208.3553
Leading retailer of contemporary tableware
and decorative accessories for the home.
Merchandise is 100% exclusive, designed
and sold exclusively at Pottery Barn. Over
fifty stores nationally and mail order.

THREE FOXES TROT
23733 Malibu Road
Suite 900
Malibu, CA 90265
310.456.1776
Jeanna Gelston
Areas served: Malibu, San Fernando
Valley, Santa Monica, W. Los Angeles
Tableware, decor, favors, home
furnishings, personal care accessories,
audio, gifts, luggage.

TIFFANY & CO.
210 N. Rodeo Drive
Beverly Hills, CA 90210
310.273.8880
Michele Sheid

South Coast Plaza
3333 Bristol Street
Costa Mesa, CA 92626
714.540.5330
The finest in engraved invitations, favors,
accessories, stationery, bridal registry, fine
crystal and china, Tiffany flatware and gifts
for all occasions.

VILLAGE KITCHEN SHOPPE
147 N. Glendora Avenue
Glendora, CA 91740
818.914.7897
Fantastic selection of every imaginable
gadget, superior bake ware and service
ware - everything for the kitchen.

WILLIAMS-SONOMA
100 Smith Ranch Road
Suite 301
San Rafael, CA 94903
415.492.2823
Pat Rinker

317 N. Beverly Drive
Beverly Hills, CA 90210
310.274.9127

Beverly Center
131 N. LaCienega Blvd.
Los Angeles, CA 90048
310.652.9117

The Commons
146 S. Lake Avenue
Pasadena, CA 91101
818.795.5045

273 Promenade
Woodland Hills, CA 91367
818.887.4355

La Cumbre Place
3835 State Street
Santa Barbara, CA 93105
805.563.0767

14006 Riverside Drive
Sherman Oaks, CA 91423
818.981.1044

1112 Glendale Galleria
Glendale, CA 91210
818.241.0154

South Coast Plaza
3333 S. Bristol Street
Costa Mesa, CA 92626
714.751.1166

Main Place
Suite 552
2800 N. Main Street
Santa Ana, CA 92701
714.542.8852

The Shops at Palos Verdes
550 Deep Valley Drive
Rolling Hills Estates, CA 90274
213.541.9545

1016 Brea Mall
Brea, CA 92621
714.256.9301
An authoritative selection of the best for the
kitchen. Complete line of cookware,
bakeware, electrics, glassware, tabletop,
kitchen furniture, cookbooks, packaged
foods. Knowledgeable staff will help choose
equipment, plan parties. Most merchandise
is exclusive to Williams-Sonoma.

VALET PARKING
**CELEBRITY VALET PARKING
SERVICE, INC.**
P.O. Box 100
Los Alamitos, CA 90720
310.430.2775
Randy Olsen
Areas served: Southern California
Valet parking company. Coordinates
complete guest reception services. Staff is
highly trained in hospitality. Services
include coat check, formal greeters,
transportation and shuttling. Named Top
Valet Parking and Guest Accommodation
Service by Long Beach Convention Visitors
Bureau, Honorable Mention *Los Angeles
Times* and *Long Beach Press Telegram*.

[Continued on next page.]

LOS ANGELES

MAJESTIC VALET PARKING
2442 S. Coast Hwy.
Suite 3
Laguna Beach, CA 92651
714.497.1465
800.831.7275
Areas served: Orange County, Los Angeles
Valet parking for all special events.
Provide a two million dollar insurance
policy. Clients include leading politicians,
businesses and celebrities.

VALET PARKING SERVICE, INC.
10555 Jefferson Blvd.
Culver City, CA 90232
800.794.PARK
310.657.2420
Joel Groves
Tony Policella
Areas served: San Francisco to San Diego
Valet parking for any size event from 1000
to 5000. Contracts valet parking for
restaurants, hotels, businesses, etc.
Specialize in any size private parties for any
type of situation. Provide ten million dollar
liability insurance, radio communications
and all other equipment necessary for
efficient and professional valet parking.
Emphasis is on car protection and safety.
Provided parking service for the Emmy
Wards, Grammy Awards, Academy
Awards, Playboy Mansion West, etc. The
originators of party parking in Los Angeles,
established in 1946.

Z-VALET PARKING & SHUTTLE
6922 Hollywood Blvd.
Los Angeles, CA 90028
213.871.0222
Kent Simmons
Areas served: Greater Los Angeles, Mid-
Wilshire, Beverly Hills, Santa Monica,
Malibu, Westlake/Agoura, Calabassas, all
San Fernando Valley, La Canada/Flintridge
& Pasadena
Professional special event valet parking,
excellent ground transportation for groups
via fifteen-passenger maxi vans. Large, gala
events for museums, movie premieres and
charities. Full scale planning for all
vehicular receptions. Commendation from
Occidental Petroleum, Armand Hammer
Museum, LA County Museum of Art, LA
County Museum of Natural History, Annual
Pediatric Aid and Parkinson.

WINE & SPIRITS

BEL-AIR WINE MERCHANT
10421 Santa Monica Blvd.
W. Los Angeles, CA 90025
310.474.9518
Bob Gold
Areas served: Los Angeles, International
Old vintage wines. Fresh Russian caviar.
Full bar supplies. Delivery, shipping
worldwide.

**CALIFORNIA BASKET COMPANY
& WINE SHOP**
20 S. Raymond Avenue
Old Pasadena, CA 91105
800.992.9992
818.577.9292
Jack Daniel Smith
Areas served: International
Custom-made gift baskets, handle large
volumes with ease. Baskets made on short
notice and include customer supplied
products and goods for special events
(company mugs, pens, etc.). Specialize in
unique gourmet foods, coffees and teas,
chocolates, cheeses and meats, bath
products. Also feature a large selection of
wines and imported beers. One of the
largest gift basket companies in California,
each basket is made to order. All bows are
hand-made and can be color coordinated
for any color scheme. Sixteen page full
color catalogue available at no charge.

DUKE OF BOURBON
20908 Roscoe Blvd.
Canoga Park, CA 91304
818.341.1234
David Breitstein
Ron Breitstein
Areas served: San Fernando Valley,
Beverly Hills, West Los Angeles, Malibu,
Westlake Village, Thousand Oaks, Agoura
Wine tasting seminars, executive wine
seminars, party and event planning with
delivery of wine, spirits, beer, wine
collecting consultation, speakers, gift

baskets, newsletter. Specialize in personalized service. Commendations from City and County of Los Angeles for twenty-five years of successful business. Chosen by *The Wine Spectator* and *Market Watch* as one of top twelve wine and spirits shops in America for 1990. *Beverage Dynamics* Retailer of the Year 1991.

GELSON'S

16450 Ventura Blvd.
Encino, CA 91436
818.906.5780
Greg Hansen

4738 Laurel Canyon Blvd.
N. Hollywood, CA 91607
818.906.5743
Bill Thompson

10250 Santa Monica Blvd.
Los Angeles, CA 90067
310.906.5793
Tim Redmond

500 Reseda Blvd.
Tarzana, CA 91356
818.906.5752
Mike Lee

1660 San Miguel Drive
Newport Beach, Ca 92660
714.906.5798
Frank Spielberger

15424 Sunset Blvd.
Pacific Palisades, CA 90272
310.906.5795
Jim McCurry

2734 Townsgate Road
Westlake Village, CA 91361
818.906.5790
John Austin

13455 Maxella Avenue
Marina Del Rey, CA 90292
310.906.5771
Rick Imamura

Extensive collection of domestic and imported wines. Dick Williams, Gelson's wine buyer and merchandiser, will recommend the taste and bouquet of wines through Gelson's Wine Department. Look for the varieties labeled "Dick Williams' Personal Choice".

LOS ANGELES WINE CO.

4935 McConnell Avenue
Unit 8
Los Angeles, CA 90066
310.306.9463
Steven Bialek
Areas served: California
Best wines, hand selected and lowest prices.

RED CARPET WINE & SPIRITS MERCHANT

400 E. Glenoaks Blvd.
Glendale, CA 91207
818.247.5544
David Dobbs
Steve Fox
Russell Shin
Areas served: Los Angeles County
Full line beverage catering, wine tasting, personalized gift baskets, bartending. Largest gift basket selection. In-store wine tasting and classes. Best Gift Basket "Liquors" Kylex Award from New York. Deliver locally. Ship nationwide.

THE WINE RESERVE

929 S. Brand
Glendale, CA 91204
818.500.8400
Barry Herbst
Areas served: California
Tastings, seminars, outside catering, dining facilities, wine storage (temperature controlled). Boutique wineries, eclectic selection of imported wines, well known California brands.

YACHT & BOAT CHARTERS

A-SUNSET SAIL YACHT CHARTERS

11684 Ventura Blvd.
Studio City, CA 91604
818.348.1797
310.578.9248
Sindee Kritzberg
Areas served: Marina Del Rey, Newport Beach, Long Beach
Specializing in custom, private, fully crewed yacht charters on sail boats, power yachts, sport fishers and luxury mega yachts. Complete event and party planning. Yachts

ranging in size from 25 feet to 120 feet.
Receptions: 2 - 260 people. Sit down: 2 -
150 people. Named one of fifteen "Most
Imaginative Amorous Adventure, " featured
in *LA Magazine's 1992 Valentine's
Handbook* - "Get Romantic."

A CHARTERED AFFAIR
13428 Maxella Avenue
Suite 404
Marina Del Rey, CA 90292
310.306.3545
Michael Deren
Areas served: Greater Los Angeles
Event coordinators specializing in luxury
yachts. Parties from 2 to 400 people.
Awarded Bridal Diamond Award on "Most
Romantic Wedding Reception Site, " 1990.

GONDOLA GETAWAY
5437 E. Ocean Blvd.
Long Beach, CA 90803
310.433.9595
Areas served: Naples - Long Beach
Unique one hour gondola cruise around the
Naples canals in Long Beach.

MARQUIS EVENTS
3007 Washington Blvd.
Suite 225
Marina Del Rey, CA 90292
310.574.6611
Full service event planning company with
exclusive locations including elegant custom
yachts, private homes, castles, mansions,
and estates. Events at land and sea.

&a &a &a

SAN DIEGO

SAN DIEGO

AUDIOVISUAL & TECHNICAL SERVICES

BEAR COMMUNICATIONS
1400 Sixth Avenue
Suite 103
San Diego, CA 92101
619.531.0933
Tim Walters
Areas served: National (Thirteen offices across the United States)
Rental, sales and service of Motorola two-way radios and accessory equipment. Largest inventory of radio equipment in the United States.

MASTERS PRESENTATION GRAPHIC SERVICES
6150 Lusk Blvd.
Suite 104
San Diego, CA 92121
619.457.4720
Jeff Pratt
Areas served: California, Nevada, Arizona
Full audiovisual, multi-image, video, computer graphics and photography services.

WESTERN SCENIC STUDIOS
1470 Citrus Ridge
Escondido, CA 92025
619.943.8847
Ted Prina
Areas served: National
Full event decor including lighting, staging, and floral design. Full trade show production. Technical services. In business since 1919.

BALLOONS

PARTY FAVORS AND RENTALS
908 Fesler Street
El Cajon, CA 92020
619.562.7888
Joyce Buchmayer
Areas served: San Diego County
Linens, tables, chairs, gazebos, arches, canopies, barbecues, china, chaffers, full selection of favors and party supplies. Paper goods, custom and catalogue invitations. Custom imprinting of napkins, ribbons, matchbooks. Balloons, helium tanks – blow up and delivery.

THE PARTY SHOP
441 Santa Fe Drive
Encinitas, CA 92024
619.753.8455
Areas served: San Diego and Orange Counties
Huge selection of retail party goods, full costume shop year 'round, balloons, helium.

BOOKS

WILLIAMS-SONOMA
1640 Camino del Rio North
San Diego, CA 92108
619.298.8851

235 Horton Plaza
San Diego, Ca 92101
619.239.3855
An authoritative selection of the best for the kitchen. Complete line of cookware, bakeware, electrics, glassware, tabletop, kitchen furniture, cookbooks, packaged foods. Knowledgeable staff will help choose equipment, plan parties. Most of their merchandise is exclusive to Williams-Sonoma.

CAKES & BAKED GOODS

THE BREAD FACTORY
2525 El Camino Real
Suite 154
Carlsbad, CA 92008
619.720.2253
Mary Lynn Weingarden
Areas served: San Diego County
Full service bakery specializing in wedding and cheese cakes, breads, rolls, pastries, fifteen kinds of bagels, NY-style breads. Can create any kind of cake – custom drawings.

CALLIGRAPHY

THE CLASSY PEN
619.560.6545
Fran Lewis
Areas served: International
Computerized and hand calligraphy
services. Custom-designed and catalogue
invitations, seating charts, menu cards, etc.

ELEGANT ADVERTISING GRAPHICS
7280-A Carrara Place
San Diego, CA 92122
619.457.3232
Peter Turner
Areas served: International
Custom-designed and catalogue invitations,
lighting and sound effects, die-cuts, foiled,
embossed, special paper folds, pop-ups,
place cards, favors, sign-in boards, full
calligraphy services.

LADYBUG ART CALLIGRAPHY SERVICES
4685 Biona Drive
San Diego, CA 92166
619.274.2510
Susan Hull
Areas served: International
Retail store specializing in custom-designed
and catalogue invitations. Seating charts,
signage, customized gift registry sheets.
Calligraphy services. Calligraphy
supplies, fine stationery, custom framing,
greeting cards.

CATERING

FRENCH GOURMET CATERING
960 Turquoise Street
Pacific Beach, CA 92109
619.488.1725
Sales Department
Area served: San Diego County
Full service catering company, fully licensed
to sell liquor. Full event planning services.
Specializing in French cuisine, but also do
incredible Italian, Mexican, Thai and Cajun
menus. Member of 1992 Louis Vuitton Cup
Team. Owner Michael Malecof is the
President of the San Diego Chapter of NACE.

PEARTREES CATERING
1503 30th Street
San Diego, CA 92102
619.232.7020
Jerrold Siegel
Areas served: San Diego County, Orange
County and Palm Springs
Full service, off-premise catering and event
planning for corporate and theme events.
Chosen to cater for Americas Cup Museum,
Ruben H. Fleet Theatre, Auto Museum and
many others.

**SWEET CELEBRATIONS CATERING
AND EVENTS**
7948 Convoy Court
San Diego, CA 92111
619.292.1414
Mary Schlesing
Areas served: San Diego County
Stunning displays accent this company's
hors d'oeuvre station and buffet
presentations. Specialties include Country
Italian, Mediterranean, Pacific Rim,
California and American regional cuisine.
Will also design a menu to the client's taste
and budget. Providing catering only or full
event planning for weddings, corporate
events or special affairs of any size.
Holiday gift baskets.

TONY KOPAS AND ASSOCIATES, CATERERS
P.O. Box 8657
La Jolla, CA 92038
619.454.9926
Tony Kopas
Areas served: San Diego County, Orange
County and Palm Springs
Upscale, full service catering and event
planning for all occasions.

❧ BAR CATERING

CALIFORNIA BAR CATERING
7898 Ostrow Street
San Diego, CA 92111
619.560.7178
Brett Johnson
Areas served: California
Fully licensed and insured beverage caterer.
All equipment included. Full liquor and
non-alcoholic catering. Sub-contractor for
all food services.

SAN DIEGO

CELEBRITY ACQUISITION

STANDING OVATIONS
8380 Miramar Mall
Suite 225
San Diego, CA 92121
619.455.1850
Nan Pratt
P.J. Fox
Areas served: International
International full service speaker bureau
serving associations and corporate clients.
Quality speakers, trainers, celebrities,
entertainers and sports stars for keynotes,
general sessions, seminars and workshops.

CHOCOLATES & CONFECTIONS

THE CHOCOLATE FACTORY
1145 Prospect
La Jolla, CA 92037
619.454.0077
Patti Buckallew
Areas served: San Diego County
Retail candy store containing handmade
truffles, assorted fruit, Australian honey-
glazed fruit, nuts, caramel apples covered
with chocolates and nuts, fifteen kinds of
fudge, chocolates galore.

A CHOCOLATIER
2710 Via de la Valle
Del Mar, CA 92014
619.755.1600
Hilby Mignone
Areas served: San Diego County
Retail chocolate and confections. Custom
molded logos, distinctive wedding favors,
gift baskets. Specialty custom molding and
arrangements. Custom and theme gifts.
Handcrafted confections. Sugarless and
seasonal specialties. Shipping and delivery
available. Winner of People's Choice
Award in San Diego. In business nine
years.

THE DINING ROOM SHOP
7645 Girard Avenue
La Jolla, CA 92037
619.454.8688
Joan Fisher

Areas served: La Jolla and surrounding areas
Tabletop accessories, giftware, delicacies,
linens, plates, glassware, vases,
candlesticks. Delicacies include pastas,
sauces, mustards, jams, olive oil, bread
mixes, chocolate, jalapeno pecan brittle.
Delivery available.

GODIVA CHOCOLATIER
1640 Camino del Rio
San Diego, CA 92108
619.291.6775
World renowned chocolatier. Belgium-style
chocolates, gift baskets and party favors.

COSTUMES

THE PARTY SHOP
441 Santa Fe Drive
Encinitas, CA 92024
619.753.8455
Areas served: San Diego and Orange Counties
Huge selection of retail party goods, full
costume shop year 'round, balloons, helium.

DELICACIES

BEST REGARDS
7898 Ostrow
Suite F
San Diego, CA 92111
619.560.9040
800.544.6234
Alan Aegerter
Areas served: National
Quality wines and champagnes with your
personal message on the label. Gourmet
foods, personalized gift baskets. Great
holiday selections. No minimum.

THE DINING ROOM SHOP
7645 Girard Avenue
La Jolla, CA 92037
619.454.8688
Joan Fisher
Areas served: La Jolla and surrounding areas
Tabletop accessories, giftware, delicacies,
linens, plates, glassware, vases,
candlesticks. Delicacies include pastas,

sauces, mustards, jams, olive oil, bread mixes, chocolate, jalapeno pecan brittle. Delivery available.

DESTINATION MANAGEMENT

CALIFORNIA LEISURE CONSULTANTS
1775 Hancock Street
Suite 280
San Diego, CA 92110
619.299.2200
Joane Wheeler

Areas served: San Diego. (Other offices in Los Angeles, Orange County, Palm Springs.) Full service destination management including: special events, private homes, tours, sporting events, entertainment, transportation. Won Site Crystal Award "Best Incentive Trip Four Nights or Less", 1991; Perfect Host Award, San Diego's Finest Service Award.

PATTI ROSCOE & ASSOCIATES, INC.
2456 Broadway
San Diego, CA 92102
619.234.9440
Annie Revel

Areas served: San Diego County
Full service destination management company. Creates, coordinates and operates special events, meetings, tours, conventions, corporate and incentive trips. Numerous awards and distinctions.

EQUIPMENT RENTALS & TENTING

A-RENTAL WORLD
7473 El Cajon Blvd.
La Mesa, CA 91941
619.286.5110
Willie Williams

Areas served: Southern California
Tents, lighting, staging, flooring, tables, chairs, tableware, glassware, wedding equipment, dance floors, food service equipment. San Diego's oldest party rental company. Chosen to serve Super Bowl

XXII, America's Cup 1992 and All Star Gala 1992.

CASINO DE PARIS, INC.
9636 Long Beach Blvd.
South Gate, CA 90280
213.566.1001
714.549.3396

Areas served: Southern California
Las Vegas-style casino equipment and dealers for fund-raisers, charity events, company parties, Christmas parties, wrap parties, grad nights, Bar Mitzvahs, anniversaries, surprise birthdays, etc. In business thirty-two years.

CASINO DEL SOL
5645 Friars Road
Suite 402
San Diego, CA 92110
619.299.5825
Don Belcher, Owner

Areas served: San Diego County, Riverside County, Imperial County, Orange County and Los Angeles on request
Professional quality casino equipment and dealers. Includes party planning consultation.

CMC DRY AND WATER ICE SERVICE
3417 30th Street
San Diego, CA 92104
619.260.0051
Carlos Shannon

Areas served: San Diego
Dry ice, party ice, block ice for all events. Fog machines, snow scenes, ice sculptures and carvings. 300 pound block ice. Delivery available.

NORTH COAST PARTY RENTALS
725 First Street
Encinitas, CA 92024
619.942.9566
Bob Carey

Areas served: San Diego County, South Orange County, South Riverside County
Party equipment rentals, tents, catering equipment rentals and themed events.

RAPHAEL'S PARTY RENTALS
8860 Production Avenue
San Diego, CA 92121-2218
619.689.7368

Raphael Silverman
Areas served: Southern California
Party consultation and equipment rentals.

EVENT PLANNING

ALLIED BOOKING COMPANY AND TALENT AGENCY

1717 Kettner Blvd.
Suite 200
San Diego, CA 92101-2533
619.696.9100
James Gates

Areas served: San Diego, Orange County, Los Angeles, San Francisco, Arizona, and Nevada

Full service entertainment agency providing nationally known artists, theme entertainers, bands, DJs, actors, MCs, dancers, ethnic performers, comedians, magicians, theme parties and specialty entertainers for any kind of event or client. They also provide event production, lighting, sound and contract musicians for shows. Winner of the 1991 Sammy Award for best San Diego Talent Agency (*Sales, Advertising & Marketing Magazine*). Provide entertainment for all of the major convention planners (DMCs) in San Diego and some in Orange County, Palm Springs and Los Angeles. Oldest agency in San Diego, opened doors in 1954. Licensed, bonded, and insured.

CALIFORNIA LEISURE CONSULTANTS

1775 Hancock Street
Suite 280
San Diego, CA 92110
619.299.2200
Joane Wheeler

Areas served: San Diego. (Other offices in Los Angeles, Orange County, Palm Springs.) Full service destination management including: special events, private homes, tours, sporting events, entertainment, transportation. Won Site Crystal Award "Best Incentive Trip Four Nights or Less", 1991; Perfect Host Award, San Diego's Finest Service Award.

CASINO DE PARIS, INC.

9636 Long Beach Blvd.
South Gate, CA 90280
213.566.1001
714.549.3396

Areas served: Southern California
Las Vegas-style casino equipment and dealers for fund-raisers, charity events, company parties, Christmas parties, wrap parties, grad nights, Bar Mitzvahs, anniversaries, surprise birthdays, etc. In business thirty-two years.

CASINO DEL SOL

5645 Friars Road
Suite 402
San Diego, CA 92110
619.299.5825
Don Belcher, Owner

Areas served: San Diego County, Riverside County, Imperial County, Orange County and Los Angeles on request

Professional quality casino equipment and dealers. Includes party planning consultation.

FRENCH GOURMET CATERING

960 Turquoise Street
Pacific Beach, CA 92109
619.488.1725
Sales Department

Area served: San Diego County
Full service catering company, fully licensed to sell liquor. Full event planning services. Specializing in French cuisine, but also do incredible Italian, Mexican, Thai and Cajun menus. Member of 1992 Louis Vuitton Cup Team. Owner Michael Malecof is the President of the San Diego Chapter of NACE.

A GRAND AFFAIR

3804 La Jolla Village Drive
La Jolla, CA 92037
619.452.7599
Beverly O'Keefe

Areas served: California, Texas, Arizona and Nevada

Full event planning and coordination for weddings, corporate functions, grand openings, social events, Bar and Bat Mitzvahs, holiday and theme parties. Vice President of the San Diego Chapter of the Association of Bridal Consultants.

SAN DIEGO

IRWIN PRODUCTIONS, INC.
PETALS 'N' LACE
6211 Yarrow Drive
Suite B
Carlsbad, CA 92009
619.931.1103
Cheryl Irwin
Areas served: San Diego, Los Angeles,
Orange County, Palm Springs and Mexico
An award-winning special events company
offering event decor, theme parties, florals
and ESCAPADE, the newest in interactive
entertainment and business theatre. Total
in-house event design and production, from
florals to custom business theatre. Won the
1989 "Most Outstanding Floral" in the
Special Events Industry and the 1985 Top
Ten Floral Award for California Gala
Competition.

PACIFIC BRENT PRODUCTIONS
8525 Camino Santa Fe
San Diego, CA 92121
619.458.9908
George Duff
Areas served: California
Event planning, set design and production.
Prop rental, floral design and decorations.
Theme events for incentive groups,
corporations and associations. Exclusive
planner and decorator for Louis Vuitton
Cup '92.

PATTI ROSCOE & ASSOCIATES, INC.
2456 Broadway
San Diego, CA 92102
619.234.9440
Annie Revel
Areas served: San Diego County
Full service destination management
company. Creates, coordinates and
operates special events, meetings, tours,
conventions, corporate and incentive trips.
Numerous awards and distinctions.

PEARTREES CATERING
1503 30th Street
San Diego, CA 92102
619.232.7020
Jerrold Siegel
Areas served: San Diego County, Orange
County and Palm Springs
Full service, off-premise catering and event
planning for corporate and theme events.

Chosen to cater for Americas Cup Museum,
Ruben H. Fleet Theatre, Auto Museum and
many others.

SWEET CELEBRATIONS CATERING
AND EVENTS
7948 Convoy Court
San Diego, CA 92111
619.292.1414
Mary Schlesing
Areas served: San Diego County
Stunning displays accent this company's
hors d'oeuvre station and buffet
presentations. Specialties include Country
Italian, Mediterranean, Pacific Rim,
California and American regional cuisine.
Will also design a menu to the client's taste
and budget. Providing catering only or full
event planning for weddings, corporate
events or special affairs of any size.
Holiday gift baskets.

TONY KOPAS AND ASSOCIATES
P.O. Box 8657
La Jolla, CA 92038
619.454.9926
Tony Kopas
Areas served: San Diego County, Orange
County and Palm Springs
Upscale, full service catering and event
planning for all occasions.

WESTERN SCENIC STUDIOS
1470 Citrus Ridge
Escondido, CA 92025
619.943.8847
Ted Prina
Areas served: National
Full event decor including lighting, staging,
and floral design. Full trade show
production. Technical services. In
business since 1919.

THE WINESELLAR
9550 Waples Street
Suite 115
San Diego, CA 92121
619.455.1414
David Clark
Terry Hudson
Areas served: National
Retail store specializing in small
production, high quality, handcrafted
wines. Foreign and domestic wines. Wine

storage facilities. Speakers on wine. Tastings in adjoining restaurant every Saturday (reservations in advance). Produce custom-designed wine tasting parties at outside locations. Custom-designed gift baskets.

selection of favors and party supplies. Paper goods, custom and catalogue invitations. Custom imprinting of napkins, ribbons, matchbooks. Balloons, helium tanks – blow up and delivery.

FAVORS

A CHOCOLATIER
2710 Via de la Valle
Del Mar, CA 92014
619.755.1600
Hilby Mignone
Areas served: San Diego County
Retail chocolate and confections. Custom molded logos, distinctive wedding favors, gift baskets. Specialty custom molding and arrangements. Custom and theme gifts. Handcrafted confections. Sugarless and seasonal specialties. Shipping and delivery available. Winner of People's Choice Award in San Diego. In business nine years.

ELEGANT ADVERTISING GRAPHICS
7280-A Carrara Place
San Diego, CA 92122
619.457.3232
Peter Turner
Areas served: International
Custom-designed and catalogue invitations, lighting and sound effects, die-cuts, foiled, embossed, special paper folds, pop-ups, place cards, favors, sign-in boards, full calligraphy services.

GODIVA CHOCOLATIER
1640 Camino del Rio
San Diego, CA 92108
619.291.6775
World renowned chocolatier. Belgium-style chocolates, gift baskets and party favors.

PARTY FAVORS AND RENTALS
908 Fesler Street
El Cajon, CA 92020
619.562.7888
Joyce Buchmayer
Areas served: San Diego County
Linens, tables, chairs, gazebos, arches, canopies, barbecues, china, chaffers, full

FIREWORKS & SPECIAL EFFECTS

PARTY LIGHTS OF CALIFORNIA
8656 Sky Rim Drive
Suite 110
Lakeside, CA 92040
619.443.9949
M. White
Areas served: International
Complete line of Cyalume Lightstick products. Lighters, necklaces, cocktail stirrers, bracelets, earrings. Worldwide shipping.

PYRO SPECTACULARS
P.O. Box 2329
Rialto, CA 92377
800.322.7732
Kevin Kelley
Areas served: International
Aerial fireworks, displays choreographed to music, low level displays and special effects. Clients include Chinese New Year, Hong Kong (annually), Los Angeles Olympics, Rolling Stones Steel Wheel Tour, America Fest, Statue of Liberty, Macy's, Dodgers, Angels, Giants, A's, Super Bowls, Hollywood Bowl, Magic Mountain and LA County Fair.

FLORISTS & FLORAL DESIGNS

IRWIN PRODUCTIONS, INC.
PETALS 'N' LACE
6211 Yarrow Drive
Suite B
Carlsbad, CA 92009
619.931.1103
Cheryl Irwin
Areas served: San Diego, Los Angeles, Orange County, Palm Springs and Mexico

SAN DIEGO

An award-winning special events company offering event decor, theme parties, florals and ESCAPADE, the newest in interactive entertainment and business theatre. Total in-house event design and production, from florals to custom business theatre. Won the 1989 "Most Outstanding Floral" in the Special Events Industry and the 1985 Top Ten Floral Award for California Gala Competition.

PACIFIC BRENT PRODUCTIONS
8525 Camino Santa Fe
San Diego, CA 92121
619.458.9908
George Duff
Areas served: California
Event planning, set design and production. Prop rental, floral design and decorations. Theme events for incentive groups, corporations and associations. Exclusive planner and decorator for Louis Vuitton Cup '92.

WESTERN SCENIC STUDIOS
1470 Citrus Ridge
Escondido, CA 92025
619.943.8847
Ted Prina
Areas served: National
Full event decor including lighting, staging, and floral design. Full trade show production. Technical services. In business since 1919.

FORMAL WEAR
GARY'S TUX SHOPS
7843 Clairemont Mesa Blvd.
619.467.9700

Horton Plaza
619.233.4277

639 Broadway
619.426.5661

Grossmont Center
619.466.1665

La Jolla Village Square
619.452.8410

North County Fair

619.743.1343
Tuxedo sales and rentals. Large selection of fine formal wear including Christian Dior, Henry Grethel, Pierre Cardin, Lord West and more. Specializing in weddings and corporate events/conventions offering special discounts and services for large groups. Served over 250,000 newly-weds since 1933. Supplied over 700 tuxedos for Super Bowl in San Diego and all tuxedos for opening ceremonies of Los Angeles Olympics.

TUX DEN AT SEARS
El Camino Real
619.729.6502

Parkway Plaza
619.593.9602

University Town Center
619.556.7880

North County Fair
619.432.8264

555 Fifth Avenue
619.427.7015
Tuxedo sales and rentals. Largest selection of fine formal wear including Christian Dior, Henry Grethel, Pierre Cardin, Lord West and more. Specialize in weddings and corporate events/conventions offering special discounts and services for large groups, including on-sight measuring, hotel pick-up and delivery.

GIFTS & GIFT BASKETS
BEST REGARDS
7898 Ostrow
Suite F
San Diego, CA 92111
619.560.9040
800.544.6234
Alan Aegerter
Areas served: National
Quality wines and champagnes with your personal message on the label. Gourmet foods, personalized gift baskets. Great holiday selections. No minimum.

[Continued on next page.]

THE BEST TO YOU
7915 Silverton Avenue
Suite 307
San Diego, CA 92126
Linda Gorin
619.578.2740
Areas served: International
Custom-designed gift baskets: theme,
holiday, corporate gifts. Showroom viewing
by appointment only.

A CHOCOLATIER
2710 Via de la Valle
Del Mar, CA 92014
619.755.1600
Hilby Mignone
Areas served: San Diego County
Retail chocolate and confections. Custom
molded logos, distinctive wedding favors,
gift baskets. Specialty custom molding and
arrangements. Custom and theme gifts.
Handcrafted confections. Sugarless and
seasonal specialties. Shipping and delivery
available. Winner of People's Choice
Award in San Diego. In business nine years.

SWEET CELEBRATIONS CATERING AND EVENTS
7948 Convoy Court
San Diego, CA 92111
619.292.1414
Mary Schlesing
Areas served: San Diego County
Stunning displays accent this company's
hors d'oeuvre station and buffet
presentations. Specialties include Country
Italian, Mediterranean, Pacific Rim,
California and American regional cuisine.
Will also design a menu to the client's taste
and budget. Providing catering only or full
event planning for weddings, corporate
events or special affairs of any size.
Holiday gift baskets.

THE WINESELLAR
9550 Waples Street
Suite 115
San Diego, CA 92121
619.455.1414
David Clark
Terry Hudson
Areas served: National
Retail store specializing in small
production, high quality, handcrafted
wines. Foreign and domestic wines. Wine
storage facilities. Speakers on wine.
Tastings in adjoining restaurant every
Saturday (reservations in advance).
Produce custom-designed wine tasting
parties at outside locations. Custom-
designed gift baskets.

ICE SERVICES

CMC DRY AND WATER ICE SERVICE
3417 30th Street
San Diego, CA 92104
619.260.0051
Carlos Shannon
Areas served: San Diego
Dry ice, party ice, block ice for all events.
Fog machines, snow scenes, ice sculptures
and carvings. 300 pound block ice.
Delivery available.

INVITATIONS & ACCESSORIES

THE CLASSY PEN
619.560.6545
Fran Lewis
Areas served: International
Computerized and hand calligraphy
services. Custom-designed and catalogue
invitations, seating charts, menu cards, etc.

ELEGANT ADVERTISING GRAPHICS
7280-A Carrara Place
San Diego, CA 92122
619.457.3232
Peter Turner
Areas served: International
Custom-designed and catalogue invitations,
lighting and sound effects, die-cuts, foiled,
embossed, special paper folds, pop-ups,
place cards, favors, sign-in boards, full
calligraphy services.

GODIVA CHOCOLATIER
1640 Camino del Rio
San Diego, CA 92108
619.291.6775
World renowned chocolatier. Belgium-style
chocolates, gift baskets and party favors.

SAN DIEGO

LADYBUG ART CALLIGRAPHY SERVICES
4685 Biona Drive
San Diego, CA 92166
619.274.2510
Susan Hull
Areas served: International
Retail store specializing in custom-designed and catalogue invitations. Seating charts, signage, customized gift registry sheets. Calligraphy services. Calligraphy supplies, fine stationery, custom framing, greeting cards.

PARTY FAVORS AND RENTALS
908 Fesler Street
El Cajon, CA 92020
619.562.7888
Joyce Buchmayer
Areas served: San Diego County
Linens, tables, chairs, gazebos, arches, canopies, barbecues, china, chaffers, full selection of favors and party supplies. Paper goods, custom and catalogue invitations. Custom imprinting of napkins, ribbons, matchbooks. Balloons, helium tanks – blow up and delivery.

LIGHTING, STAGING & SOUND

A-RENTAL WORLD
7473 El Cajon Blvd.
La Mesa, CA 91941
619.286.5110
Willie Williams
Areas served: Southern California
Tents, lighting, staging, flooring, tables, chairs, tableware, glassware, wedding equipment, dance floors, food service equipment. San Diego's oldest party rental company. Chosen to serve Super Bowl XXII, America's Cup 1992 and All Star Gala 1992.

ALLIED BOOKING COMPANY AND TALENT AGENCY
1717 Kettner Blvd.
Suite 200
San Diego, CA 92101-2533
619.696.9100
James Gates

Areas served: San Diego, Orange County, Los Angeles, San Francisco, Arizona, and Nevada
Full service entertainment agency providing nationally known artists, theme entertainers, bands, DJs, actors, MCs, dancers, ethnic performers, comedians, magicians, theme parties and specialty entertainers for any kind of event or client. They also provide event production, lighting, sound and contract musicians for shows. Winner of the 1991 Sammy Award for best San Diego Talent Agency (*Sales, Advertising & Marketing Magazine*). Provide entertainment for all of the major convention planners (DMCs) in San Diego and some in Orange County, Palm Springs and Los Angeles. Oldest agency in San Diego, opened doors in 1954. Licensed, bonded, and insured.

WESTERN SCENIC STUDIOS
1470 Citrus Ridge
Escondido, CA 92025
619.943.8847
Ted Prina
Areas served: National
Full event decor including lighting, staging, and floral design. Full trade show production. Technical services. In business since 1919.

LIMOUSINE & TRANSPORTATION

CAREY LIMOUSINE
619.225.9551
800.336.4646
Areas served: International
Privately chauffeured sedans, limousines, vans and mini buses in 372 cities.

COUNTRY CARRIAGES
P.O. Box 607
Julian, CA 92036
619.765.1471
Suzanne Porter
Areas served: National
Elegant horse-drawn carriages for all special events.

[Continued on next page.]

SAN DIEGO

**DAV EL CHAUFFEURED
TRANSPORTATION NETWORK**
>**800.328.3526** (outside CA)
>**800.826.5779** (inside CA)

Areas Served: International
Luxury chauffeured services in over 350
cities worldwide. Centralized reservations
and billing. Airport concierge services.

LONDON TOWN CARS
>P.O. Box 4100
>Leucadia, CA 92024
>**619.297.8967**
>Joe Egan

Areas Served: San Diego
Limousines and sedans for corporate
groups.

OLD TOWN TROLLEY TOURS
>2175 Hancock Street
>San Diego, CA 92110
>**619.298.8687**

Areas served: San Diego, Washington DC,
Miami, Boston, Cambridge, Key West
Tours, transportation, shuttle services. For
individuals, groups, weddings. Largest fleet
operator of theme-styled vehicles in the
United States.

PRESIDENTIAL LIMOUSINE SERVICE
>2085 Hotel Circle South
>San Diego, CA 92108
>**619.291.2820**
>Mark Kasmer

Areas Served: San Diego
Chauffeured limousines, sedans, Mercedes
and Rolls Royces.

LINENS

PARTY FAVORS AND RENTALS
>908 Fesler Street
>El Cajon, CA 92020
>**619.562.7888**
>Joyce Buchmayer

Areas served: San Diego County
Linens, tables, chairs, gazebos, arches,
canopies, barbecues, china, chaffers, full
selection of favors and party supplies.
Paper goods, custom and catalogue
invitations. Custom imprinting of napkins,
ribbons, matchbooks. Balloons, helium
tanks – blow up and delivery.

MUSIC & ENTERTAINMENT

**ALLIED BOOKING COMPANY
AND TALENT AGENCY**
>1717 Kettner Blvd.
>Suite 200
>San Diego, CA 92101-2533
>**619.696.9100**
>James Gates

Areas served: San Diego, Orange County,
Los Angeles, San Francisco, Arizona,
and Nevada
Full service entertainment agency providing
nationally known artists, theme
entertainers, bands, DJs, actors, MCs,
dancers, ethnic performers, comedians,
magicians, theme parties and specialty
entertainers for any kind of event or client.
They also provide event production,
lighting, sound and contract musicians for
shows. Winner of the 1991 Sammy Award
for best San Diego Talent Agency (*Sales,
Advertising & Marketing Magazine*).
Provide entertainment for all of the major
convention planners (DMCs) in San Diego
and some in Orange County, Palm Springs
and Los Angeles. Oldest agency in San
Diego, opened doors in 1954. Licensed,
bonded, and insured.

CASINO DEL SOL
>5645 Friars Road
>Suite 402
>San Diego, CA 92110
>**619.299.5825**
>Don Belcher, Owner

Areas served: San Diego County, Riverside
County, Imperial County, Orange County
and Los Angeles on request
Professional quality casino equipment and
dealers. Includes party planning
consultation.

**ENTERTAINMENT CONSULTANTS
& E.C. VIDEO PRODUCTIONS**
>801 Washington Street
>San Diego, CA 92103
>**800.273.7221**

Areas served: San Diego, Orange County,
Los Angeles, Riverside and Santa Barbara
Bands, DJs, entertainment, video taping,
services. Other offices in Costa Mesa and
Los Angeles.

GOODE COMPANY

P.O. Box 1961
Wrightwood, CA 92397
619.249.3180
818.985.6982
Laura Kelly

Areas served: Southern California
Entertaining performances of Christmas
carols or Renaissance madrigals in
elaborate, authentic costumes – either
Dickens or Elizabethan costumes. Strolling
carolers. All occasions. Won several first
place awards for best musical performance
at Southern California Renaissance
Pleasure Faire.

IRWIN PRODUCTIONS, INC.
PETALS 'N' LACE

6211 Yarrow Drive
Suite B
Carlsbad, CA 92009
619.931.1103
Cheryl Irwin

Areas served: San Diego, Los Angeles,
Orange County, Palm Springs and Mexico
An award-winning special events company
offering event decor, theme parties, florals
and ESCAPADE, the newest in interactive
entertainment and business theatre. Total
in-house event design and production, from
florals to custom business theatre. Won the
1989 "Most Outstanding Floral" in the
Special Events Industry and the 1985 Top
Ten Floral Award for California Gala
Competition.

MUSIC AS YOU LIKE IT PRODUCTIONS

4633 Pescadero Avenue
San Diego, CA 92107
619.223.5732
Keith Danon

Areas served: San Diego, Los Angeles and
Orange County
Entertainment for all occasions – DJs, live
music, novelty acts, etc.

THE MUSIC PEOPLE

6251 Rockhurst Drive
San Diego, CA 92120-4607
619.583.7265
800.243.2066
Bernie Kaye

Areas served: San Diego, Palm Springs,
Los Angeles, Orange and Riverside Counties

Live music, DJs, entertainment, orchestras,
bands, ethnic talent. Winner of Gold Key
Award and Allied Member Award from the
hotel industry.

SAN DIEGO SYMPHONY ORCHESTRA
ASSOCIATION/SAN DIEGO'S COPLEY
SYMPHONY HALL

1245 Seventh Avenue
San Diego, CA 92101
619.699.4200
Eloise Manker

Catered dinners for pre- and post-concert
receptions. Music ranging from Bobbie
McFerrin to an all-Beethoven concert.

STANDING OVATIONS

8380 Miramar Mall
Suite 225
San Diego, CA 92121
619.455.1850
Nan Pratt
P.J. Fox

Areas served: International
International full service speaker bureau
serving associations and corporate clients.
Quality speakers, trainers, celebrities,
entertainers and sports stars for keynotes,
general sessions, seminars and workshops.

SUPER STAR FANTASY

731 Nolan Avenue
Chula Vista, CA 91910
619.426.7394
Rosemarie Ballard

Areas served: San Diego, Palm Springs and
Los Angeles
Celebrity look-alikes and impersonators.

TONY HELLER

619.561.9694
Areas served: International
Humphrey Bogart impersonator. Many
awards and distinctions.

[Continued on next page.]

PARTY SITES

CAFE PACIFICA
2414 San Diego Avenue
San Diego, CA 92110
619.291.6666
Donna LaFremiere

Cozy restaurant located in San Diego's Old Town with patio-type atmosphere. Seafood and non-fish entrees. Contemporary. Receptions: 100 people. Sit down: 120 people. Featured in *Zagat '92, Epicurean Rendezvous* and *San Diego Magazine's* "Best".

DOUBLETREE HOTEL AT HORTON PLAZA
910 Broadway Circle
San Diego, CA 92101
619.239.2200
Brenda Nielson
Jan Underwood

Located in downtown San Diego. Adjacent to the spectacular Horton Plaza shopping and entertainment complex. Walking distance from the San Diego Convention Center. Exceptional cuisine and impeccable service. 18,000 square feet. Receptions: 1200 people. Sit down: 850 people.

GEORGE'S AT THE COVE
1250 Prospect Street
La Jolla, CA 92037
619.454.4244
Kathy Murray

Restaurant and banquet facilities. Creative regional cuisine with emphasis on fresh seafood and produce. Four separate banquet facilities. Countless awards of excellence locally and nationally.

LA COSTA
Costa Del Mar Road
Carlsbad, CA 92009
619.438.9111
Al Dauber
Gerard Theveny

Full event and meeting facilities for all size groups up to 600. World renowned for their spa, golf courses and tennis courts. 50,000 square foot conference center. Outdoor lawns, terraces, patios, pool areas. State-of-the-art theatre seats 175 people. Specializing in unusual theme parties – jungle safaris with lions and tigers, skydiving, fireworks.

PACIFICA DEL MAR
1535 Camino Del Mar
Del Mar, CA 92014
619.792.0476
Donna LaFremiere

Beautiful ocean view restaurant. Located on top of the Del Mar Plaza. Ample patio dining. Seafood focus with Asian Pacific flare. Receptions: 200 people. Sit down: 165 people. Featured in *Zagat's '92, Epicurean Rendezvous* and many other magazines.

PACIFICA GRILL
1202 Keltner Blvd.
San Diego, CA 92101
619.696.9226
Donna LaFremiere

Located in downtown San Diego. Restaurant opens into atrium of historical building. Outside patio dining. Seafood focus with Southwestern accent. Art gallery in building also available as reception space. Receptions: 100 people. Sit down: 130 people. Many local and national awards.

SAN DIEGO SYMPHONY ORCHESTRA ASSOCIATION/SAN DIEGO'S COPLEY SYMPHONY HALL
1245 Seventh Avenue
San Diego, CA 92101
619.699.4200
Eloise Manker

Catered dinners for pre- and post-concert receptions. Music ranging from Bobbie McFerrin to an all-Beethoven concert.

SAN DIEGO WILD ANIMAL PARK
P.O. Box 551
San Diego, CA 92112-0551
619.557.3966
Group Sales

SAN DIEGO ZOO
P.O. Box 551
San Diego, CA 92112-0551
619.557.3966
Group Sales

SEA WORLD
1720 S. Shores Road
San Diego, CA 92109-7995
619.226.3845
800.325.3150 (California)

800.732.9753 (Nationwide)
Bess Eberhardt
Limitless possibilities for events up to 5000
people. Dinner inside their shark
encounter, formal wear optional at their
penguin encounter, a beach party with
dolphins. Full service event specialists plan
out-of-this-world events.

SPRECKELS THEATRE
121 Broadway
San Diego, CA 92101
619.235.0494
David Chandler
Theatre. Seats: 1450 people. On-site
parking for 150 vehicles.

PARTY SUPPLIES

PARTY FAVORS AND RENTALS
908 Fesler Street
El Cajon, CA 92020
619.562.7888
Joyce Buchmayer
Areas served: San Diego County
Linens, tables, chairs, gazebos, arches,
canopies, barbecues, china, chaffers, full
selection of favors and party supplies.
Paper goods, custom and catalogue
invitations. Custom imprinting of napkins,
ribbons, matchbooks. Balloons, helium
tanks – blow up and delivery.

PARTY LIGHTS OF CALIFORNIA
8656 Sky Rim Drive
Suite 110
Lakeside, CA 92040
619.443.9949
M. White
Areas served: International
Complete line of Cyalume Lightstick
products. Lighters, necklaces, cocktail
stirrers, bracelets, earrings.
Worldwide shipping.

THE PARTY SHOP
441 Santa Fe Drive
Encinitas, CA 92024
619.753.8455
Areas served: San Diego and Orange Counties
Huge selection of retail party goods, full
costume shop year 'round, balloons, helium.

PERSONNEL & STAFFING

PARTY 123
619.576.7320
Julie Wartell
Areas served: San Diego County
Staffing and personnel – bartenders,
waitresses, servers, clean-up and set-up.

STAFFPRO INC.
4420 Hotel Circle Court
Suite 210
San Diego, CA 92108
619.294.3990
Gus Kontopuls
Area served: San Diego
Hosts, hostesses, security, ticket takers, set-
up crews, box office parking, custodial,
janitorial, traffic control for all events.
Various attires for all services.

PHOTOGRAPHY & VIDEO

DALE E. BINGHAM PHOTOGRAPHY
619.221.8022
Areas served: San Diego County
Full event photography and video services
for all events. Clients include
San Diego Home and Garden Magazine,
USX Corporation.

ENTERTAINMENT CONSULTANTS & E.C. VIDEO PRODUCTIONS
801 Washington Street
San Diego, CA 92103
800.273.7221
Areas served: Los Angeles, Orange County,
San Diego, Riverside and Santa Barbara
Banks, DJs, entertainment, video
taping services. Other offices in Costa Mesa
and Los Angeles.

MASTERS PRESENTATION GRAPHIC SERVICES
6150 Lusk Blvd.
Suite 104
San Diego, CA 92121
619.457.4720
Jeff Pratt
Areas served: California, Nevada, Arizona
Full audiovisual, multi-image, video,
computer graphics and photography services.

SAN DIEGO

PROPS & DECOR

BILL BAKER PRODUCTIONS
4154 Cartagesa Drive
San Diego, CA 92115
619.287.8000
Bill Baker
Randy Prendergost
Areas served: Southern California and
other regions
Custom designers and manufacturers of
thematic props and decor.

CASINO DE PARIS, INC.
9636 Long Beach Blvd.
South Gate, CA 90280
213.566.1001
714.549.3396
Areas served: Southern California
Las Vegas-style casino equipment and
dealers for fund-raisers, charity events,
company parties, Christmas parties, wrap
parties, grad nights, Bar Mitzvahs,
anniversaries, surprise birthdays, etc. In
business thirty-two years.

CASINO DEL SOL
5645 Friars Road
Suite 402
San Diego, CA 92110
619.299.5825
Don Belcher, Owner
Areas served: San Diego County, Riverside
County, Imperial County, Orange County
and Los Angeles on request
Professional quality casino equipment
and dealers. Includes party planning
consultation.

CMC DRY AND WATER ICE SERVICE
3417 30th Street
San Diego, CA 92104
619.260.0051
Carlos Shannon
Areas served: San Diego
Dry ice, party ice, block ice for all events.
Fog machines, snow scenes, ice sculptures
and carvings. 300 pound block ice.
Delivery available.

COUNTRY CARRIAGES
P.O. Box 607
Julian, CA 92036
619.765.1471
Suzanne Porter

Areas served: National
Elegant horse drawn carriages for all
special events.

IMPACT PROFESSIONAL DECORATING
1402 Willow Street
San Diego, CA 92106
619.222.5360
Jean Leighton
Areas served: San Diego, Riverside,
Orange, Los Angeles Counties
Complete decorating services. Custom-
designed props warehoused in San Diego.
Theme parties, trade shows, conventions,
holiday decorating. In business since 1974.

IRWIN PRODUCTIONS, INC.
PETALS 'N' LACE
6211 Yarrow Drive
Suite B
Carlsbad, CA 92009
619.931.1103
Cheryl Irwin
Areas served: San Diego, Los Angeles,
Orange County, Palm Springs and Mexico
An award-winning special events company
offering event decor, theme parties, florals
and ESCAPADE, the newest in interactive
entertainment and business theatre. Total
in-house event design and production, from
florals to custom business theatre. Won
the 1989 "Most Outstanding Floral" in the
Special Events Industry and the 1985
Top Ten Floral Award for California
Gala Competition.

PACIFIC BRENT PRODUCTIONS
8525 Camino Santa Fe
San Diego, CA 92121
619.458.9908
George Duff
Areas served: California
Event planning, set design and production.
Prop rental, floral design and decorations.
Theme events for incentive groups,
corporations and associations. Exclusive
planner and decorator for Louis Vuitton
Cup '92.

WESTERN SCENIC STUDIOS
1470 Citrus Ridge
Escondido, CA 92025
619.943.8847
Ted Prina

SAN DIEGO

Areas served: National
Full event decor including lighting, staging, and floral design. Full trade show production. Technical services. In business since 1919.

SECURITY

STAFFPRO, INC.
4420 Hotel Circle Court
Suite 210
San Diego, CA 92108
619.294.3990
Gus Kontopuls
Area served: San Diego
Hosts, hostesses, security, ticket takers, set-up crews, box office parking, custodial, janitorial, traffic control for all events. Various attires for all services.

SIGNAGE

INSTANT SIGN CENTERS OF SAN DIEGO
3555 Rosecrantz
Suite 113
San Diego, CA 92110
619.225.8230
Nancy Rossi
Areas served: San Diego and surrounding areas
Custom signs, banners, vehicle lettering, window lettering. Specializing in party and trade show banners.

SPEAKERS

SPEAK, INC.
6540 Lusk Blvd.
San Diego, CA 92121
619.457.9880
Jennifer Walker
Ruth Levin
Richard Gibbons
Areas served: International
Full service speaker and trainer bureau. Over 1000 internationally known motivational speakers, sports stars, business and entertainment speakers.

STANDING OVATIONS
8380 Miramar Mall
Suite 225
San Diego, CA 92121
619.455.1850
Nan Pratt
P.J. Fox
Areas served: International
International full service speaker bureau serving associations and corporate clients. Quality speakers, trainers, celebrities, entertainers and sports stars for keynotes, general sessions, seminars and workshops.

THE WINESELLAR
9550 Waples Street
Suite 115
San Diego, CA 92121
619.455.1414
David Clark
Terry Hudson
Areas served: National
Retail store specializing in small production, high quality, handcrafted wines. Foreign and domestic wines. Wine storage facilities. Speakers on wine. Tastings in adjoining restaurant every Saturday (reservations in advance). Produce custom-designed wine tasting parties at outside locations. Custom-designed gift baskets.

TABLETOP ACCESSORIES & KITCHENWARE

CRATE & BARREL
Fashion Valley
San Diego, CA 92108
619.295.6600
Full line of unique contemporary home furnishings and accessories featuring tabletop accessories and gourmet kitchenware.

THE DINING ROOM SHOP
7645 Girard Avenue
La Jolla, CA 92037
619.454.8688
Joan Fisher
Areas served: La Jolla and surrounding areas
Tabletop accessories, giftware, delicacies, linens, plates, glassware, vases,

candlesticks. Delicacies include pastas, sauces, mustards, jams, olive oil, bread mixes, chocolate, jalapeno pecan brittle. Delivery available.

POTTERY BARN

> 583 Fashion Valley
> San Diego, CA 92108
> **619.296.8014**

Leading retailer of contemporary tableware and decorative accessories for the home. Merchandise is 100% exclusive, designed and sold exclusively at Pottery Barn. Over fifty stores nationally and mail order.

WILLIAMS-SONOMA

> 1640 Camino del Rio North
> San Diego, CA 92108
> **619.298.8851**

> 235 Horton Plaza
> San Diego, CA 92101
> **619.239.3855**

An authoritative selection of the best for the kitchen. Complete line of cookware, bakeware, electrics, glassware, tabletop, kitchen furniture, cookbooks, packaged foods. Knowledgeable staff will help choose equipment, plan parties. Most of their merchandise is exclusive to Williams-Sonoma.

VALET PARKING

SUNSET VALET SERVICE, INC.

> P.O. Box 551
> Solana Beach, CA 92075
> **619.755.5298**
> **714.831.3311**
> John Streeter

Areas served: San Diego, Orange County, Los Angeles, Palm Springs
Parking consultations, valet parking, traffic attendants. $1,000,000 liability insurance. Clients include Nordstrom.

WINE & SPIRITS

BEST REGARDS

> 7898 Ostrow
> Suite F
> San Diego, CA 92111
> Alan Aegerter
> **619.560.9040**
> **800.544.6234**

Quality wines and champagnes with your personal message on the label. Gourmet foods, personalized gift baskets. Great holiday selections. No minimum.

THE WINESELLAR

> 9550 Waples Street
> Suite 115
> San Diego, CA 92121
> **619.455.1414**
> David Clark
> Terry Hudson

Areas served: National
Retail store specializing in small production, high quality, handcrafted wines. Foreign and domestic wines. Wine storage facilities. Speakers on wine. Tastings in adjoining restaurant every Saturday (reservations in advance). Produce custom-designed wine tasting parties at outside locations. Custom-designed gift baskets.

YACHT & BOAT CHARTERS

SAN DIEGO YACHT CHARTERS

> 1880 Harbor Island Drive
> San Diego, CA 92101
> **619.297.4555**
> **800.456.0222**

Yachts and charters from fifty feet to eighty-six feet. Receptions: 144 people. Sit down: 80 people.

INVADER CRUISES

> 1066 North Harbor Drive
> San Diego, CA 92101
> **619.234.8687**
> David Strait

Regularly scheduled events as well as private charters available. Diverse schedule. Group rates available. Receptions: 600 people. Sit down: 575 people.

SAN FRANCISCO

SAN FRANCISCO

AUDIOVISUAL & TECHNICAL SERVICES

3B PRODUCTIONS
575 N. Seventh Street
San Jose, CA 95112
408.289.1383
Kevin Boone
Areas served: Northern California
Complete sound, lighting and production
services for corporate events, trade shows
and concerts. Build sets and also provide
complete power distributor systems.

McCALL AND ASSOCIATES
888 Brannen Street
San Francisco, CA 94103
415.552.8550
Claire Jolley
Areas served: National
Full service event planning, catering, floral
design, sound, lighting, staging, event design
and production, entertainment and
audiovisual services. Over ten years in
business.

McCUNE AUDIO VISUAL
951 Howard Street
San Francisco, CA 94103
415.885.2510
Dave Molnar
Areas served: International
Complete audiovisual services, sound
systems, videos, multimedia, etc., for
corporate events, meetings and conventions.

WESTERN SCENIC STUDIOS
1185 32nd Street
Oakland, CA 94608
510.658.3139
Areas served: National
Full event decor. Lighting, staging and
floral design. Full trade show production.
Technical services. In business since 1919.

BALLOONS

BALLOON BOUQUETS OF SAN FRANCISCO
80 Panorama Drive
San Francisco, CA 94131
415.282.2626
Elizabeth Grace

Areas served: San Francisco/East Bay area
Balloon bouquets, delivery and decorating
for all events. In business since 1978.

PARTY WAREHOUSE
2121 Harrison Street
San Francisco, CA 94110
415.863.0912

13 - 43rd Avenue
San Mateo, CA 94403
415.377.0646

458 San Mateo Avenue
San Bruno, CA 94066
415.873.0792

221 Oak Street
Oakland, CA 94607
510.893.1951
Discount party supplies: balloons, paper
products, decorations, invitations,
imprinting services, helium tank rentals.

STREAMERS
Capitola Mall
1855 41st Avenue
Capitola, CA 95010
408.479.4556

401 Corte Madera Town Center
Corte Madera, CA 94925
415.927.1003

39121 Fremont Hub
Fremont, CA 94538
510.792.5777

18 N. Santa Cruz Avenue
Los Gatos, CA 95030
408.395.1165

1689 Arden Way
Suite 1356
Sacramento, CA 95815
916.923.1821

2061 Chestnut Street
San Francisco, CA 94123
415.922.5888

282 Hillsdale Mall
San Mateo, CA 94403
415.578.0131

Valley Fair Shopping Center
2855 Stevens Creek Blvd.

SAN FRANCISCO

Suite 2273
Santa Clara, CA 95050
408.248.9495

1286 Broadway Plaza
Walnut Creek, CA 94596
510.937.3630
One-stop shopping for party supplies:
invitations, balloons, paper supplies,
imprinting and machine calligraphy,
decorations.

BOOKS
WILLIAMS-SONOMA
150 Post Street
San Francisco, CA 94108
415.362.6904

865 Market Street
Suite 206
San Francisco, CA 94103
415.546.0171
An authoritative selection of the best for the
kitchen. Complete line of cookware,
bakware, electrics, glassware, tabletop,
kitchen furniture, cookbooks, packaged
foods. Knowledgeable staff will help choose
equipment, plan parties. Most merchandise
is exclusive to Williams-Sonoma.

CAKES & BAKED GOODS
NARSAIS MARKET, I. MAGNIN
135 Stockton Street
San Francisco, CA 94108
415.403.2046
Jim Mills
Areas served: San Francisco Bay
A full service cafe providing full event
planning, catering, delicacies, cakes and
confections. Mustards, chocolate and
caramel sauces, coffee, vintage wines,
prepared foods, custom-designed cakes,
tarts, petit fours, etc.

CALLIGRAPHY
ABC CALLIGRAPHY
1903 Broderick
Suite 7
San Francisco, CA 94115
415.668.4994
Robin Hall
Areas served: National
Custom-designed and catalogue invitations,
English calligraphy, Hebrew calligraphy,
illuminated wedding contracts, menus, hand
painted place cards, wine labels,
illustrations. Handmade and rice papers.

BARBARA CALLOW CALLIGRAPHY
1686 Union Street
Suite 204
San Francisco, CA 94123
415.928.3303
Barbara Callow
Areas served: National
Custom-designed invitations, accessories
and calligraphy services.

PAPYRUS
2 Embarcadero Center
San Francisco, CA 94111
415.781.8777
Anne Fulton
Areas served: National
Twenty-eight locations nationwide.
Custom-designed and catalogue invitations,
accessories, place cards, menu cards,
programs. Full calligraphy services.

STREAMERS
Capitola Mall
1855 41st Avenue
Capitola, CA 95010
408.479.4556

401 Corte Madera Town Center
Corte Madera, CA 94925
415.927.1003

39121 Fremont Hub
Fremont, CA 94538
510.792.5777

18 N. Santa Cruz Avenue
Los Gatos, CA 95030
408.395.1165

[Continued on next page]

1689 Arden Way
Suite 1356
Sacramento, CA 95815
916.923.1821

2061 Chestnut Street
San Francisco, CA 94123
415.922.5888

282 Hillsdale Mall
San Mateo, CA 94403
415.578.0131

Valley Fair Shopping Center
2855 Stevens Creek Blvd.
Suite 2273
Santa Clara, CA 95050
408.248.9495

1286 Broadway Plaza
Walnut Creek, CA 94596
510.937.3630

One-stop shopping for party supplies:
invitations, balloons, paper supplies,
imprinting and machine calligraphy,
decorations.

CATERING

CREATIVE CATERING
2800 Bryant
San Francisco, CA 94110
415.285.2555
Allison Rodman
Areas served: Northern California
Full event planning and catering for all
occasions.

MCCALL AND ASSOCIATES
888 Brannen Street
San Francisco, CA 94103
415.552.8550
Claire Jolley
Areas served: National
Full service event planning, catering, floral
design, sound, lighting, staging, event design
and production, entertainment and
audiovisual services. Over ten years in
business.

MON CHERIE COOKING SCHOOL AND CATERING
461 S. Murphy Avenue
Sunnyvale, CA 94086

408.736.0892
Sharon Shipley
Areas served: Northern California
Full service catering and box lunches for all
occasions. Specializing in corporate events
and upscale private parties. Cooking school
is offered through UC Extension, Santa
Cruz – four week seminars in different
cuisines of the world. They also custom-
design corporate team building cooking
classes.

NARSAIS MARKET, I. MAGNIN
135 Stockton Street
San Francisco, CA 94108
415.403.2046
Jim Mills
Areas served: San Francisco Bay
A full service cafe providing full event
planning, catering, delicacies, cakes and
confections. Mustards, chocolate and
caramel sauces, coffee, vintage wines,
prepared foods, custom-designed cakes,
tarts, petit fours, etc.

TASTE
3450 Third Street
Suite 4D
San Francisco, CA 94124
415.550.6464
Tambra Harck
Areas served: Northern California
Full service catering and event planning.
Taste and Edible Art Catering have merged
into one company. Over eleven years in
business. Top corporate and private
clientele. Fine cuisine and gracious service.

❧ BAR CATERING

BARTENDERS UNLIMITED
1560 Fourth Street
San Rafael, CA 94901
415.454.3731
John Radovich
Areas served: California
Full-bar catering and staffing for all events.
Oldest and largest beverage catering
company in the state of California. Can
handle any size group up to 20,000. Fully
licensed and insured, clients include The
American Bar Association, Apple

Computer, Trans America Insurance Co. and many other major corporations.

CHOCOLATES & CONFECTIONS

GODIVA CHOCOLATIER
Crooker Galleria
50 Post Street
San Francisco, CA 94104
415.982.6798
World renowned chocolatier. Belgium-style chocolates, gift baskets and party favors. Two other locations in Northern California.

JOSEPH SCHMIDT CONFECTIONS
3489 16th Street
San Francisco, CA 94114
415.861.8682
Audrey Ryan
Areas served: U.S. and Canada
Custom-designed chocolates for all events. They create and sculpt anything in chocolate. They love to create one-of-a-kind things and also provide custom-designed gift baskets. Catalogue available.

NARSAIS MARKET, I. MAGNIN
135 Stockton Street
San Francisco, CA 94108
415.403.2046
Jim Mills
Areas served: San Francisco Bay
A full service cafe providing full event planning, catering, delicacies, cakes and confections. Mustards, chocolate and caramel sauces, coffee, vintage wines, prepared foods, custom-designed cakes, tarts, petit fours, etc.

CLASSES & SEMINARS

MON CHERIE COOKING SCHOOL AND CATERING
461 S. Murphy Avenue
Sunnyvale, CA 94086
408.736.0892
Sharon Shipley
Areas served: Northern California

Full service catering and box lunches for all occasions. Specializing in corporate events and upscale private parties. Cooking school is offered through UC Extension, Santa Cruz – four week seminars in different cuisines of the world. They also custom-design corporate team building cooking classes.

TANTE MARIE'S COOKING SCHOOL
271 Francisco Street
San Francisco, CA 94133
415.788.6699
Mary Risley
A wide variety of culinary and pastry courses, ranging in length from one day to six months. French and California cooking. Catalogue available.

COSTUMES

BOB MANDELL'S COSTUME SHOP, INC.
1137 Mission Street
San Francisco, CA 94103
415.863.7755
Bob Mandell
Areas served: International
Northern California's largest costume rental shop. 5000 costumes for sale. 40,000 costumes for rent. Novelties, masks, wigs, beards, makeup. Makeup artist on staff during Halloween week.

DELICACIES

NARSAIS MARKET, I. MAGNIN
135 Stockton Street
San Francisco, CA 94108
415.403.2046
Jim Mills
Areas served: San Francisco Bay
A full service cafe providing full event planning, catering, delicacies, cakes and confections. Mustards, chocolate and caramel sauces, coffee, vintage wines, prepared foods, custom-designed cakes, tarts, petit fours, etc.

[Continued on next page]

SAN FRANCISCO

DESTINATION MANAGEMENT
CAPPA AND GRAHAM DESTINATION
401 China Basin Street
Suite 212
San Francisco, CA 94107
415.543.3488
Barbara Cappa
Areas served: Northern California
Full service destination management
company for all special events – airport
transfers, tours, shuttles. Transportation
for all size groups.

EQUIPMENT RENTALS & TENTING
3B PRODUCTIONS
575 N. Seventh Street
San Jose, CA 95112
408.289.1383
Kevin Boone
Areas served: Northern California
Complete sound, lighting and production
services for corporate events, trade shows
and concerts. Build sets and also provide
complete power distributor systems.

HDO PRODUCTIONS
1465 N. Gordon Avenue
Burlingame, CA 94010
415.375.0331
415.375.1200
800.225.1471
Areas served: National
Tents, canopies, freestanding structures,
floors, lights, heat. Outdoor event
planning. Offices in Washington, DC and
Chicago.

THE STUART RENTAL COMPANY
1650 Industrial Road
San Carlos, CA 94070
415.591.4414
Susan Bennett
Areas served: Northern California
Provide equipment rentals, custom tenting,
linens, lighting, staging, dance floors,
tables, chairs, flatware, catering
equipment, glassware, etc.

WESTERN SCENIC STUDIOS
1185 32nd Street
Oakland, CA 94608
510.658.3139
Areas served: National
Full event decor. Lighting, staging and
floral design. Full trade show production.
Technical services. In business since
1919.

EVENT PLANNING
3B PRODUCTIONS
575 N. Seventh Street
San Jose, CA 95112
408.289.1383
Kevin Boone
Areas served: Northern California
Complete sound, lighting and production
services for corporate events, trade shows
and concerts. Build sets and also provide
complete power distributor systems.

ANN BENNETT AND ASSOCIATES
1177 California Street
Suite B
San Francisco, CA 94108
415.928.3622
Ann Bennett
Areas served: International
Complete special event production, travel
services, conference coordination and
limousine service.

CREATIVE CATERING
2800 Bryant
San Francisco, CA 94110
415.285.2555
Allison Rodman
Areas served: Northern California
Full event planning and catering for all
occasions.

MCCALL AND ASSOCIATES
888 Brannen Street
San Francisco, CA 94103
415.552.8550
Claire Jolley
Areas served: National
Full service event planning, catering, floral
design, sound, lighting, staging, event

design and production, entertainment, audiovisual services. Over ten years in business.

MOONLIGHTING
3880 Chestnut Avenue
Concord, CA 94519
510.798.MOON
Mary Frevele

Full service event co-ordination. Theme parties, fundraising development, etc. Mary is president of the Northern California chapter of ISES.

NARSAIS MARKET, I. MAGNIN
135 Stockton Street
San Francisco, CA 94108
415.403.2046
Jim Mills

Areas served: San Francisco Bay
A full service cafe providing full event planning, catering, delicacies, cakes and confections. Mustards, chocolate and caramel sauces, coffee, vintage wines, prepared foods, custom-designed cakes, tarts, petit fours, etc.

TASTE
3450 Third Street
Suite 4D
San Francisco, CA 94124
415.550.6464
Tambra Harck

Areas served: Northern California
Full service catering and event planning. Taste and Edible Art Catering have merged into one company. Over eleven years in business. Top corporate and private clientele. Fine cuisine and gracious service.

FAVORS
GODIVA CHOCOLATIER
Crooker Galleria
50 Post Street
San Francisco, CA 94104
415.982.6798

World renowned chocolatier. Belgium-style chocolates, gift baskets and party favors. Two other locations in Northern California.

TIFFANY & CO.
252 Grant Avenue
San Francisco, CA 94108
415.781.7000

The finest in engraved invitations, favors, accessories, stationery, bridal registry, fine crystal and china, Tiffany flatware and gifts for all occasions.

FIREWORKS & SPECIAL EFFECTS
CTA LASERS
1100 Gough Street
Suite 19F
San Francisco, CA 94109
415.221.6005
Paul Rosenberg

Areas served: California and Western U.S., Hawaii, Mexico
Laser effects and laser shows customized to specific budgets. Spectacular effects and high-powered equipment. Winners of International Laser Display Association award for most outrageous effects 1988-89.

JOEL NELSON PRODUCTIONS
1157 Saratoga Avenue
San Jose, CA 95129
916.648.0100
800.578.5780

1390 Market Street
San Francisco, CA 94102
415.573.7664
800.578.5780
Joel Nelson

Areas served: Northern California
Music and entertainment agency specializing in theme parties, celebrity look-alikes, bands, DJ's, magic theme entertainment. Lighting, decor, props, sound and lasers.

[Continued on next page]

FLORISTS & FLORAL DESIGNS

BLOOMERS
340 Presideo Avenue
San Francisco, CA 94115
415.563.3266
Patrik Powell
Areas served: San Francisco and
Surrounding Areas
Complete florist and floral designer
specializing in loose garden-like
arrangements and a wonderful selection of
cut flowers.

THE GREENERY
3237 Pierce Street
San Francisco, CA 94123
415.567.4991
Mike Mahoney
Rick Tremeroli
Areas served: San Francisco Bay
Full service indoor/outdoor plant store
providing plant rentals and floral decor for
all special events. Free delivery within San
Francisco.

McCALL AND ASSOCIATES
888 Brannen Street
San Francisco, CA 94103
415.552.8550
Claire Jolley
Areas served: National
Full service event planning, catering, floral
design, sound, lighting, staging, event design
and production, entertainment and
audiovisual services. Over ten years in
business.

WESTERN SCENIC STUDIOS
1185 32nd Street
Oakland, CA 94608
510.658.3139
Areas served: National
Full event decor. Lighting, staging and
floral design. Full trade show production.
Technical services. In business since 1919.

FORMAL WEAR

BLACK AND WHITE FORMALS
1233 Sutter Street
San Francisco, CA 94109
415.673.0626

2093 Mission Street
San Francisco, CA 94110
415.552.7613
Nick Tigos
Areas served: Northern California
Formal wear and wedding attire for men
and women. Rentals and Sales.

GIFTS & GIFT BASKETS

GODIVA CHOCOLATIER
Crooker Galleria
50 Post Street
San Francisco, CA 94104
415.982.6798
World renowned chocolatier. Belgium-style
chocolates, gift baskets and party favors.
Two other locations in Northern California.

JOHN WALKER & CO.
175 Sutter Street
San Francisco, CA 94104
415.986.2707
Mike Hogan
Areas served: International
A well known wine store with a London
carriage look, specializing in International and
California wines as well as a huge selection of
single malt scotches. Wine storage space
available for rent. Known for reasonable
prices and extensive personal service. Custom
designed gift baskets. In business since 1933.

JOSEPH SCHMIDT CONFECTIONS
3489 16th Street
San Francisco, CA 94114
415.861.8682
Audrey Ryan
Areas served: U.S. and Canada
Custom-designed chocolates for all events.
They create and sculpt anything in
chocolate. They love to create one-of-a-
kind things and also provide custom-
designed gift baskets. Catalogue available.

TIFFANY & CO.
252 Grant Avenue
San Francisco, CA 94108
415.781.7000
The finest in engraved invitations, favors,
accessories, stationery, bridal registry, fine
crystal and china, Tiffany flatware and gifts
for all occasions.

SAN FRANCISCO

INVITATIONS & ACCESSORIES

ABC CALLIGRAPHY
> 1903 Broderick
> Suite 7
> San Francisco, CA 94115
> **415.668.4994**
> Robin Hall

Areas served: National
Custom-designed and catalogue invitations,
English calligraphy, Hebrew calligraphy,
illuminated wedding contracts, menus, hand
painted place cards, wine labels,
illustrations. Handmade and rice papers.

BARBARA CALLOW CALLIGRAPHY
> 1686 Union Street
> Suite 204
> San Francisco, CA 94123
> **415.928.3303**
> Barbara Callow

Areas served: National
Custom-designed invitations, accessories
and calligraphy services.

PAPYRUS
> 2 Embarcadero Center
> San Francisco, CA 94111
> **415.781.8777**
> Anne Fulton
> Areas served: National

Twenty-eight locations nationwide.
Custom-designed and catalogue invitations,
accessories, place cards, menu cards,
programs. Full calligraphy services.

PARTY WAREHOUSE
> 2121 Harrison Street
> San Francisco, CA 94110
> **415.863.0912**
> 13 - 43rd Avenue
> San Mateo, CA 94403
> **415.377.0646**

> 458 San Mateo Avenue
> San Bruno, CA 94066
> **415.873.0792**

> 221 Oak Street
> Oakland, CA 94607
> **510.893.1951**

Discount party supplies: balloons, paper
products, decorations, invitations,
imprinting services, helium tank rentals.

SHREVE AND COMPANY
> 200 Post Street
> San Francisco, CA 94108
> **415.421.2600**
> Jim Jiminez

Areas served: San Francisco Bay
Shreve and Company provides wedding
invitations and social stationery by Crane
and Company.

STREAMERS
> Capitola Mall
> 1855 41st Avenue
> Capitola, CA 95010
> **408.479.4556**

> 401 Corte Madera Town Center
> Corte Madera, CA 94925
> **415.927.1003**

> 39121 Fremont Hub
> Fremont, CA 94538
> **510.792.5777**

> 18 N. Santa Cruz Avenue
> Los Gatos, CA 95030
> **408.395.1165**

> 1689 Arden Way
> Suite 1356
> Sacramento, CA 95815
> **916.923.1821**

> 2061 Chestnut Street
> San Francisco, CA 94123
> **415.922.5888**

> 282 Hillsdale Mall
> San Mateo, CA 94403
> **415.578.0131**

> Valley Fair Shopping Center
> 2855 Stevens Creek Blvd.
> Suite 2273
> Santa Clara, CA 95050
> **408.248.9495**

> 1286 Broadway Plaza
> Walnut Creek, CA 94596
> **510.937.3630**

One-stop shopping for party supplies:
invitations, balloons, paper supplies,
imprinting and machine calligraphy,
decorations.

[Continued on next page]

SAN FRANCISCO

TIFFANY & CO.
252 Grant Avenue
San Francisco, CA 94108
415.781.7000
The finest in engraved invitations, favors, accessories, stationery, bridal registry, fine crystal and china, Tiffany flatware and gifts for all occasions.

LIGHTING, STAGING & SOUND

3B PRODUCTIONS
575 N. Seventh Street
San Jose, CA 95112
408.289.1383
Kevin Boone
Areas served: Northern California
Complete sound, lighting and production services for corporate events, trade shows and concerts. Build sets and also provide complete power distributor systems.

CTA LASERS
1100 Gough Street
Suite 19F
San Francisco, CA 94109
415.221.6005
Paul Rosenberg
Areas served: California and Western U.S., Hawaii, Mexico
Laser effects and laser shows customized to specific budgets. Spectacular effects and high-powered equipment. Winners of International Laser Display Association award for most outrageous effects 1988-89.

HDO PRODUCTIONS
1465 N. Gordon Avenue
Burlingame, CA 94010
415.375.0331
415.375.1200
800.225.1471
Areas served: National
Tents, canopies, freestanding structures, floors, lights, heat. Outdoor event planning. Offices in Washington, DC and Chicago.

JOEL NELSON PRODUCTIONS
1157 Saratoga Avenue
San Jose, CA 95129
916.648.0100
800.578.5780

1390 Market Street
San Francisco, CA 94102
415.573.7664
800.578.5780
Joel Nelson
Areas served: Northern California
Music and entertainment agency specializing in theme parties, celebrity look-alikes, bands, DJ's, magic theme entertainment. Lighting, decor, props, sound and lasers.

McCALL AND ASSOCIATES
888 Brannen Street
San Francisco, CA 94103
415.552.8550
Claire Jolley
Areas served: National
Full service event planning, catering, floral design, sound, lighting, staging, event design and production, entertainment and audiovisual services. Over ten years in business.

THE STUART RENTAL COMPANY
1650 Industrial Road
San Carlos, CA 94070
415.591.4414
Susan Bennett
Areas served: Northern California
Provide equipment rentals, custom tenting, linens, lighting, staging, dance floors, tables, chairs, flatware, catering equipment, glassware, etc.

WESTERN SCENIC STUDIOS
1185 32nd Street
Oakland, CA 94608
510.658.3139
Areas served: National
Full event decor. Lighting, staging and floral design. Full trade show production. Technical services. In business since 1919.

LIMOUSINE & TRANSPORTATION

AAA LIMOUSINE
1685 Rogers Avenue
San Jose, CA 95112
408.453.6259
800.969.5466
Dan Nelson
Areas served: San Francisco Bay
Limousines, charters, airport
transportation.

ANN BENNETT AND ASSOCIATES
1177 California Street
Suite B
San Francisco, CA 94108
415.928.3622
Ann Bennett
Areas served: International
Complete special event production, travel
services, conference coordination and
limousine service.

CAPPA AND GRAHAM DESTINATION
401 China Basin Street
Suite 212
San Francisco, CA 94107
415.543.3488
Barbara Cappa
Areas served: Northern California
Full service destination management
company for all special events – airport
transfers, tours, shuttles. Transportation
for all size groups.

CAREY LIMOUSINE
415.468.7550
800.336.4646
Areas served: International
Privately chauffeured sedans, limousines,
vans and mini buses in 372 cities.

CELEBRITY VALET PARKING SERVICE, INC.
105 San Pablo
San Francisco, CA 94127
415.584.2035
Jay Skylor
Areas served: Bay area and all of Northern
California
Northern California's premier valet parking
company. Coordinates complete guest

reception services. Staff is highly trained in
hospitality. Services include coat check,
formal greeters, transportation and
shuttling. Named top valet company by San
Francisco SOMA Business Association.
Honorable mention by San Francisco
Chronicle.

CHAUFFEURED LIMOUSINES
1210 Cypress Avenue
San Mateo, CA 94401
415.344.4400
Mr. Minky
Areas served: Northern California
Limousines, vans and sedans for all
occasions.

DAV EL CHAUFFEURED TRANSPORTATION NETWORK
800.328.3526 (outside
California)
800.826.5779 (inside
California)
Areas Served: International
Luxury chauffeured services in over 350
cities worldwide. Centralized reservations
and billing. Airport concierge services.

THE FLYING DUTCHMEN
Pier 27
Administration Building
San Francisco, CA 94111
415.397.6644
Scott Becker
Areas served: San Francisco Bay
Full valet parking and shuttle services.
Coordinate all transportation needs.

WHIM AGENCY
2148 Union Street
San Francisco, CA 94123
415.951.9446

90 E. Blithedale Avenue
Mill Valley, CA 94941
415.383.9446

629 East D Street
Petaluma, CA 94925
707.545.9446
Suzanne Brady

[Continued on next page]

Areas served: San Francisco Bay area
Party servers, bartenders, entertainers,
celebrity look-alikes, valet parking,
childcare, drivers, etc. Same day service.

LINENS

THE STUART RENTAL COMPANY
1650 Industrial Road
San Carlos, CA 94070
415.591.4414
Susan Bennett
Areas served: Northern California
Provide equipment rentals, custom tenting,
linens, lighting, staging, dance floors,
tables, chairs, flatware, catering
equipment, glassware, etc.

MUSIC & ENTERTAINMENT

EARL & ERNIE HECKSCHER ORCHESTRA
10 Miller Place
Suite 603
San Francisco, CA 94108
415.362.3990
Earl Heckscher
Areas served: National
Full orchestra available in any size,
providing dance music and back up for
weddings, corporate events, conventions
and private parties.

JOEL NELSON PRODUCTIONS
1157 Saratoga Avenue
San Jose, CA 95129
916.648.0100
800.578.5780

1390 Market Street
San Francisco, CA 94102
415.573.7664
800.578.5780
Joel Nelson
Areas served: Northern California
Music and entertainment agency
specializing in theme parties, celebrity look-
alikes, bands, DJ's, magic theme
entertainment. Lighting, decor, props,
sound and lasers.

MCCALL AND ASSOCIATES
888 Brannen Street
San Francisco, CA 94103
415.552.8550
Claire Jolley
Areas served: National
Full service event planning, catering, floral
design, sound, lighting, staging, event design
and production, entertainment and
audiovisual services. Over ten years in
business.

WHIM AGENCY
2148 Union Street
San Francisco, CA 94123
415.951.9446

90 E. Blithedale Avenue
Mill Valley, CA 94941
415.383.9446

629 East D Street
Petaluma, CA 94925
707.545.9446
Suzanne Brady
Areas served: San Francisco Bay area
Party servers, bartenders, entertainers,
celebrity look-alikes, valet parking,
childcare, drivers, etc. Same day service.

PARTY SITES

FOUR SEASONS CLIFT HOTEL
495 Geary Street
San Francisco, CA 94102
415.775.4700
Rosanne Karlbach
San Francisco's Grand Dame Hotel, in heart
of Theatre District near Union Square. The
only Mobil five-star, AAA five-diamond
hotel. Conde Nast Traveler Magazine
readers poll top 10, Wine Spectator "Grand
Award." Full event and meeting facilities.
Business Center. Complete catering and
audio visual services. Receptions: 300
people. Sit down: 200 people.

NORTH BEACH RESTAURANT

1512 Stockton Street
San Francisco, CA 94133
415.392.1700
Huey Bui
Ruby Centony

Located in the heart of San Franciso's
North Beach area. Northern Italian
Cuisine, all fresh seafood, homemade pastas
and desserts. Art and paintings in dining
room, white walls and napkins, voted as one
of "Top 100 Restaurants" by Wine
Spectator Magazine for their wine list.
Many awards of excellence since 1980.
Three event spaces: Main Dining Room, sit
down: 150 people; Wine Cellar, receptions:
120 people, sit down: 90 people; Private
Stanza, sit down: 12 people.

MANDARIN ORIENTAL HOTEL
SAN FRANCISCO

222 Sansome Street
San Francisco, CA 94104
415.885.0999
Rick Arcari

Located downtown in the Financial District.
Beautiful, light pastel colors, crystal
chandeliers, hand painted murals. Named
by *CondeNast Traveler* as one of the top
100 hotels in the world. Voted best hotel in
San Francisco by *Institutional Investor*.
Three banquet rooms. Receptions: 150
people. Sit down: 100 people.

SAN FRANCISCO MART

1355 Market Street
San Francisco, CA 94103
415.552.2311
John Radovich

Recently refurbished. Two event facilities:
Grand Lobby (rotunda with mezzanine),
receptions: 800 people, sit down: 550
people; and The Mart Exchange (art deco);
receptions: 500 people, sit down: 250
people. On-site parking for over 200
vehicles.

PARTY SUPPLIES

PARTY WAREHOUSE

2121 Harrison Street
San Francisco, CA 94110
415.863.0912

13 - 43rd Avenue
San Mateo, CA 94403
415.377.0646

458 San Mateo Avenue
San Bruno, CA 94066
415.873.0792

221 Oak Street
Oakland, CA 94607
510.893.1951

Discount party supplies: balloons, paper
products, decorations, invitations,
imprinting services, helium tank rentals.

STREAMERS

Capitola Mall
1855 41st Avenue
Capitola, CA 95010
408.479.4556

401 Corte Madera Town Center
Corte Madera, CA 94925
415.927.1003

39121 Fremont Hub
Fremont, CA 94538
510.792.5777

18 N. Santa Cruz Avenue
Los Gatos, CA 95030
408.395.1165

1689 Arden Way
Suite 1356
Sacramento, CA 95815
916.923.1821

2061 Chestnut Street
San Francisco, CA 94123
415.922.5888

282 Hillsdale Mall
San Mateo, CA 94403
415.578.0131

Valley Fair Shopping Center
2855 Stevens Creek Blvd.
Suite 2273
Santa Clara, CA 95050
408.248.9495

1286 Broadway Plaza
Walnut Creek, CA 94596
510.937.3630

One-stop shopping for party supplies:
invitations, balloons, paper supplies,
imprinting and machine calligraphy,
decorations.

PERSONNEL & STAFFING

BARTENDERS UNLIMITED
1560 Fourth Street
San Rafael, CA 94901
415.454.3731
John Radovich
Areas served: California
Full-bar catering and staffing for all events.
Oldest and largest beverage catering
company in the state of California. Can
handle any size group up to 20,000. Fully
licensed and insured, clients include The
American Bar Association, Apple
Computer, Trans America Insurance Co.
and many other major corporations.

WHIM AGENCY
2148 Union Street
San Francisco, CA 94123
415.951.9446

90 E. Blithedale Avenue
Mill Valley, CA 94941
415.383.9446

629 East D Street
Petaluma, CA 94925
707.545.9446
Suzanne Brady
Areas served: San Francisco Bay area
Party servers, bartenders, entertainers,
celebrity look-alikes, valet parking,
childcare, drivers, etc. Same day service.

PHOTOGRAPHY & VIDEO

DAVE BUSH PHOTOGRAPHY
2 Saint George Alley
San Francisco, CA 94108
415.981.2874
Areas served: National
Offer complete photography and video
services for meetings, events, groups,
weddings and private parties. Have
complete color lab on the premises and are
the official photographers for MPI and
other large associations.

JONATHAN PERRY
51 Park Avenue
Mill Valley
San Francisco, CA 94941
415.388.5493

Areas served: San Francisco
Photography services for fundraisers,
political events, parties, weddings,
corporate events, radio and TV, sports.
Specialty is candid photos of people at live
events.

MCCUNE AUDIO VISUAL
951 Howard Street
San Francisco, CA 94103
415.885.2510
Dave Molnar
Areas served: International
Complete audiovisual services, sound
systems, videos, multimedia, etc., for
corporate events, meetings and conventions.

PLANT RENTALS

THE GREENERY
3237 Pierce Street
San Francisco, CA 94123
415.567.4991
Mike Mahoney
Rick Tremeroli
Areas served: San Francisco Bay
Full service indoor/outdoor plant store
providing plant rentals and floral decor for
all special events. Free delivery within San
Francisco.

PROPS & DECOR

JOEL NELSON PRODUCTIONS
1157 Saratoga Avenue
San Jose, CA 95129
916.648.0100
800.578.5780

1390 Market Street
San Francisco, CA 94102
415.573.7664
800.578.5780
Joel Nelson
Areas served: Northern California
Music and entertainment agency
specializing in theme parties, celebrity look-
alikes, bands, DJ's, magic theme
entertainment. Lighting, decor, props,
sound and lasers.

McCall and Associates
888 Brannen Street
San Francisco, CA 94103
415.552.8550
Claire Jolley
Areas served: National
Full service event planning, catering, floral
design, sound, lighting, staging, event design
and production, entertainment and
audiovisual services. Over ten years in
business.

Party Warehouse
2121 Harrison Street
San Francisco, CA 94110
415.863.0912

13 - 43rd Avenue
San Mateo, CA 94403
415.377.0646

458 San Mateo Avenue
San Bruno, CA 94066
415.873.0792

221 Oak Street
Oakland, CA 94607
510.893.1951
Discount party supplies: balloons, paper
products, decorations, invitations,
imprinting services, helium tank rentals.

Streamers
Capitola Mall
1855 41st Avenue
Capitola, CA 95010
408.479.4556

401 Corte Madera Town Center
Corte Madera, CA 94925
415.927.1003

39121 Fremont Hub
Fremont, CA 94538
510.792.5777

18 N. Santa Cruz Avenue
Los Gatos, CA 95030
408.395.1165

1689 Arden Way
Suite 1356
Sacramento, CA 95815
916.923.1821

2061 Chestnut Street
San Francisco, CA 94123
415.922.5888

282 Hillsdale Mall
San Mateo, CA 94403
415.578.0131

Valley Fair Shopping Center
2855 Stevens Creek Blvd.
Suite 2273
Santa Clara, CA 95050
408.248.9495

1286 Broadway Plaza
Walnut Creek, CA 94596
510.937.3630
One-stop shopping for party supplies:
invitations, balloons, paper supplies,
imprinting and machine calligraphy,
decorations.

Western Scenic Studios
1185 32nd Street
Oakland, CA 94608
510.658.3139
Areas served: National
Full event decor. Lighting, staging and
floral design. Full trade show production.
Technical services. In business since 1919.

TABLETOP ACCESSORIES & KITCHENWARE

Crate & Barrel
125 Grant Avenue
San Francisco, CA 94108
415.985.4000

The Village at Corte Madera
Corte Madera, CA 94925
415.924.5412

Stanford Shopping Center
Palo Alto, CA 94304
415.321.7800

Valley Fair Shopping Center
Santa Clara, CA 95050
408.243.7500

Broadway Plaza
Walnut Creek, CA 94596
510.947.3500

Outlet Store
1785 Fourth Street
Berkeley, CA 94710
510.528.5500

[Continued on next page]

SAN FRANCISCO

Full line of unique contemporary home furnishings and accessories, featuring tabletop accessories and gourmet kitchenware.

POTTERY BARN
2000 Chestnut Street
San Francisco, CA 94123
415.441.1787

One Embarcadero Center
Street Level
San Francisco, CA 94111
415.788.6810

Leading retailer of contemporary tableware and decorative accessories for the home. Merchandise is 100% exclusive, designed and sold exclusively at Pottery Barn. Over fifty stores nationally and mail order. Several other locations in Northern California.

TIFFANY & CO.
252 Grant Avenue
San Francisco, CA 94108
415.781.7000

The finest in engraved invitations, favors, accessories, stationery, bridal registry, fine crystal and china, Tiffany flatware and gifts for all occasions.

WILLIAMS-SONOMA
150 Post Street
San Francisco, CA 94108
415.362.6904

865 Market Street
Suite 206
San Francisco, CA 94103
415.546.0171

An authoritative selection of the best for the kitchen. Complete line of cookware, bakware, electrics, glassware, tabletop, kitchen furniture, cookbooks, packaged foods. Knowledgeable staff will help choose equipment, plan parties. Most merchandise is exclusive to Williams-Sonoma.

VALET PARKING
CELEBRITY VALET PARKING SERVICE, INC.
105 San Pablo
San Francisco, CA 94127

415.584.2035
Jay Skylor
Areas served: Bay area and all of Northern California
Northern California's premier valet parking company. Coordinates complete guest reception services. Staff is highly trained in hospitality. Services include coat check, formal greeters, transportation and shuttling. Named top valet company by San Francisco SOMA Business Association. Honorable mention by *San Francisco Chronicle*.

THE FLYING DUTCHMEN
Pier 27
Administration Building
San Francisco, CA 94111
415.397.6644
Scott Becker
Areas served: San Francisco Bay
Full valet parking and shuttle services. Coordinate all transportation needs.

WHIM AGENCY
2148 Union Street
San Francisco, CA 94123
415.951.9446

90 E. Blithedale Avenue
Mill Valley, CA 94941
415.383.9446

629 East D Street
Petaluma, CA 94925
707.545.9446
Suzanne Brady
Areas served: San Francisco Bay area
Party servers, bartenders, entertainers, celebrity look-alikes, valet parking, childcare, drivers, etc. Same day service.

WINE & SPIRITS
D & M WINES
2200 Fillmore Street
San Francisco, CA 94115
415.346.1325
Joe Politz
Areas served: National
A California boutique wine store offering one of the largest champagne selections in the United States as well as all hard to find California wines. In business since 1935.

SAN FRANCISCO

JOHN WALKER & CO.
175 Sutter Street
San Francisco, CA 94104
415.986.2707
Mike Hogan
Areas served: International
A well known wine store with a London
carriage look, specializing in International
and California wines as well as a huge
selection of single malt scotches. Wine
storage space available for rent. Known for
reasonable prices and extensive personal
service. Custom designed gift baskets. In
business since 1933.

NARSAIS MARKET, I. MAGNIN
135 Stockton Street
San Francisco, CA 94108
415.403.2046
Jim Mills
Areas served: San Francisco Bay
A full service cafe providing full event
planning, catering, delicacies, cakes and
confections. Mustards, chocolate and
caramel sauces, coffee, vintage wines,
prepared foods, custom-designed cakes,
tarts, petit fours, etc.

YACHT & BOAT CHARTERS

HORN BLOWER DINING YACHTS
Pier 33
San Francisco, CA 94111
415.394.8900
One of the largest dining yacht companies in
the country. Corporate events, private
parties, business meetings, cocktail and
dinner cruises. Nautically attired crew,
cuisine prepared fresh on board. In
business over ten years.

MONTE CARLO CRUISES
Pier 3
Ferryboat Santa Rosa
San Francisco, CA 94111
415.394.7999 x270
Kathy Green
Offers a unique way to see the San
Francisco Bay. Karaoke Sing-a-Long on
board, a DJ, two dance floors, two bars and
charity casino available complete with
Roulette, Black Jack and Craps tables. A
Taste of San Francisco Buffet with a

sampling of Northbeach, Fisherman's
Wharf, The Mission and Chinatown.
Receptions: 500 people. Sit down: 350
people.

≈ ≈ ≈

ATLANTA

ATLANTA

AUDIOVISUAL & TECHNICAL SERVICES

ATLANTA MUSIC AGENCY
P.O. Box 720297
Atlanta, GA 30358
404.552.8220

10820 Shallowford Road
Roswell, GA 30075
404.552.8220
Tony N. Garstin
Areas served: National
Entertainment contractors, technical
production: sound, lights, stages, stage
sets, technical administration, labor
administration.

MAGNUM COMPANIES
170-A Ohley Drive, NE
Atlanta, GA 30324
404.872.0553
Erik Magnuson
Areas served: National
Stage lighting, sound, video, audiovisual
services. Rent, sell, produce and design
lighting equipment.

TOTAL AUDIO VISUAL SERVICES, INC.
811 Marietta Street, NW
Atlanta, GA 30318
404.875.7555
Areas served: International
Equipment, personnel and planning
expertise for all audiovisual needs. All size
events.

BALLOONS

FUNNY BUSINESS
Ansley Mall
1544 Piedmont Avenue
Atlanta, GA 30324
404.876.3747
Gary Divan
Areas served: Atlanta
Retail store offering wide selection of party
supplies, balloons, cards, paper plates, gift
items, gift bags.

BOOKS

WILLIAMS-SONOMA
3393 Peachtree Road, NE
Atlanta, GA 30326
404.237.4878
Barbara Metz, Manager
Jeannette Marsh, Assistant
Manager

4400 Ashford Dunwoody Road
Atlanta, GA 30346
404.698.8584
Jennifer Moss, Manager
Marty Luke, Assistant Manager
An authoritative selection of the best for the
kitchen. Complete line of cookware,
bakeware, electrics, glassware, tabletop,
kitchen furniture, cookbooks, packaged
foods. Knowledgeable staff will help choose
equipment, plan parties. Most merchandise
is exclusive to Williams-Sonoma.

CAKES & BAKED GOODS

ALONS BAKERY
1394 N. Highland Avenue
Atlanta, GA 30306
404.872.6000
Alon Balshan
Areas served: Atlanta
Custom-designed cakes and pastries -
wedding cakes, logos, scones, desserts,
cookies, croissants. Voted best croissant by
Atlanta Magazine.

THE EASY WAY OUT
2449 Peachtree Road
Atlanta, GA 30305
404.262.9944
David Warren
Jane Long
Areas served: Atlanta
Gourmet foods and catering to go. Cheeses,
pate, salads, entrees, picnic baskets, cakes,
pastries. Specializing in Southern and
gourmet products. Corporate box lunches
and dinners.

ATLANTA

CALLIGRAPHY

CHARLES WILLIS
465 E. Paces Ferry Road, NE
Atlanta, GA 20355
404.233.9487
Edith Shaburn
Areas served: Atlanta
Retail store offering tabletop accessories, catalogue invitations, accessories and favors. Full calligraphy services. Bridal registry of several hundred patterns.

CATERING

BLACK TIE SERVICES
5446 Peachtree Industrial Boulevard
Suite 173
Atlanta, GA 30341
404.457.5649
Marc Fraser
Areas served: Georgia
Catering, service personnel, coordination of weddings. Servers, bartenders, invitations.

CELEBRATIONS, INC.
3130 Maple Drive, NE
Suite 21-C
Atlanta, GA 30305
404.261.5995
Gail Prescott
Stacie Rogers
Areas served: Metro & surrounding Atlanta area; other cities in the Southeast
Full service catering and event planning. Specializing in cocktail buffets. Clients include Lexus, Dean Witter, Reynolds, Democratic National Convention and many others. In business since 1976.

THE EASY WAY OUT
2449 Peachtree Road
Atlanta, GA 30305
404.262.9944
David Warren
Jane Long
Areas served: Atlanta
Gourmet foods and catering to go. Cheeses, pate, salads, entrees, picnic baskets, cakes, pastries. Specializing in Southern and gourmet products. Corporate box lunches and dinners.

PROOF OF THE PUDDING INC.
489 Courtland Street, NE
Atlanta, GA 30308
404.892.2359
Guy Thomson
Areas served: Atlanta and surrounding areas
Full service, upscale catering for all events.

TOP BANANAS CATERING
103 Roswell Street
Atlanta, GA 30201
404.475.8677
David Shuppert
Areas served: Atlanta Metropolitan area, but will travel to other areas
Full service party planning, production and catering of major corporate and social events for 30 to 5000. Major weddings and social galas, large-scale tented events, themed productions and creative events their specialty. Top quality, innovative foods including a one-of-a-kind wedding "cake" consisting of chocolate Frangelico mousse frosted with white chocolate buttercream. One of thirty original founders of The International Special Events Society. Featured as a cover story in *Catering Today Magazine*; editorially featured in numerous local and national publications. Known for site-cooked, a la carte quality foods. Custom-designed party plans and menus to match the needs of clientele. In business since 1982.

CELEBRITY ACQUISITION

ATLANTA SPEAKERS BUREAU
2859 Paces Ferry Road
Suite 1830
Atlanta, GA 30339
404.432.1394
Sherry Conner
Speakers, celebrities, entertainers. For meetings, parties and special events.

[Continued on next page]

ATLANTA

CHOCOLATES & CONFECTIONS

GODIVA CHOCOLATIER
Lenox Square Mall
404.262.2108

Perimeter Mall
404.671.9650
World renowned chocolatier. Belgium-style chocolates, gift baskets and party favors.

MADDIX DELUXE
1034 N. Highland Avenue
Atlanta, GA 30306
404.892.9337
Michael Phillips
Areas served: Southeast US
Full service florist and chocolatier providing full service event planning for all occasions. Known for their natural approach to flowers, handmade chocolate bowls, truffles from around the world, exotic candy confections, extensive and romantic gifts, Japanese rice paper writing sets, Italian bubble bath.

CLASSES & SEMINARS

GREEN'S
737 Ponce De Leon Avenue
Atlanta, GA 30306
404.872.1109

2612 Buford Highway, NE
Atlanta, GA 30324
404.321.6232
Michael Bishop
Areas served: Atlanta
Full service wine, liquor and beer, party ice, holiday gift baskets. Michael Bishop, the wine director, is available for private seminars on all aspects of wine appreciation.

COSTUMES

COSTUME ARCHITECTS
1536 Monroe Drive, NE
Atlanta, GA 30324
404.875.6275

Areas served: National
Costume rentals, custom made costumes, wigs, make-up, masks, mascots, hats. Make-up artist and staff during holidays and Mardi Gras.

DELICACIES

THE EASY WAY OUT
2449 Peachtree Road
Atlanta, GA 30305
404.262.9944
David Warren
Jane Long
Areas served: Atlanta
Gourmet foods and catering to go. Cheeses, pate, salads, entrees, picnic baskets, cakes, pastries. Specializing in Southern and gourmet products. Corporate box lunches and dinners.

DESTINATION MANAGEMENT

PRESENTING ATLANTA, INC.
110 E. Andrews Drive, NW
Suite 303
Atlanta, GA 30305
404.231.0200
Cindy Fowler
Areas served: Atlanta
Full service destination management, event and meeting planning.

EQUIPMENT RENTALS & TENTING

TABLES AND CHAIRS
2135 American Industrial Way
Atlanta, GA 30341
404.458.2757
Areas served: Southeast United States
Tables, chairs, linens, tenting, flower carts, ice caddies, patio umbrellas and tables, etc.

TAYLOR RENTAL
2144 Masonwood Circle
Snellville, GA 30278
404.985.1070
Dottie Palmer

Areas served: Southeast US
Rental equipment and tents. Delivery,
pick-up, set-up, take-down, coordination of
event, consultation, tent decoration
(brochure included). ISES/NACE Allie
Awards '92 for Best Use of Tenting, and
Best Logistics for Rental.

EVENT PLANNING

BLACK TIE SERVICES
5446 Peachtree Industrial
Boulevard
Suite 173
Atlanta, GA 30341
404.457.5649
Marc Fraser
Areas served: Georgia
Catering, service personnel, coordination of
weddings. Servers, bartenders, invitations.

CELEBRATIONS, INC.
3130 Maple Drive, NE
Suite 21-C
Atlanta, GA 30305
404.261.5995
Gail Prescott
Stacie Rogers
Areas served: Metro & surrounding
Atlanta area; other cities in the Southeast
Full service catering and event planning.
Specializing in cocktail buffets. Clients
include Lexus, Dean Witter, Reynolds,
Democratic National Convention and many
others. In business since 1976.

MADDIX DELUXE
1034 N. Highland Avenue
Atlanta, GA 30306
404.892.9337
Michael Phillips
Areas served: Southeast US
Full service florist and chocolatier
providing full service event planning for all
occasions. Known for their natural
approach to flowers, handmade chocolate
bowls, truffles from around the world,
exotic candy confections, extensive and
romantic gifts, Japanese rice paper writing
sets, Italian bubble bath.

MICHAEL EVANS FLORAL DESIGN
34 Irby Avenue
Atlanta, GA 30305
404.365.0200
Michael Evans
Areas served: Metro Atlanta
Complete party planning, floral and decor
services for all special events. Full service
florist. Delivery available. Fine flowers
imported from Europe. Sophisticated
elegance with a dash of casual abandon.

MONTE CARLO PRODUCTIONS
1810 Plymouth Road, NW
Atlanta, GA 30318
404.351.9012
Christine Cazayoux
Areas served: Southeast US
Participatory theme events for conventions,
trade shows, receptions, private parties.
Specializing in Las Vegas Casino parties,
Kentucky Derby nites, Riverboat Gambler,
Mardi Gras, 1950's, etc.

PRESENTING ATLANTA, INC.
110 E. Andrews Drive, NW
Suite 303
Atlanta, GA 30305
404.231.0200
Cindy Fowler
Areas served: Atlanta
Full service destination management, event
and meeting planning.

TOP BANANAS CATERING
103 Roswell Street
Atlanta, GA 30201
404.475.8677
David Shuppert
Areas served: Atlanta Metropolitan area,
but will travel to other areas
Full service party planning, production and
catering of major corporate and social
events for 30 to 5000. Major weddings and
social galas, large-scale tented events,
themed productions and creative events
their specialty. Top quality, innovative
foods including a one-of-a-kind wedding
"cake" consisting of chocolate Frangelico
mousse frosted with white chocolate
buttercream. One of thirty original
founders of The International Special
Events Society. Featured as a cover story

[Continued on next page]

in Catering Today Magazine; editorially featured in numerous local and national publications. Known for site-cooked, a la carte quality foods. Custom-designed party plans and menus to match the needs of clientele. In business since 1982.

FAVORS

CHARLES WILLIS
465 E. Paces Ferry Road, NE
Atlanta, GA 20355
404.233.9487
Edith Shaburn
Areas served: Atlanta
Retail store offering tabletop accessories, catalogue invitations, accessories and favors. Full calligraphy services. Bridal registry of several hundred patterns.

GODIVA CHOCOLATIER
Lenox Square Mall
404.262.2108

Perimeter Mall
404.671.9650
World renowned chocolatier. Belgium-style chocolates, gift baskets and party favors.

TIFFANY & CO.
Phipps Plaza
3500 Peachtree Road, NE
Atlanta, GA 30326
404.261.0075
The finest in engraved invitations, favors, accessories, stationery, bridal registry, fine crystal and china, Tiffany flatware and gifts for all occasions.

FIREWORKS & SPECIAL EFFECTS

CLASSIC FIREWORKS BY EVENTS, INC.
P.O. Box 205
Mandeville, LA 70470-0205
504.893.8800
800.783.2513
David Spear
Areas served: National & International
Indoor pyrotechnic productions and aerial

fireworks displays. Produced pyrotechnics at last three Super Bowls.

SOUTHEASTERN INTERNATIONAL FIREWORKS
P.O. Box 1
Woodstock, GA 30188
404.924.1777
John Feigert
Areas served: Southeast US
Turnkey fireworks displays, special effects and indoor pyrotechnics.

FLORISTS & FLORAL DESIGNS

DAN MARTIN FLOWERS, INC.
3205 Peachtree Road, NE
Atlanta, GA 30305
404.261.1161
Dan Martin
Areas served: Greater Atlanta
Full service florist and floral design services for special events. In business thirty-five years serving top Atlanta clientele.

MADDIX DELUXE
1034 N. Highland Avenue
Atlanta, GA 30306
404.892.9337
Michael Phillips
Areas served: Southeast US
Full service florist and chocolatier providing full service event planning for all occasions. Known for their natural approach to flowers, handmade chocolate bowls, truffles from around the world, exotic candy confections, extensive and romantic gifts, Japanese rice paper writing sets, Italian bubble bath.

MICHAEL EVANS FLORAL DESIGN
34 Irby Avenue
Atlanta, GA 30305
404.365.0200
Michael Evans
Areas served: Metro Atlanta
Complete party planning, floral and decor services for all special events. Full service florist. Delivery available. Fine flowers imported from Europe. Sophisticated elegance with a dash of casual abandon.

FORMAL WEAR

GINGISS FORMALWEAR
> 3400 Woodale Boulevard
> Atlanta, GA 30326
> **404.266.2115**
> Jeff Harris

Areas served: Atlanta
Formal wear rentals for both men and women. Men's formal wear for sale. Special event services available for large groups. Ten other stores throughout Atlanta.

GIFTS & GIFT BASKETS

GODIVA CHOCOLATIER
> Lenox Square Mall
> **404.262.2108**
>
> Perimeter Mall
> **404.671.9650**

World renowned chocolatier. Belgium-style chocolates, gift baskets and party favors.

GREEN'S
> 737 Ponce De Leon Avenue
> Atlanta, GA 30306
> **404.872.1109**
>
> 2612 Buford Highway, NE
> Atlanta, GA 30324
> **404.321.6232**
> Michael Bishop

Areas served: Atlanta
Full service wine, liquor and beer, party ice, holiday gift baskets. Michael Bishop, the wine director, is available for private seminars on all aspects of wine appreciation.

MADDIX DELUXE
> 1034 N. Highland Avenue
> Atlanta, GA 30306
> **404.892.9337**
> Michael Phillips

Areas served: Southeast US
Full service florist and chocolatier providing full service event planning for all occasions. Known for their natural approach to flowers, handmade chocolate bowls, truffles from around the world, exotic candy confections, extensive and romantic gifts, Japanese rice paper writing sets, Italian bubble bath.

TIFFANY & CO.
> Phipps Plaza
> 3500 Peachtree Road, NE
> Atlanta, GA 30326
> **404.261.0075**

The finest in engraved invitations, favors, accessories, stationery, bridal registry, fine crystal and china, Tiffany flatware and gifts for all occasions.

ICE SERVICES

GREEN'S
> 737 Ponce De Leon Avenue
> Atlanta, GA 30306
> **404.872.1109**
>
> 2612 Buford Highway, NE
> Atlanta, GA 30324
> **404.321.6232**
> Michael Bishop

Areas served: Atlanta
Full service wine, liquor and beer, party ice, holiday gift baskets. Michael Bishop, the wine director, is available for private seminars on all aspects of wine appreciation.

INVITATIONS & ACCESSORIES

BLACK TIE SERVICES
> 5446 Peachtree Industrial Boulevard
> Suite 173
> Atlanta, GA 30341
> **404.457.5649**
> Marc Fraser

Areas served: Georgia
Catering, service personnel, coordination of weddings. Servers, bartenders, invitations.

CHARLES WILLIS
> 465 E. Paces Ferry Road, NE
> Atlanta, GA 20355
> **404.233.9487**
> Edith Shaburn

[Continued on next page]

Areas served: Atlanta
Retail store offering tabletop accessories, catalogue invitations, accessories and favors. Full calligraphy services. Bridal registry of several hundred patterns.

TIFFANY & CO.

Phipps Plaza
3500 Peachtree Road, NE
Atlanta, GA 30326
404.261.0075

The finest in engraved invitations, favors, accessories, stationery, bridal registry, fine crystal and china, Tiffany flatware and gifts for all occasions.

LIGHTING, STAGING & SOUND

ATLANTA MUSIC AGENCY

P.O. Box 720297
Atlanta, GA 30358
404.552.8220

10820 Shallowford Road
Roswell, GA 30075
404.552.8220
Tony Garstin

Areas served: National
Entertainment contractors, technical production: sound, lights, stages, stage sets, technical administration, labor administration.

MAGNUM COMPANIES

170-A Ohley Drive, NE
Atlanta, GA 30324
404.872.0553
Erik Magnuson

Areas served: National
Stage lighting, sound, video, audiovisual services. Rent, sell, produce and design lighting equipment.

LIMOUSINE & TRANSPORTATION

CAREY LIMOUSINE

404.681.3366
800.336.4646

Privately chauffeured sedans, limousines, vans and mini buses in 372 cities.

DAV EL CHAUFFEURED TRANSPORTATION NETWORK

800.328.3526 (outside CA)
800.826.5779 (inside CA)

Areas Served: International
Luxury chauffeured services in over 350 cities worldwide. Centralized reservations and billing. Airport concierge services.

LINENS

TABLES AND CHAIRS

2135 American Industrial Way
Atlanta, GA 30341
404.458.2757

Areas served: Southeast United States
Tables, chairs, linens, tenting, flower carts, ice caddies, patio umbrellas and tables, etc.

MUSIC & ENTERTAINMENT

ATLANTA MUSIC AGENCY

P.O. Box 720297
Atlanta, GA 30358
404.552.8220

10820 Shallowford Road
Roswell, GA 30075
404.552.8220
Tony Garstin

Areas served: National
Entertainment contractors, technical production: sound, lights, stages, stage sets, technical administration, labor administration.

ATLANTA SPEAKERS BUREAU

2859 Paces Ferry Road
Suite 1830
Atlanta, GA 30339
404.432.1394
Sherry J. Conner

Speakers, celebrities, entertainers. For meetings, parties and special events.

ATLANTA

MONTE CARLO PRODUCTIONS
1810 Plymouth Road, NW
Atlanta, GA 30318
404.351.9012
Christine Cazayoux
Areas served: Southeast US
Participatory theme events for conventions, trade shows, receptions, private parties. Specializing in Las Vegas Casino parties, Kentucky Derby nites, Riverboat Gambler, Mardi Gras, 1950's, etc.

PARTY SITES

ATLANTA BOTANICAL GARDEN
Piedmont Avenue
Prado Entrance
P.O. Box 77246
Atlanta, GA 30357
404.876.5859
Ann Siebert
Thirty acres of botanical gardens, hall and classroom for special events. Parties, wedding receptions, corporate retreats, lectures. The hall is 5000 square feet. Receptions: 450 people. Sit down: 300 people. On site parking for 350 vehicles.

CALLANWOLDE FINE ARTS CENTER
980 Briarcliff Road, NE
Atlanta, GA 30306
404.872.5338
Sam Goldman
Tudor Mansion located on twelve acres of land. Listed on Historical Register. 30,000 square feet. Receptions: 500 people. Sit down: 400 people.

THE FOX THEATRE
660 Peachtree Street, NE
Atlanta, GA 30365
404.881.2110
Charlotte Margolin, Director
Sales & Marketing
The opulent Fox Theatre, with its mosque-like facade, is located in midtown Atlanta. It has a 4518-seat auditorium and two exquisite ballrooms for private events. The Egyptian Ballroom evokes mysticism of an Egyptian temple while the architecture of the Grand Salon is Moorish inspired. The Egyptian Ballroom is 6776 square feet, the Grand

Salon is 3468 square feet, and combined is 10,244 square feet. Receptions: Egyptian Ballroom 675 people, Grand Salon 337 people, combined 1012 people. Sit down: Egyptian Ballroom 464 people, Grand Salon 240 people, combined 704 people.

THE RITZ CARLTON ATLANTA – DOWNTOWN
181 Peachtree Street, NE
Atlanta, GA 30303
404.659.0400
Karen Kushner
Special event facilities from small meetings of 10 up to 700 in a ballroom. Provide full event planning services. Arrange every detail.

STUDIO TWO
1275 Ellsworth Industrial Boulevard
Atlanta, GA 30318
404.350.9764
Steve Jezerinac
32,000 square foot building. Atmosphere of a movie studio back lot using theatre-style sets and backdrops to create different themes. Old time movie theatre marquee, five major theme areas including sports bar set with air hockey and basketball, the Victory Diner and Soda Shoppe sets, and an authentic-looking ante-bellum mansion front. Over thirty-five different theme sets available. Receptions: 2500 people. Sit down: 1500 people. Secured parking for up to 500 vehicles.

THE WORLD TRADE CLUB ATLANTA
270 Peachtree Street, NE
Atlanta, GA 30303
404.525.4144
David Pecher
Private club available evenings and weekends for special events. Terrace encircles club and indoor facilities. Receptions: 400. Sit down: 250. Ten years old. Affiliated with World Trade Center Association. Dark green and purple decor. Glass enclosed Main Dining Room overlooking Atlanta.

[Continued on next page]

ATLANTA

PARTY SUPPLIES

FUNNY BUSINESS
Ansley Mall
1544 Piedmont Avenue
Atlanta, GA 30324
404.876.3747
Gary Divan
Areas served: Atlanta
Retail store offering wide selection of party supplies, balloons, cards, paper plates, gift items, gift bags.

PERSONNEL & STAFFING

BLACK TIE SERVICES
5446 Peachtree Industrial
Boulevard
Suite 173
Atlanta, GA 30341
404.457.5649
Marc Fraser
Areas served: Georgia
Catering, service personnel, coordination of weddings. Servers, bartenders, invitations.

PHOTOGRAPHY & VIDEO

FOSTER AND ASSOCIATES
1012 Piedmont Avenue, NE
Atlanta, GA 30309
404.892.3533
Louis Foster
Areas served: National
Photography and video services. Specializes in convention and special event photography. In business over twenty years.

MAGNUM COMPANIES
170-A Ohley Drive, NE
Atlanta, GA 30324
404.872.0553
Erik Magnuson
Areas served: National
Stage lighting, sound, video, audiovisual services. Rent, sell, produce and design lighting equipment.

MICHAEL RIGGALL
403 Eighth Street, NE
Atlanta, GA 30309
404.872.8242
Michael Riggal
Areas served: Georgia
Public relations and special event photography.

PROPS & DECOR

DAN MARTIN FLOWERS, INC.
3205 Peachtree Road, NE
Atlanta, GA 30305
404.261.1161
Dan Martin
Areas served: Greater Atlanta
Full service florist and floral design services for special events. In business for thirty-five years serving top Atlanta clientele.

MICHAEL EVANS FLORAL DESIGN
34 Irby Avenue
Atlanta, GA 30305
404.365.0200
Michael Evans
Areas served: Metro Atlanta
Complete party planning, floral and decor services for all special events. Full service florist. Delivery available. Fine flowers imported from Europe. Sophisticated elegance with a dash of casual abandon.

SPEAKERS

ATLANTA SPEAKERS BUREAU
2859 Paces Ferry Road
Suite 1830
Atlanta, GA 30339
404.432.1394
Sherry Conner
Speakers, celebrities, entertainers. For meetings, parties and special events.

ATLANTA

TABLETOP ACCESSORIES & KITCHENWARE

CHARLES WILLIS
465 E. Paces Ferry Road, NE
Atlanta, GA 20355
404.233.9487
Edith Shaburn
Areas served: Atlanta
Retail store offering tabletop accessories, catalogue invitations, accessories and favors. Full calligraphy services. Bridal registry of several hundred patterns.

TIFFANY & CO.
Phipps Plaza
3500 Peachtree Road, NE
Atlanta, GA 30326
404.261.0075
The finest in engraved invitations, favors, accessories, stationery, bridal registry, fine crystal and china, Tiffany flatware and gifts for all occasions.

WILLIAMS-SONOMA
3393 Peachtree Road, NE
Atlanta, GA 30326
404.237.4878
Barbara Metz, Manager
Jeannette Marsh, Assistant Manager

4400 Ashford Dunwoody Road
Atlanta, GA 30346
404.698.8584
Jennifer Moss, Manager
Marty Luke, Assistant Manager
An authoritative selection of the best for the kitchen. Complete line of cookware, bakeware, electrics, glassware, tabletop, kitchen furniture, cookbooks, packaged foods. Knowledgeable staff will help choose equipment, plan parties. Most merchandise is exclusive to Williams-Sonoma.

WINE AND SPIRITS

GREEN'S
737 Ponce De Leon Avenue
Atlanta, GA 30306
404.872.1109

2612 Buford Highway, NE
Atlanta, GA 30324
404.321.6232
Michael Bishop
Areas served: Atlanta
Full service wine, liquor and beer, party ice, holiday gift baskets. Michael Bishop, the wine director, is available for private seminars on all aspects of wine appreciation.

BOSTON

BOSTON

AUDIOVISUAL & TECHNICAL SERVICES

ADAMS LIGHTING COMPANY
33 Bristol Street
Cambridge, MA 02141
617.492.6363
Deborah Adams
Andrew McGuigan
Areas served: New England
Theatrical production services including
decorative and theatrical lighting,
entertainment sound systems, temporary
power distribution, audiovisual
presentations and scale drawings. Lighting
in hotels, office buildings, school facilities
and tents, with selection of custom-designed
decorative fixtures, as well as pattern
projection and centerpiece spotlighting.
Computerized scale drawings showing guest
tables and chairs, decorative elements,
dance floors, bars and buffets. Won the
1980 IES Guth Memorial Lighting Design
Award of Excellence.

BOOKS

WILLIAMS-SONOMA
Marketplace Center
200 State Street
Boston, MA 02109
617.439.7035

Copley Place
100 Huntington Avenue
Boston, MA 02116
617.262.3080
An authoritative selection of the best for the
kitchen. Complete line of cookware,
bakeware, electrics, glassware, tabletop,
kitchen furniture, cookbooks, packaged
foods. Knowledgeable staff will help choose
equipment, plan parties. Most merchandise
is exclusive to Williams-Sonoma.

CAKES & BAKED GOODS

CAKES BY CHARLIE
32 Park Street
Wilmington, MA 01887
508.658.4190

Charlotte Guthrie
Areas served: Most of Massachusetts east of
Worcester (except Cape Cod) and Southern
New Hampshire
Specialty cakes for all occasions, wedding
cakes, full service bridal consultant,
wedding packages.

CONFECTIONS
231 New Boston Road
Fall River, MA 02720
508.674.4976
James Kennedy, Jr.
Areas served: Rhode Island,
Massachusetts, Connecticut
Wedding cakes, pastries, bakes Australian
style cakes. Handmade sugar flowers and
lacework.

THE ICING ON THE CAKE, INC.
212 Adams Street
Newton, MA 02158
617.969.1830
Amy Schwartz
Areas served: Greater Boston area
Uniquely designed, professionally decorated
cakes for all occasions. Specializing in
wedding cakes, cake sculptures.

SWEET CREATIONS
23 R Water Street
Wakefield, MA 01880
617.246.9792
617.246.0836
Eileen Worthley
Areas served: Boston, surrounding area,
and North Shore of Massachusetts
Special occasion cakes, wedding cakes,
dessert buffets, fancy European desserts
and pastries. Specializing in theme cakes
for special parties, wedding cakes. Made
Rose Kennedy's 100th birthday party cake.
Made cakes and pastries for visiting
"notables" to Boston: Prince Charles,
Corazan Aquino, Nelson Mandella, Jimmy
Buffett, Julia Child, Aerosmith. Julia Child
described the wedding cake as one of the
very few she had ever tasted that was a
pleasure from crumb to frosting, and so
beautiful as well.

CALLIGRAPHY
PAPER POTPOURRI
> 93 Broadway
> Haverhill, MA 01832
> **508.372.3861**
> Elaine Barker

Areas served: Massachusetts (mail order)
Invitation and calligraphy services. Won
first and third prize at the National
Stationery Show in New York, 1992.

CATERING
AL & PAT'S CATERING
> 11 Hawthorne Street
> Woburn, MA 01801
> **617.935.5606**
> Al Gangi, Jr.

Areas served: Middlesex County
Off premise catering. Italian and American
Cuisine.

DIFFERENT TASTES, INC.
> 103A Broadway
> Boston, MA 02116
> **617.884.3791**
> Jack Milaon

Areas served: Northeast US
Full service catering. Innovative, original
menus served with elegance. Won
Massachusetts choice - Best Chocolate
Dessert '92. Clients include many
personalities and dignitaries.

❧ PRIVATE CHEFS
THE PARTY PEOPLE, INC.
> 2 Carlisle Terrace
> Natick, MA 01760
> **508.650.9220**
> Rachel Goldstein, President

Areas served: Metro Boston including Cape
Cod and Southern New Hampshire
Professional, friendly accommodators.
Outstanding staff of servers, bartenders and
chefs. Offers pre-party set-up, food
service, and unsurpassed clean up. The
staff wears black & white or can dress for a
theme party. Full service event planning
for social and corporate clients.

Omelet parties a specialty. Rachel
Goldstein is in her second term as Secretary
of ISES/New England and was recently
featured in *Boston Magazine*.

CELEBRITY ACQUISITION
LORDLY & DAME
> 51 Church Street
> Boston, MA 02116
> **617.482.3596**
> Sam Dame

Areas served: International
Full event planning, music, entertainment,
speakers, celebrity acquisition, name acts.

CHOCOLATES & CONFECTIONS
THE CHOCOLATE TRUFFLE
> 200 W. Cummings Park
> Woburn, MA 01801
> **617.933.4616**
> Norma Herscott
> Barbara Yankovich

Areas served: Continental US
Specializing in swiss chocolate truffles,
corporate gifts in theme chocolate, wedding
favors, chocolate roses, swans, and baskets.
Won *Boston Magazine's* "Best" Chocolate
Award 1990 and 1991. Muscular Dystrophy
People's Choice Silver Medal Award.

GODIVA CHOCOLATIER
> Copley Place
> **617.437.8490**
>
> Burlington Mall
> **617.229.8999**
>
> The Atrium at Chestnut Hill
> **617.969.6992**

World renowned chocolatier. Belgium-style
chocolates, gift baskets and party favors.

[Continued on next page.]

BOSTON

DESTINATION MANAGEMENT

DAME ASSOCIATES, INC.
51 Church Street
Boston, MA 02116
617.482.3596
Douglas Dame
Areas served: International
Destination management, trade show
production, convention coordination,
exhibit and display rentals, corporate
seminars.

UNCOMMON BOSTON LTD.
437 Boylston Street
Fourth floor
Boston, MA 02116
617.731.6353
Susan Berk
Areas served: Boston and New England
Special customized tours and events from 2
- 2000, complete from idea and inception to
flowers and desserts. Events, parties,
dinners, luncheons, board meetings, tours,
entertainment, packaged weekends,
transportation, theme tours, wine,
antiques, gardens.

EQUIPMENT RENTALS & TENTING

ABC RENT-A-TENT, INC.
21 Heritage Drive
Westport, MA 02790
508.676.9214
401.846.3111
Donald Raposa, President
Areas served: Southeastern Massachusetts
and Rhode Island
Tents, tables, chairs, etc.

DAME ASSOCIATES, INC.
51 Church Street
Boston, MA 02116
617.482.3596
Douglas Dame
Areas served: International
Destination management, trade show
production, convention coordination,
exhibit and display rentals, corporate
seminars.

THE PARTY SPIRIT
74 Elm Street
Salisbury, MA 01952
508.465.2016
800.999.3398
Loretta & Stephen Dietch
Areas served: Greater Boston, Southern
New Hampshire, North Shore
Massachusetts, Merrimac Valley
(Massachusetts)
Party and tent rentals...complete party
supplies from invitations to palm tree
confetti.

TABLEFASHIONS, LTD.
116 Will Drive
Canton, MA 02021
617.821.1160
Sandi Chudnow
Areas served: International
Specialty linens, chair covers, upscale
specialty table treatments (all
manufacturing and processing is handled in
house).

EVENT PLANNING

BACON-CONCANNON ASSOCIATES
P.O. Box 246
Prudential Center
Boston, MA 02199
617.536.1448
Smoki Bacon
Areas served: New England
Registered fundraisers with the Attorney
General's Office. Fundraising, advertising,
community planning, event planning, public
relations, festivals, publicity, promotions,
theatre events. Organized "Jubilee 350"
Grand Ball in Copley Square, 1980 for
6,000 people. *Boston Magazine* cited Smoki
Bacon as one of the 100 most powerful
women in Boston. Papers were put in
Radcliffe College's time capsule. "Footlight
Parade" a party for the Boston Theatre
District Association, cited by *Boston
Magazine* as best party of the year.

CAKES BY CHARLIE
32 Park Street
Wilmington, MA 01887
508.658.4190

BOSTON

Charlotte Guthrie
Areas served: Most of Massachusetts east of Worcester (except Cape Cod) and Southern New Hampshire
Specialty cakes for all occasions, wedding cakes, full service bridal consultant, wedding packages.

CHRISTOPHER'S FLOWERS, INC.
56 Church Street
Cambridge, MA 02138
800.666.8384
Bill Rowe
Kathy Pickett
Areas served: Boston and New England
Event planner, florist, decorator. Specializing in weddings, corporate events. Work closely with Boston area hotel catering departments, as well as many local caterers.

CREATIVE TALENT, INC.
214 Lincoln Street
Suite 301
Allston, MA 02134
617.789.4747
Andy Espo, President
Areas served: New England and Eastern New York state
Entertainment, scenery and prop rentals, theme events and decor, lighting design, visual environments. Specialize in theme events.

DAME ASSOCIATES, INC.
51 Church Street
Boston, MA 02116
617.482.3596
Douglas Dame
Areas served: International
Destination management, trade show production, convention coordination, exhibit and display rentals, corporate seminars.

LORDLY & DAME
51 Church Street
Boston, MA 02116
617.482.3596
Sam Dame
Areas served: International
Full event planning, music, entertainment, speakers, celebrity acquisition, name acts.

THE ORIGINAL TOUCH
14 Partridge Road
Lexington, MA 02173
617.862.6471
Carol Silverston
Areas served: Eastern US
Complete party coordinating/planning services and floral design for weddings, Bar/Bat Mitzvah celebrations, corporate functions and other special occasions. Writer for *Greater Boston Events* and *Boston Magazine*.

THE PARTY PEOPLE, INC.
2 Carlisle Terrace
Natick, MA 01760
508.650.9220
Rachel Goldstein, President
Areas served: Metro Boston including Cape Cod and Southern New Hampshire
Professional, friendly accommodators. Outstanding staff of servers, bartenders and chefs. Offers pre-party set-up, food service, and unsurpassed clean up. The staff wears black & white or can dress for a theme party. Full service event planning for social and corporate clients. Omelet parties a specialty. Rachel Goldstein is in her second term as Secretary of ISES/New England and was recently featured in *Boston Magazine*.

SLEUTH & COMPANY
The Statler Building
20 Park Plaza
Suite 510
Boston, MA 02116
617.542.2525
Carol Schreck, President
Areas served: New England
Boston's Twilight Mystery Tour: A journey through Boston's history of mysteries, crimes and infamous deeds. Customized participatory mystery/fantasy events for conventions and groups of all sizes.

UNCOMMON BOSTON LTD.
437 Boylston Street
Fourth floor
Boston, MA 02116
617.731.6353
Susan Berk
Areas served: Boston and New England

BOSTON

Special customized tours and events from 2 - 2000, complete from idea and inception to flowers and desserts. Events, parties, dinners, luncheons, board meetings, tours, entertainment, packaged weekends, transportation, theme tours, wine, antiques, gardens.

WATNICK PROMOTIONS & EVENTS
31 Sherborne Circle
Ashland, MA 01721
508.881.6959
Sheila Watnick
Areas served: New England
Planning, producing and publicizing theme events, giving 150% service. Corporate, association, retail and private events. Specializing in events with wit and humor, and unique souvenir printed programs. President, New England chapter of ISES 1991-1993. 1986 Bell Ringer Award from The Publicity Club of New England. Contributing editor on special events in *Development Today: A Guide for Nonprofit Organizations.*

FAVORS

THE CHOCOLATE TRUFFLE
200 W. Cummings Park
Woburn, MA 01801
617.933.4616
Norma Herscott
Barbara Yankovich
Areas served: Continental US
Specializing in swiss chocolate truffles, corporate gifts in theme chocolate, wedding favors, chocolate roses, swans, and baskets. Won *Boston Magazine's* "Best" Chocolate Award 1990 and 1991. Muscular Dystrophy People's Choice Silver Medal Award.

GODIVA CHOCOLATIER
Copley Place
617.437.8490

Burlington Mall
617.229.8999

The Atrium at Chestnut Hill
617.969.6992
World renowned chocolatier. Belgium-style chocolates, gift baskets and party favors.

TIFFANY & CO.
Copley Place
100 Huntington Avenue
Boston, MA 02116
617.353.0222
The finest in engraved invitations, favors, accessories, stationery, bridal registry, fine crystal and china, Tiffany flatware and gifts for all occasions.

WATNICK PROMOTIONS & EVENTS
31 Sherborne Circle
Ashland, MA 01721
508.881.6959
Sheila Watnick
Areas served: New England
Planning, producing and publicizing theme events, giving 150% service. Corporate, association, retail and private events. Specializing in events with wit and humor, and unique souvenir printed programs. President, New England chapter of ISES 1991-1993. 1986 Bell Ringer Award from The Publicity Club of New England. Contributing editor on special events in *Development Today: A Guide for Nonprofit Organizations.*

FIREWORKS & SPECIAL EFFECTS

WET LIGHT
564 Putnam Avenue
Cambridge, MA 02139
617.876.8882
Jackson Madnick
Lasers, fireworks, fountains. Public large scale celebrations, conservation education spectacles. Won Gala Award 1991 for Best Entertainment Concept over $30,000 from *Special Event Magazine.*

FLORISTS & FLORAL DESIGNS

CHRISTOPHER'S FLOWERS, INC.
56 Church Street
Cambridge, MA 02138
800.666.8384

B O S T O N

Bill Rowe
Kathy Pickett
Areas served: Boston and general New England area.
Events planner, florist, decorator. Specializing in weddings, corporate events. Work closely with Boston area hotel catering departments, as well as many local caterers.

THE ORIGINAL TOUCH
14 Partridge Road
Lexington, MA 02173
617.862.6471
Carol Silverston
Areas served: Eastern US
Complete party coordinating/planning services and floral design for weddings, Bar/Bat Mitzvah celebrations, corporate functions and other special occasions. Writer for *Greater Boston Events* and *Boston Magazine*.

FORMAL WEAR
GINGISS FORMALWEAR
Arsenal Mall
Watertown, MA 02172
617.923.0841
Richard Lemire
Formal wear rentals and sales. Wide selection of designer styles. Pick up and delivery to hotels.

GIFTS & GIFT BASKETS
THE CHOCOLATE TRUFFLE
200 W. Cummings Park
Woburn, MA 01801
617.933.4616
Norma Herscott
Barbara Yankovich
Areas served: Continental US
Specializing in swiss chocolate truffles, corporate gifts in theme chocolate, wedding favors, chocolate roses, swans, and baskets. Won *Boston Magazine's* "Best" Chocolate Award 1990 and 1991. Muscular Dystrophy People's Choice Silver Medal Award.

JOHN GILBERT, JR. COMPANY
107 South Street
Boston, MA 02111
617.542.8900
Areas served: Massachusetts
Full service wine and liquor store. Wine and liquor consultation for special events. Specializing in fine wines from around the world. Custom gift baskets.

GODIVA CHOCOLATIER
Copley Place
617.437.8490

Burlington Mall
617.229.8999

The Atrium at Chestnut Hill
617.969.6992
World renowned chocolatier. Belgium-style chocolates, gift baskets and party favors.

TIFFANY & CO.
Copley Place
100 Huntington Avenue
Boston, MA 02116
617.353.0222
The finest in engraved invitations, favors, accessories, stationery, bridal registry, fine crystal and china, Tiffany flatware and gifts for all occasions.

ICE SERVICES
BROOKLINE ICE COMPANY, INC.
610 Brookline Avenue
Brookline, MA 02146
617.232.0941
617.ICE.CUBE
Areas served: Eastern Massachusetts/ Southern New Hampshire and Maine/Rhode Island, parts of Connecticut twenty-four hour/seven-day delivery service of ice, dry ice, ice sculptures, ice bowls, charcoal, exotic cooking woods. Rentals of mobile refrigerators/freezers and cooler storage units. Family owned and operated since 1924.

[Continued on next page.]

BOSTON

INVITATIONS & ACCESSORIES

PAPER POTPOURRI
93 Broadway
Haverhill, MA 01832
508.372.3861
Elaine Barker
Areas served: Massachusetts (mail order)
Invitation and calligraphy services. Won
first and third prize at the National
Stationery Show in New York, 1992.

TIFFANY & CO.
Copley Place
100 Huntington Avenue
Boston, MA 02116
617.353.0222
The finest in engraved invitations, favors,
accessories, stationery, bridal registry, fine
crystal and china, Tiffany flatware and gifts
for all occasions.

LIGHTING, STAGING & SOUND

ADAMS LIGHTING COMPANY
33 Bristol Street
Cambridge, MA 02141
617.492.6363
Deborah Adams
Andrew McGuigan
Areas served: New England
Theatrical production services including
decorative and theatrical lighting,
entertainment sound systems, temporary
power distribution, audiovisual
presentations and scale drawings. Lighting
in hotels, office buildings, school facilities
and tents, with selection of custom-designed
decorative fixtures, as well as pattern
projection and centerpiece spotlighting.
Computerized scale drawings showing guest
tables and chairs, decorative elements,
dance floors, bars and buffets. Won the
1980 IES Guth Memorial Lighting Design
Award of Excellence.

CAPRON LIGHTING & SOUND CO., INC.
Statler Building
20 Park Plaza
Suite 932
Boston, MA 02116
617.445.8850
Leslie Buckmaster
Providing sound systems, lighting design,
staging, audiovisual equipment, radio
communications, sports timing and silenced
generator power. Their project portfolio
includes the last four Presidential
Inaugurations, the annual Boston
Marathon, the US Men's and Women's Pro
Ski Tour, The Who and Rolling Stones
concerts and the Papal and Mandela visits
to Boston, to name a few. In addition,
Capron has provided services for hundreds
of customized parties, weddings, fashion
shows, product announcements,
conventions and like events. Corporate
clients include Reebok, Digital, IBM,
Gillette, Polaroid, Fidelity Investments,
Saks Fifth Avenue and many others. Fully
licensed and insured. In business for over
fifty years.

CREATIVE TALENT, INC.
214 Lincoln Street
Suite 301
Allston, MA 02134
617.789.4747
Andy Espo, President
Areas served: New England and Eastern
New York state
Entertainment, scenery and prop rentals,
theme events and decor, lighting design,
visual environments. Specialize in theme
events.

VISUAL DESIGN ASSOCIATES
25 East Street
Cambridge, MA 02141
617.868.9200
Len Schnabel
Areas served: National, Offshore
Corporate meeting stages, theme party
scenics, lighting and audio systems. Custom
and stock inventory of stages, creative
lighting.

WET LIGHT
564 Putnam Avenue
Cambridge, MA 02139
617.876.8882
Jackson Madnick
Lasers, fireworks, fountains. Public large

BOSTON

scale celebrations, conservation education spectacles. Won Gala Award 1991 for Best Entertainment Concept over $30,000 from *Special Event Magazine*.

LIMOUSINE & TRANSPORTATION

CAREY LIMOUSINE
617.623.8700
800.336.4646
Privately chauffeured sedans, limousines, vans and mini buses in 372 cities.

DAV EL CHAUFFEURED TRANSPORTATION NETWORK
800.328.3526 (outside CA)
800.826.5779 (inside CA)
Areas Served: International
Luxury chauffeured services in over 350 cities worldwide. Centralized reservations and billing. Airport concierge services.

OLD TOWN TROLLEY TOURS
329 W. Second Street
S. Boston, MA 02127
617.269.7150
Leslie Nagy
Areas served: Boston, Cambridge, Miami, Key West, San Diego, Washington
Tours, transportation, shuttle services for individuals, groups, weddings. Largest fleet operator of theme styled vehicles in the United States.

LINENS

TABLEFASHIONS, LTD.
116 Will Drive
Canton, MA 02021
617.821.1160
Sandi Chudnow
Areas served: International
Specialty linens, chair covers, upscale specialty table treatments (all manufacturing and processing is handled in house).

MUSIC & ENTERTAINMENT

CREATIVE TALENT, INC.
214 Lincoln Street
Suite 301
Allston, MA 02134
617.789.4747
Andy Espo, President
Areas served: New England and Eastern New York state
Entertainment, scenery and prop rentals, theme events and decor, lighting design, visual environments. Specialize in theme events.

LORDLY & DAME
51 Church Street
Boston, MA 02116
617.482.3596
Sam Dame
Areas served: International
Full event planning, music, entertainment, speakers, celebrity acquisition, name acts.

MARGE GHILARDUCCI AGENCY
724 Berkley Street
Berkley, MA 02779
508.822.3735
Marge & Chris Ghilarducci
Areas served: International
Performing artists for family entertainment in storytelling, music, juggling, physical comedy, theatre, dance. Family entertainment series for community events, festivals and theatres.

PRETTY POLLY PRODUCTIONS
P.O. Box 938
Boston, MA 02117
617.965.1245
Kathe Burbach
Areas served: Nationwide
All forms of entertainment and production. National and local bands and comedians. National acts produced for corporate conventions. Eighteen years in business. Member of Greater Boston Visitors & Convention Bureau.

SIAGEL PRODUCTIONS, INC.
P.O. Box 208
Newton, MA 02161
617.527.0493
Marc and Steve

BOSTON

Areas served: Massachusetts, New
Hampshire, Connecticut, and Rhode Island
DJs, bands, entertainment packages.
Specializing in Bar and Bat Mitzvahs.

SLEUTH & COMPANY
The Statler Building
20 Park Plaza
Suite 510
Boston, MA 02116
617.542.2525
Carol Schreck, President
Areas served: New England
Boston's Twilight Mystery Tour: A journey
through Boston's history of mysteries,
crimes and infamous deeds. Customized
participatory mystery/fantasy events for
conventions and groups of all sizes.

**ZIDEL & CO. PRESENTS
MANHATTAN EXPRESS**
9 Dean Street
Medway, MA 02053
508.533.5547
Marshall Zidel
Areas served: Northeast
Disc jockey show.

PARTY SITES

BOSTON MARRIOTT HOTEL NEWTON
2345 Commonwealth Avenue
Newton, MA 02166
617.630.3506
Marcia Lichtenwalner
Beautifully situated on the tranquil banks
of the Charles River, just 15 minutes from
downtown Boston, 430 deluxe guest rooms.
Standard features include individual
climate control, color TV with free cable
and in-room pay movies. Indoor and
outdoor swimming pool, fully equipped
health club with sauna, whirlpool. Paddle
boats and horseshoe pit for outdoor
activities. 15,244 square feet. Receptions:
1000 people. Sit down: 630 people. Rated
three stars by AAA and Mobil.

THE COLONNADE HOTEL
120 Huntington Avenue
Boston, MA 02116
617.424.7000

Terrence Vallee
Situated in the Heart of Back Bay directly
behind the Prudential Center and the
Hynes Convention Center. Earned a
reputation as Boston's private, personal
hotel by providing the quality service
desired by international guests as well as the
sophisticated business and leisure traveler.
In addition to 288 luxury sleeping rooms,
suites and recently refurbished executive
business suites, The Colonnade offers over
10,000 square feet of space suitable for
meetings, conferences, receptions,
banquets, and weddings, and is the only
Boston hotel with and outdoor rooftop pool.
Newly renovated ballroom. Receptions:
400 people in Huntington Ballroom;
Dinner/Dance: 250 people, Theater Style:
400 people, Classroom: 240 people.

CREST VIEW PLAZA
36 Montvale Avenue
Woburn, MA 01801
617.935.4994
Al Gangi, Jr.
Full service function facility, in-house
catering, wedding packages, social and
business functions, Italian and American
cuisine.

ENDICOTT ESTATE
656 East Street
Dedham, MA 02026
617.326.0012
Ginny McLaughlin
Offers an elegant style and relaxed
atmosphere in this stately mansion, where
guests can focus on both indoor and outdoor
functions. The manor house, consists of a
ballroom, four adjoining function rooms,
and a well-equipped kitchen. On the upper
level is a bride's room, a groom's room and
six additional meeting rooms. The Grand
Ballroom, 25 x 36 feet, framed by majestic
Ionic columns and duel balustrades, is ideal
for receptions, lectures, meetings, and
events that require a special touch. Here
guests may dance, feast or socialize in
accommodating splendor. The equally
impressive adjoining rooms are both
amiable and personal. These rooms are
decorated with period furnishings, works of
art, Italian marble fireplaces, rich

mahogany paneling and elegant Oriental carpeting. The manor house can comfortably accommodate groups of 200 people. For larger groups it can be expanded to include the entire estate. Ample on-site parking is available. For small private gatherings, the estate can provide a charm and elegance rarely found today. The special function rooms on the upper level offer intimacy, and are ideal for individual workshops or group meetings.

GUEST QUARTERS SUITE
HOTEL WALTHAM
550 Winter Street at Route 128
Waltham, MA 02154
617.890.6767
Susan Goldschmidt
Ellen Rooney

Deluxe all suite hotel. Building is eight stories with a dramatic atrium lobby. Nine function rooms, including 3000 square foot ballroom, two board rooms and 2000 square foot mezzanine for receptions. In-hotel restaurant and lobby lounge. Excellent food. Drake Ballroom: 3000 square feet, Hastings Room: 1560 square feet, Mezzanine Lounge: 2000 square feet. Receptions: 250 people. Sit down: 250 theatre style seats and 200 people for banquets using round tables. Outside catering also available.

LONG HILL RESERVATION
572 Essex Street
Beverly, MA 01915
508.356.4351
Heidi Carlson

Replica of early 19th century Ball House of Charleston, South Carolina. Five acres of gardens containing rare and unusual plants. Receptions: 150 people. Sit down: 80 people without tenting, 150 people with tenting.

MUSEUM OF SCIENCE
Science Park
Boston, MA 02114
617.589.0190
Julie McConchie

Unique meeting and event space with function areas available throughout the museum and the exhibit halls. Omni

Theater, Planetarium and Theater of Electricity shows also available. Outdoor space, overlooking the Charles River, is available in the summer. Six different function spaces. Receptions: 3000 people. Sit down: 400 people. No private parties or events, but concentrate on corporate groups, convention groups, associations and organizations.

NEW ENGLAND AQUARIUM
Central Wharf
Boston, MA 02110-3399
617.973.5200
Lynn Hughes

Three different areas can be rented for the particular needs of the client. The Main Exhibit Building creates a fascinating atmosphere for any function and is available after public hours. The Harbor View Room aboard the ship *Discovery* has a panoramic view of Boston harbor, and is available for any day or evening event. From May through September, an outdoor setting on the fully tented Harbor Terrace, can be rented with either facility. Other options include divers in giant ocean tank or a marine mammal presentation. Receptions: Main Building - 1000 people, *Discovery* - 300 people. Sit down: Main Building - 300 people, Harbor Terrace - 600 people. Banquet style: Discovery - 200 people.

OMNI PARKER HOUSE
60 School Street
Boston, MA 02108
617.227.8600
Michelle Quigley

Located in downtown Boston on the Freedom Trail, 12,000 square feet. Receptions: 500 people. Sit down: 450 people in theatre, 250 people in classroom.

THE VALE
185 Lyman Street
Waltham, MA 02154
617.893.7232
Jean Salvucci
Happy DiFranza
Virginia Platt

Located twenty minutes west of Boston, "The Vale" is one of the finest examples of an American country house laid out in the

English manner. Designated a National Historic Landmark, the property is owned and operated by the Society for the Preservation of New England Antiquities. The estate comprises 35 acres of landscaped grounds. The main floor has approximately 8000 square feet divided into 5 large rooms, one of which is an elegant ballroom with crystal chandeliers. A spacious hall system connects the rooms on the main floor. Two 20' x 23' rooms are available on the second floor. Receptions: 175 people. Sit down: 150 people.

TREMONT HOUSE HOTEL
275 Tremont Street
Boston, MA 02116
617.426.1400
800.331.9998
Donna Bruno

281 guest rooms. 7 function rooms. 14,200 square feet. Receptions: 450 people. Sit down: 280 people with dance floor, 350 people without dance floor.

VENEZIA RESTAURANT
20 Ericsson Street
Neponset Circle
Boston, MA 02122
617.329.8563

Boston's only waterfront Italian restaurant. Dockage available. Newly renovated. 5000 square feet. Receptions: 250 - 300 people. Sit down: 250 - 300 people.

PARTY SUPPLIES
PARTY NEEDS, INC.
411 Waverly Oaks Road
Waltham, MA 02154
617.893.9181
Gwen Robbins

Areas served: Greater Boston
Paper and plastic party supplies and decorations. 12,000 square feet. Showroom with over 22,000 different items in stock.

THE PARTY SPIRIT
74 Elm Street
Salisbury, MA 01952
508.465.2016
800.999.3398
Loretta & Stephen Dietch

Areas served: Greater Boston, Southern New Hampshire, North Shore Massachusetts, Merrimac Valley (Massachusetts)
Party and tent rentals...complete party supplies from invitations to palm tree confetti.

PERSONNEL & STAFFING
THE PARTY PEOPLE, INC.
2 Carlisle Terrace
Natick, MA 01760
508.650.9220
Rachel Goldstein, President

Areas served: Metro Boston including Cape Cod and Southern New Hampshire
Professional, friendly accommodators. Outstanding staff of servers, bartenders and chefs. Offers pre-party set-up, food service, and unsurpassed clean up. The staff wears black & white or can dress for a theme party. Full service event planning for social and corporate clients. Omelet parties a specialty. Rachel Goldstein is in her second term as Secretary of ISES/New England and was recently featured in *Boston Magazine*.

PHOTOGRAPHY & VIDEO
KENNETH BERMAN PHOTOGRAPHER
108 N. Main Street
Sharon, MA 02067
617.784.9600
Ken Berman

Areas served: National
Professional wedding photography. Natural, spontaneous approach.

PROPS & DECOR

ADAMS LIGHTING COMPANY
33 Bristol Street
Cambridge, MA 02141
617.492.6363
Deborah Adams
Andrew McGuigan
Areas served: New England
Theatrical production services including decorative and theatrical lighting, entertainment sound systems, temporary power distribution, audiovisual presentations and scale drawings. Lighting in hotels, office buildings, school facilities and tents, with selection of custom-designed decorative fixtures, as well as pattern projection and centerpiece spotlighting. Computerized scale drawings showing guest tables and chairs, decorative elements, dance floors, bars and buffets. Won the 1980 IES Guth Memorial Lighting Design Award of Excellence.

CHRISTOPHER'S FLOWERS, INC.
56 Church Street
Cambridge, MA 02138
800.666.8384
Bill Rowe
Kathy Pickett
Areas served: Boston and New England
Event planner, florist, decorator. Specializing in weddings, corporate events. Work closely with Boston area hotel catering departments, as well as many local caterers.

CREATIVE TALENT, INC.
214 Lincoln Street
Suite 301
Allston, MA 02134
617.789.4747
Andy Espo, President
Areas served: New England and Eastern New York state
Entertainment, scenery and prop rentals, theme events and decor, lighting design, visual environments. Specialize in theme events.

DAME ASSOCIATES, INC.
51 Church Street
Boston, MA 02116
617.482.3596
Douglas Dame
Areas served: International
Destination management, trade show production, convention coordination, exhibit and display rentals, corporate seminars.

PARTY NEEDS, INC.
411 Waverly Oaks Road
Waltham, MA 02154
617.893.9181
Gwen Robbins
Areas served: Greater Boston
Paper and plastic party supplies and decorations. 12,000 square feet. Showroom with over 22,000 different items in stock.

VISUAL DESIGN ASSOCIATES
25 East Street
Cambridge, MA 02141
617.868.9200
Len Schnabel
Areas served: National, Offshore
Corporate meeting stages, theme party scenics, lighting and audio systems. Custom and stock inventory of stages, creative lighting.

PUBLIC RELATIONS

BACON-CONCANNON ASSOCIATES
P.O. Box 246
Prudential Center
Boston, MA 02199
617.536.1448
Smoki Bacon
Areas served: New England
Registered fundraisers with the Attorney General's Office. Fundraising, advertising, community planning, event planning, public relations, festivals, publicity, promotions, theatre events. Organized "Jubilee 350" Grand Ball in Copley Square, 1980 for 6,000 people. Boston Magazine cited Smoki Bacon as one of the 100 most powerful women in Boston. Papers were put in Radcliffe College's time capsule. "Footlight Parade" a party for the Boston Theatre District Association, cited by Boston Magazine as best party of the year.

BOSTON

SPEAKERS

LORDLY & DAME
51 Church Street
Boston, MA 02116
617.482.3596
Sam Dame
Areas served: International
Full event planning, music, entertainment, speakers, celebrity acquisition, name acts.

TABLETOP ACCESSORIES & KITCHENWARE

CRATE & BARREL
48 Brattle Street
Cambridge, MA 02138
617.876.6300

Fancuil Hall Marketplace
Boston, MA 02109
617.742.6025

The Mall at Chestnut Hill
Chestnut Hill, MA 02167
617.964.8400

Copley Place
Boston, MA 02116
617.536.9400

Furniture Stores:
1045 Massachusetts Avenue
Cambridge, MA 02138
617.547.3994

The Mall at Chestnut Hill
Chestnut Hill, MA 02167
617.964.1800

Outlet Store:
460 Wildwood Street
Woburn, MA 01801
617.938-8777

Full line of unique contemporary home furnishings and accessories featuring tabletop accessories and gourmet kitchenware.

POTTERY BARN
351 Newbury Street
Boston, MA 02116
617.536.9130

Leading retailer of contemporary tableware and decorative accessories for the home. Merchandise is 100% exclusive, designed and sold exclusively at Pottery Barn. Over fifty stores nationally and mail order.

TIFFANY & CO.
Copley Place
100 Huntington Avenue
Boston, MA 02116
617.353.0222
The finest in engraved invitations, favors, accessories, stationery, bridal registry, fine crystal and china, Tiffany flatware and gifts for all occasions.

WILLIAMS-SONOMA
Marketplace Center
200 State Street
Boston, MA 02109
617.439.7035

Copley Place
100 Huntington Avenue
Boston, MA 02116
617.262.3080
An authoritative selection of the best for the kitchen. Complete line of cookware, bakeware, electrics, glassware, tabletop, kitchen furniture, cookbooks, packaged foods. Knowledgeable staff will help chooseequipment, plan parties. Most merchandise is exclusive to Williams-Sonoma.

VALET PARKING

EXCLUSIVE VALET
45 Newbury Street
Suite 309
Boston, MA 02116
617.421.9565
Areas served: New England
Parking attendant services, specializing in weddings and private functions.

WINE & SPIRITS

JOHN GILBERT, JR. COMPANY
107 South Street
Boston, MA 02111
617.542.8900
Areas served: Massachusetts
Full service wine and liquor store. Wine
and liquor consultation for special events.
Specializing in fine wines from around the
world. Custom gift baskets.

YACHT & BOAT CHARTERS

**BOSTON HARBOR, MASSACHUSETTS BAY
SOUTHEASTERN MASSACHUSETTS**
P.O. Box 379
Stoughton, MA 02072
617.344.1749
Barry Nickerson, President
Historic sailing vessels for day sails and
multi-day adventures. Vessels range from
80 to 170 feet in length. Receptions: 200
people dockside. Sit down: 30 people
overnight, 100 people for the day.

෴ ෴ ෴

CHICAGO

CHICAGO

AUDIOVISUAL & TECHNICAL SERVICES

THE SHOW DEPARTMENT, INC.
1555 N. Sheffield
Chicago, IL 60622
312.787.2600
Areas served: International
Complete industrial show staging: large
inventory of state-of-the-art equipment for
rental. Multi-image projection. Video and
data projection, live audio mixing,
computerized lighting systems, video
recording, velour drapery system, custom
scenic system. Emphasis on industrial show
staging/corporate meetings.

BALLOONS

A-1 ENTERTAINMENT AND CONCESSIONS, INC.
2644 N. Ashland Avenue.
Chicago, IL 60614
312.880.8000
Customer Service
Areas served: Illinois, Indiana, Michigan,
Wisconsin, Minnesota, Kansas
Provides theme party props and decorating
services; Las Vegas nights and casino
equipment rentals; catering equipment and
antique food cart rentals; entertainment,
music, specialty and animal acts; balloons:
decorating, printing, helium and supplies;
amusements, kiddy rides and carnival
games; full service events, corporate picnics
and parties; tents, tables, chairs, BBQs and
general rentals. Specializing in corporate
events, custom theme parties, balloon
decorating, prop and decor, design and
construction from in-house shops and hard-
to-find rental items. Won Gala Award at
Special Event Convention for Most
Imaginative Use of Equipment.

BOOKS

WILLIAMS-SONOMA
104 Oakbrook Center
Oakbrook, IL 60521
708.571.2702

Chestnut Galleria
17 E. Chestnut Street
Chicago, IL 60611
312.642.1593

Woodfield Mall, F333
Schaumburg, IL 60173
708.619.0940

271 Market Square
Lake Forest, IL 60045
708.295.7045

700 N. Michigan Avenue
Suite 202
Chicago, IL 60611
312.787.8991

2100 Northbrook Court Mall
Northbrook IL 60062
708.291.3626

121 Town Square
Wheaton, IL 60187
708.665.7250
An authoritative selection of the best for the
kitchen. Complete line of cookware,
baking, electrics, glassware, tabletop,
kitchen furniture, cookbooks, packaged
foods. Knowledgeable staff will help choose
equipment, plan parties. Most of their
merchandise is exclusive to Williams-
Sonoma.

CAKES & BAKED GOODS

RJ'S PARTY TRAYS AND CAKES FOR ALL OCCASIONS
309 Illinois Street
Park Forest, IL 60466
708.748.7130
Areas served: Southern Chicagoland
Provides cold trays, custom party cakes,
custom wedding cakes. Specialties include
gum paste flowers and the ability to take
care of most client requests.

CHICAGO

CALLIGRAPHY

ANI'S CALLIGRAPHY
>4500 Concord Lane
>Skokie, IL 60076
>**708.674.5581**
>**800.676.5581**
>Ani Topouzian, President

Provides envelopes, place cards, return address, love letters, vows, songs, name tags, stamping and stuffing, poems, invitations for weddings, parties, special occasions, corporate events. Clients include: White House, WW Grainger, Tribune Entertainment Co.

WRITE IMPRESSIONS
>211 W. Huron
>Chicago, IL 60610
>**312.943.3306**
>Barbara Ruben

Areas served: Chicago Metropolitan
Custom invitations, personal stationery, boxed invitations, stationery, wrap, ribbon, assorted gift items. Calligraphy services: laser printing, colored laser, computerized, hand. Specialties include: custom stationery and invitations.

CATERING

FAT BOY'S BBQ
>328 N. Carpenter
>Chicago, IL 60607
>**312.588.5050**
>Greg Nauman

Areas served: Chicagoland
Complete outdoor BBQ and picnic services. Entertainment, special attractions also available. Company picnics, family reunions, etc.

FERREE' FLORSHEIM CATERING, LTD.
>5080 N. Kimberly
>Chicago, IL 60630
>**312.282.6100**
>Anne Ferree'
>Susan Florsheim

Areas served: Chicago, suburbs and 200-mile radius
Full service catering with style – emphasis on quality and personalized service. Chefs are European trained. Deluxe corporate, social and charity events from 20 to 2000 guests.

RJ'S PARTY TRAYS AND CAKES FOR ALL OCCASIONS
>309 Illinois Street
>Park Forest, IL 60466
>**708.748.7130**

Areas served: Southern Chicagoland
Provides cold trays, custom party cakes, custom wedding cakes. Specialties include gum paste flowers and the ability to do almost anything our client requests.

SIMPLY ELEGANT CATERING
>328 N. Carpenter
>Chicago, IL 60607
>**312.728.1919**
>Debra Nauman
>Greg Nauman

Areas served: Chicagoland
Complete off-premise catering, including personnel and all accessories. Corporate events, weddings, anniversary and birthday parties, fund-raisers, etc.

THE BOX LUNCH CHEF
>328 N. Carpenter
>Chicago, IL 60607
>**312.226.0666**
>Debra Nauman
>Greg Nauman

Areas served: Chicago
Complete, self-contained individual lunches for groups of five and larger. Business meetings/seminars, corporate/school outings, bus/plane/boat trips.

❧ BAR CATERING

TO THE RESCUE, INC.
>612 N. Michigan Avenue
>Chicago, IL 60611
>**312.951.0626**
>Lisa Montgomery

Areas served: Greater Chicago
Party personnel (servers, bartenders), private chefs, bar catering, full event planning services for social and corporate events.

❧ PRIVATE CHEFS

To The Rescue, Inc.
612 N. Michigan Avenue
Chicago, IL 60611
312.951.0626
Lisa Montgomery
Areas served: Greater Chicago
Party personnel (servers, bartenders),
private chefs, bar catering, full event
planning services for social and corporate
events.

CELEBRITY ACQUISITION

**A-1 Entertainment
and Concessions, Inc.**
2644 N. Ashland Avenue.
Chicago, IL 60614
312.880.8000
Customer Service
Areas served: Illinois, Indiana, Michigan,
Wisconsin, Minnesota, Kansas
Provides theme party props and decorating
services; Las Vegas nights and casino
equipment rentals; catering equipment and
antique food cart rentals; entertainment,
music, specialty and animal acts; balloons:
decorating, printing, helium and supplies;
amusements, kiddy rides and carnival
games; full service events, corporate picnics
and parties; tents, tables, chairs, BBQs and
general rentals. Specializing in corporate
events, custom theme parties, balloon
decorating, prop and decor, design and
construction from in-house shops and hard-
to-find rental items. Won Gala Award at
Special Event Convention for Most
Imaginative Use of Equipment.

CHOCOLATES & CONFECTIONS

Godiva Chocolatier
Michigan Avenue Area
Water Tower Place
312.280.1133

Woodfield Mall
708.619.1161

Oakbrook Center
708.990.0660
World renowned chocolatier. Belgium-style
chocolates, gift baskets and party favors.

CLASSES & SEMINARS

**Gold Standard Liquors
Chalet Wine & Cheese Shops**
5100 W. Dempster Street
Skokie, IL 60077
708.674.4200
Dale Maple
Areas served: Chicago and suburbs
No obligation beverage planning. Custom
gifts for any occasion. Wine consultations,
tastings, and special offerings. Beverage
serving equipment and supplies. Free
monthly catalog. Over 9000 products in
stock. Food trays (meat, pate, cheese, fruit
and dessert). Coffees, imported cheese and
pate – freshness guaranteed. Nationwide
shipping service. Local delivery and pick-
up. Corporate services to event planners
and caterers. Sandwiches, snacks and
beverages delivered to office boardrooms
and break rooms. Awards include:
"Best United States Retailer" from The
Wine Spectator, "Award of Distinction for
Retailing Excellence" from Beverage
Dynamics, "Best Cheese Shop" and "Best
Liquor Store" from *North Shore Magazine*,
"Superstar Retail Entrepreneur in the US
Wine and Spirits Industry" from *Market
Watch Magazine* and "1st Place Barbara
Hermann – Fine Wine Buyer" from Geja's
Professional Wine Tasting competition.

COSTUMES

Broadway Costumes, Inc.
954 W. Washington Blvd.
4th Floor
Chicago, IL 60607-2217
312.829.6400
Areas served: National
Costume rental and sales. Providing
masquerade party costumes since 1886.

DELICACIES

GOLD STANDARD LIQUORS
CHALET WINE & CHEESE SHOPS
5100 W. Dempster Street
Skokie, IL 60077
708.674.4200
Dale Maple
Areas served: Chicago and suburbs
No obligation beverage planning. Custom
gifts for any occasion. Wine consultations,
tastings, and special offerings. Beverage
serving equipment and supplies. Free
monthly catalog. Over 9000 products in
stock. Food trays (meat, pate, cheese, fruit
and dessert). Coffees, imported cheese and
pate – freshness guaranteed. Nationwide
shipping service. Local delivery and pick-
up. Corporate services to event planners
and caterers. Sandwiches, snacks and
beverages delivered to office boardrooms
and break rooms. Awards include:
"Best United States Retailer" from The
Wine Spectator, "Award of Distinction for
Retailing Excellence" from Beverage
Dynamics, "Best Cheese Shop" and "Best
Liquor Store" from *North Shore Magazine*,
"Superstar Retail Entrepreneur in the US
Wine and Spirits Industry" from *Market
Watch Magazine* and "1st Place Barbara
Hermann – Fine Wine Buyer" from Geja's
Professional Wine Tasting competition.

DESTINATION MANAGEMENT

ON THE SCENE, INC.
54 W. Illinois
Suite 1250
Chicago, IL 60610
312.661.1440
Eleanor Woods
Areas served: Midwest
Full event and meeting planning.
Destination management. Clients include
major corporations and associations. In
business for twenty-three years.

EQUIPMENT RENTALS
& TENTING

A-1 ENTERTAINMENT
AND CONCESSIONS, INC.
2644 N. Ashland Avenue.
Chicago, IL 60614
312.880.8000
Customer Service
Areas served: Illinois, Indiana, Michigan,
Wisconsin, Minnesota, Kansas
Provides theme party props and decorating
services; Las Vegas nights and casino
equipment rentals; catering equipment and
antique food cart rentals; entertainment,
music, specialty and animal acts; balloons:
decorating, printing, helium and supplies;
amusements, kiddy rides and carnival
games; full service events, corporate picnics
and parties; tents, tables, chairs, BBQs and
general rentals. Specializing in corporate
events, custom theme parties, balloon
decorating, prop and decor, design and
construction from in-house shops and hard-
to-find rental items. Won Gala Award at
Special Event Convention for Most
Imaginative Use of Equipment.

FROST LIGHTING COMPANY
OF ILLINOIS, INC.
P.O. Box 750
Glenview, IL 60025
708.729.8200
David Kelly
Areas served: Chicagoland/Midwest
Full service lighting and electrical rentals
and production. Specializes in decorative
atmospheric lighting. Numerous awards.

HALLS RENTAL SERVICE, INC.
3950 W. Devon
Lincolnwood, IL 60659
708.982.9200
Areas served: National
Rental of tables, chairs, silver, china,
crystal, glassware, catering equipment.
Over 30,000 chairs; 10,000 tables; 20,000
place settings in traditional and
contemporary styles. Featured in *Special
Events Magazine*.

TABLESCAPES, LTD.
1840 W. Hubbard Street
Chicago, IL 60622

CHICAGO

312.733.9700
Kathy Ruff
Areas served: Chicago and suburbs
From budget to top-of-the-line rental items
–fine china, crystal, tables and chairs,
Christian Dior dinnerware for finest
occasions to the very casual blue
enamelware for picnic and barbecues. Full
range of selections.

EVENT PLANNING

**A-1 ENTERTAINMENT
AND CONCESSIONS, INC.**
2644 N. Ashland Avenue.
Chicago, IL 60614
312.880.8000
Customer Service
Areas served: Illinois, Indiana, Michigan,
Wisconsin, Minnesota, Kansas
Provides theme party props and decorating
services; Las Vegas nights and casino
equipment rentals; catering equipment and
antique food cart rentals; entertainment,
music, specialty and animal acts; balloons:
decorating, printing, helium and supplies;
amusements, kiddy rides and carnival
games; full service events, corporate picnics
and parties; tents, tables, chairs, BBQs and
general rentals. Specializing in corporate
events, custom theme parties, balloon
decorating, prop and decor, design and
construction from in-house shops and hard-
to-find rental items. Won Gala Award at
Special Event Convention for Most
Imaginative Use of Equipment.

AUDREY GORDON PARTIES
833 Laurel Avenue
Chicago, IL 60614
708.433.2748
Audrey Gordon
Full service event planning and invitations.
On-site event management. Specializing in
"Sweet Tables".

CHICAGO BY AIR, INC.
P.O. Box 16634
Chicago, IL 60616-0634
708.524.1172
Areas served: Chicagoland – Sightseeing

tours; US – Air charters
Aerial sightseeing tours; champagne tours;
birthday, anniversary or celebration tours
(flowers and champagne); aerial
photography; air charter; helicopters for
groups of four or more.

ON THE SCENE, INC.
54 W. Illinois
Suite 1250
Chicago, IL 60610
312.661.1440
Eleanor Woods
Areas served: Midwest
Full event and meeting planning.
Destination management. Clients include
major corporations and associations. In
business for twenty-three years.

PAINT ME A PARTY, INC.
1035 W. Webster
Chicago, IL 60614
312.935.5400
Sally Schwartz
Areas served: National
Event planning, entertainment and music
booking. Two divisions: Events As Art and
Just Entertainment. Highly visual, high-
impact parties. Subtle, layered marketing
events from concept to logo.

TO THE RESCUE, INC.
612 N. Michigan Avenue
Chicago, IL 60611
312.951.0626
Lisa Montgomery
Areas served: Greater Chicago
Party personnel (servers, bartenders),
private chefs, bar catering, full event
planning service for social and corporate
events.

FAVORS
GODIVA CHOCOLATIER
Michigan Avenue Area
Water Tower Place
312.280.1133

Woodfield Mall
708.619.1161

Oakbrook Center
708.990.0660
World renowned chocolatier. Belgium-style
chocolates, gift baskets and party favors.

TIFFANY & COMPANY
715 N. Michigan Avenue
Chicago, IL 60611
312.944.7500
The finest in engraved invitations, favors,
accessories, stationery, bridal registry, fine
crystal and china, Tiffany flatware and gifts
for all occasions.

FIREWORKS & SPECIAL EFFECTS

A-1 ENTERTAINMENT AND CONCESSIONS, INC.
2644 N. Ashland Avenue.
Chicago, IL 60614
312.880.8000
Customer Service
Areas served: Illinois, Indiana, Michigan,
Wisconsin, Minnesota, Kansas
Provides theme party props and decorating
services; Las Vegas nights and casino
equipment rentals; catering equipment and
antique food cart rentals; entertainment,
music, specialty and animal acts; balloons:
decorating, printing, helium and supplies;
amusements, kiddy rides and carnival
games; full service events, corporate picnics
and parties; tents, tables, chairs, BBQs and
general rentals. Specializing in corporate
events, custom theme parties, balloon
decorating, prop and decor, design and
construction from in-house shops and hard-
to-find rental items. Won Gala Award at
Special Event Convention for Most
Imaginative Use of Equipment.

FLORISTS & FLORAL DESIGN

THE FLOWER CART, INC.
3819 N. Broadway
Chicago, IL 60613
312.477.7755
Nicholas Galatte

Full service florist specializing in weddings,
parties and social events. Winner of 1991
Best Tabletop Award. Floral and decor
consultant for Super Bowl 1987 and 1989 at
Special Event Convention.

VIRGINIA WOLFF, INC.
1332 W. Lake Street
Chicago, IL 60607
312.226.1777
Virginia Wolff
Areas served: Chicago and suburbs
Gorgeous flowers and imaginative decor.
Events of all kinds. Weddings, corporate,
benefits. Named Best Chicago Florist For
Weddings by *Bon Appetit Magazine*, June
1992.

GIFTS & GIFT BASKETS

GODIVA CHOCOLATIER
Michigan Avenue Area
Water Tower Place
312.280.1133

Woodfield Mall
708.619.1161

Oakbrook Center
708.990.0660
World renowned chocolatier. Belgium-style
chocolates, gift baskets and party favors.

GOLD STANDARD LIQUORS
CHALET WINE & CHEESE SHOPS
5100 W. Dempster Street
Skokie, IL 60077
708.674.4200
Dale Maple
Areas served: Chicago and suburbs
No obligation beverage planning. Custom
gifts for any occasion. Wine consultations,
tastings, and special offerings. Beverage
serving equipment and supplies. Free
monthly catalog. Over 9000 products in
stock. Food trays (meat, pate, cheese, fruit
and dessert). Coffees, imported cheese and
pate – freshness guaranteed. Nationwide
shipping service. Local delivery and pick-
up. Corporate services to event planners
and caterers. Sandwiches, snacks and
beverages delivered to office boardrooms

CHICAGO

and break rooms. Awards include: "Best United States Retailer" from The Wine Spectator, "Award of Distinction for Retailing Excellence" from Beverage Dynamics, "Best Cheese Shop" and "Best Liquor Store" from *North Shore Magazine*, "Superstar Retail Entrepreneur in the US Wine and Spirits Industry" from *Market Watch Magazine* and "1st Place Barbara Hermann – Fine Wine Buyer" from Geja's Professional Wine Tasting competition.

TIFFANY & COMPANY
715 N. Michigan Avenue
Chicago, IL 60611
312.944.7500
The finest in engraved invitations, favors, accessories, stationery, bridal registry, fine crystal and china, Tiffany flatware and gifts for all occasions.

INVITATIONS & ACCESSORIES

ANI'S CALLIGRAPHY
4500 Concord Lane
Skokie, IL 60076
708.674.5581
800.676.5581
Ani Topouzian, President
Provides envelopes, place cards, return address, love letters, vows, songs, name tags, stamping and stuffing, poems, invitations for weddings, parties, special occasions, corporate events. Clients include: White House, WW Grainger, Tribune Entertainment Co.

AUDREY GORDON PARTIES
833 Laurel Avenue
Chicago, IL 60614
708.433.2748
Audrey Gordon
Full service event planning and invitations. On-site event management. Specializing in "Sweet Tables".

TIFFANY & COMPANY
715 N. Michigan Avenue
Chicago, IL 60611
312.944.7500
The finest in engraved invitations, favors, accessories, stationery, bridal registry, fine crystal and china, Tiffany flatware and gifts for all occasions.

WRITE IMPRESSIONS
211 W. Huron
Chicago, IL 60610
312.943.3306
Barbara Ruben
Areas served: Chicago Metropolitan
Custom invitations, personal stationery, boxed invitations, stationery, wrap, ribbon, assorted gift items. Calligraphy services: laser printing, colored laser, computerized, hand. Specialties include: custom stationery and invitations.

LIGHTING, STAGING & SOUND

A-1 ENTERTAINMENT AND CONCESSIONS, INC.
2644 N. Ashland Avenue.
Chicago, IL 60614
312.880.8000
Customer Service
Areas served: Illinois, Indiana, Michigan, Wisconsin, Minnesota, Kansas
Provides theme party props and decorating services; Las Vegas nights and casino equipment rentals; catering equipment and antique food cart rentals; entertainment, music, specialty and animal acts; balloons: decorating, printing, helium and supplies; amusements, kiddy rides and carnival games; full service events, corporate picnics and parties; tents, tables, chairs, BBQs and general rentals. Specializing in corporate events, custom theme parties, balloon decorating, prop and decor, design and construction from in-house shops and hard-to-find rental items. Won Gala Award at Special Event Convention for Most Imaginative Use of Equipment.

FROST LIGHTING COMPANY OF ILLINOIS, INC.
P.O. Box 750
Glenview, IL 60025
708.729.8200

David Kelly
Areas served: Chicagoland/Midwest
Full service lighting and electrical rentals
and production. Specializes in decorative
atmospheric lighting. Numerous awards.

THE SHOW DEPARTMENT, INC.
1555 N. Sheffield
Chicago, IL 60622
312.787.2600
Areas served: International
Complete industrial show staging: large
inventory of state-of-the-art equipment for
rental. Multi-image projection. Video and
data projection, live audio mixing,
computerized lighting systems, video
recording, velour drapery system, custom
scenic system. Emphasis on industrial show
staging/corporate meetings.

LIMOUSINE & TRANSPORTATION

CAREY LIMOUSINE
312.763.0009
800.336.4646
Privately chauffeured sedans, limousines,
vans and mini buses in 372 cities.

CHICAGO BY AIR, INC.
P.O. Box 16634
Chicago, IL 60616-0634
708.524.1172
Areas served: Chicagoland – Sightseeing
tours; US – Air charter
Aerial sightseeing tours; champagne tours;
birthday, anniversary or celebration tours
(flowers and champagne); aerial
photography; air charter; helicopters for
groups of four or more.

DAV EL CHAUFFEURED TRANSPORTATION NETWORK
800.328.3526 (outside CA)
800.826.5779 (inside CA)
Areas Served: International
Luxury chauffeured services in over 350
cities worldwide. Centralized reservations
and billing. Airport concierge services.

PONTARELLI LIMOUSINE & GROUP CHARTERS
2213 W. Wabansia
Chicago, IL 60660
800.322.5466
Areas Served: Chicago and Metro area
Ground transportation services.

LINENS

CAROUSEL LINEN RENTAL, INC.
454 Sheridan Road
Highwood, IL 60040
708.432.8182
800.238.8182
Scott, Pari, Anna Marie
Areas served: National
Linen rental for special events. Theme
prints, florals, lame, lurex, solid colors. In
business for twenty-seven years.

LINEN EFFECTS AND BBJ BOUTIQUE
7020 Lawndale
Lincolnwood, IL 60645
708.679.9200
Steven Handelman
Areas served: International
Fine linen rentals. Patterned, formal,
metallic and theme linens. 1st Place Award
Winner for Table Design 1992 Special
Events Convention.

TABLETOPPERS, INC.
450-B Lake Cook Road
Deerfield, IL 60015
708.945.4470
Areas served: United States
Quality linen rental. Thirty-one solid colors
and over seventy prints and specialty
cloths, chair covers, laces and table
skirtings. One of the Midwest's largest linen
rental companies, with in-house sewing
department and over 20,000 yards of
material. Serviced last three US Opens,
Ryder Cup and last two Super Bowls.
Weddings their specialty. Set-up crews
available if needed, for that special touch.

[Continued on next page]

CHICAGO

MUSIC & ENTERTAINMENT

A-1 ENTERTAINMENT AND CONCESSIONS, INC.
2644 N. Ashland Avenue.
Chicago, IL 60614
312.880.8000
Customer Service
Areas served: Illinois, Indiana, Michigan, Wisconsin, Minnesota, Kansas
Provides theme party props and decorating services; Las Vegas nights and casino equipment rentals; catering equipment and antique food cart rentals; entertainment, music, specialty and animal acts; balloons: decorating, printing, helium and supplies; amusements, kiddy rides and carnival games; full service events, corporate picnics and parties; tents, tables, chairs, BBQs and general rentals. Specializing in corporate events, custom theme parties, balloon decorating, prop and decor, design and construction from in-house shops and hard-to-find rental items. Won Gala Award at Special Event Convention for Most Imaginative Use of Equipment.

DR. BOP AND THE HEADLINERS
1220 N. State Pkwy.
Suite 709
Chicago, IL 60610
312.787.8787
Ed Engelhart
Areas served: National
Rock 'n Roll entertainment. Played for Prince Charles.

JD MUSIC PRODUCTIONS
1610 W. Highland
Suite 34
Chicago, IL 60660
800.659.0762
James Hahn
Areas served: National (predominately Midwest)
Live musical entertainment (classical, jazz, rock, big band, Dixieland, country western). National conventions, trade shows, corporate hospitality parties. Private parties.

PAINT ME A PARTY, INC.
1035 W. Webster
Chicago, IL 60614
312.935.5400

Sally Schwartz
Areas served: National
Event planning, entertainment and music booking. Two divisions: Events As Art and Just Entertainment. Highly visual, high-impact parties. Subtle, layered marketing events from concept to logo.

SCOTT OLSON ORCHESTRA
101 Stratford Place
Mount Prospect, IL 60056
708.255.7345
Scott Olson
Areas served: Chicago, Kohler, Wisconsin, Milwaukee, Bloomington, IL
Wedding ceremonies, dance band, background music, MC, step-by-step help in party planning. Dance band covering 1900-1993 music. Always use three vocalists for variety. Played: Opera Ball, Children's Hospital Ball, Harold Washington Library Opening Ball, Bureau of Convention & Tourism Ball and others.

SOUND MACHINE
3700 Lake Shore
Chicago, IL 60605
312.525.2787
Avron Fagez
Areas served: Chicago and suburbs
DJs, sound, lighting, background music. In business since 1974.

STANLEY PAUL ORCHESTRA
1511 N. Wells Street
Chicago, IL 60610
312.751.2000
One of Chicago's most popular band leaders. Performed for major celebrities, fund-raisers and events. Music tailored to any occassion.

❧ CELEBRITY LOOK-ALIKES

A-1 ENTERTAINMENT AND CONCESSIONS, INC.
2644 N. Ashland Avenue.
Chicago, IL 60614
312.880.8000
Customer Service
Areas served: Illinois, Indiana, Michigan, Wisconsin, Minnesota, Kansas

CHICAGO

Provides theme party props and decorating services; Las Vegas nights and casino equipment rentals; catering equipment and antique food cart rentals; entertainment, music, specialty and animal acts; balloons: decorating, printing, helium and supplies; amusements, kiddy rides and carnival games; full service events, corporate picnics and parties; tents, tables, chairs, BBQs and general rentals. Specializing in corporate events, custom theme parties, balloon decorating, prop and decor, design and construction from in-house shops and hard-to-find rental items. Won Gala Award at Special Event Convention for Most Imaginative Use of Equipment.

PARTY SITES

BAJA BEACH CLUB
401 E. Illinois Street
Chicago, IL 60611
312.222.1993
Denise Sabol

Several rooms to hold private events. Piano Bar: seats 500, two grand pianos, oak bar, karaokee stage and glass veranda facing Chicago skyline. Arcade Room: seats 50-75, every arcade and video game imaginable, pool tables and modern bar. Main Club: seats 500, multi-level dance floor, reception of 1000, five full service bars throughout and all-glass veranda faces Chicago River. Receptions: 2500 people. Sit down: 1600 people.

THE FRANCIS J. DEWES MANSION
503 W. Wrightwood Avenue
Chicago, IL 60614
312.477.3075

A Landmark property. Elegant circa 1896 home with private courtyard. 5000 square feet – 4 floors of house. 2000 square feet – outdoor courtyard. Receptions: 550 people. Sit down: 150 people.

KABOOM NIGHTCLUB
BIG TIME PRODUCTIONS
747 N. Green
Chicago, IL 60622
312.243.8600 (Club)
Carol Johnson

770 N. Halstead Street
Chicago, IL 60622
312.243.4800 (Office)

Seven banquet facilities, indoor and outdoor. In-house production, sound, lighting, catering, invitation and graphic design, decoration and theme installations, lasers, etc. Over 20,000 square feet.

STANDING ROOM ONLY, INC.
Park West
1256 N. Wells Street
Chicago, IL 60610
312.440.9191
Donna Sue Van Cleaf
Corporate Events Director

Venue with 750 capacity. State-of-the-art audiovisual system. Won Club of the Year 1991 and 1991 from Pollstar.

THE MUSEUM OF BROADCAST COMMUNICATIONS
Chicago Cultural Center
Michigan Ave. at Washington St.
Chicago, IL 60602-3407
312.629.6000
Kimberly Shadle
Audrey Pass

Unique venue and interactive facility for all types of private events. With many hands-on exhibits, Museum comes complete with its own entertainment! Experience a working television studio in the Kraft TeleCenter, as you and your guests become anchor for a day! Also, visit the Radio Hall of Fame, Advertising Hall of Fame, Television Exhibition Gallery and much, much more! 15, 300 square feet. Receptions: 400 people. Sit down: 100 people.

PARTY SUPPLIES

A-1 ENTERTAINMENT AND CONCESSIONS, INC.
2644 N. Ashland Avenue.
Chicago, IL 60614
312.880.8000
Customer Service

Areas served: Illinois, Indiana, Michigan, Wisconsin, Minnesota, Kansas
Provides theme party props and decorating

services; Las Vegas nights and casino equipment rentals; catering equipment and antique food cart rentals; entertainment, music, specialty and animal acts; balloons: decorating, printing, helium and supplies; amusements, kiddy rides and carnival games; full service events, corporate picnics and parties; tents, tables, chairs, BBQs and general rentals. Specializing in corporate events, custom theme parties, balloon decorating, prop and decor, design and construction from in-house shops and hard-to-find rental items. Won Gala Award at Special Event Convention for Most Imaginative Use of Equipment.

COVE WAX WORKS
2311 W. Main Street
Melrose Park, IL 60160
708.344.7220
Ray Tinucci
Areas served: National, Canada, South America, The Orient
Suppliers of high quality tabletop decor and outdoor Chronella Products. Flower Float floating candles, self extinguishing.

PERSONNEL & STAFFING

SERVICE IS US, INC.
P.O. Box 25974
Chicago, IL 60625
312.784.2225
Garth Livingston
Staffing agency specializing in only "Top Notch" waiters and bartenders. Hotels, corporate dining rooms, restaurants, catering firms and private parties –business or residential. Specialty is ability to meet last minute requests. Professionally-trained staff, hired only after a rigorous screening process.

TO THE RESCUE, INC.
612 N. Michigan Avenue
Chicago, IL 60611
312.951.0626
Lisa Montgomery
Areas served: Greater Chicago
Party personnel, private chefs, bar catering, full event planning service for social and corporate events.

PHOTOGRAPHY & VIDEO

DAVID BLACHMAN PHOTOGRAPHY
Glenview, IL 60025
708.729.2780
David Blachman
Areas served: National
Photography services for weddings, Bar and Bat Mitzvahs, corporate events. Photographs have appeared in numerous national publications.

NEIL ENTERPRISES
940 Forest Edge Drive
Vernon Hills, IL 60061
708.913.8866
800.621.5584
Steve Loiner
Areas served: International
Manufacturer of photo promotional products and special events cameras. Photo buttons, photo mugs, photo key chains, photo watches, photo frames, etc. One of the largest manufacturers of photo novelties in the world.

THE SHOW DEPARTMENT, INC.
1555 N. Sheffield
Chicago, IL 60622
312.787.2600
Areas served: International
Complete industrial show staging: large inventory of state-of-the-art equipment for rental. Multi-image projection. Video and data projection, live audio mixing, computerized lighting systems, video recording, velour drapery system, custom scenic system. Emphasis on industrial show staging/corporate meetings.

PROPS & DECOR

A-1 ENTERTAINMENT AND CONCESSIONS, INC.
2644 N. Ashland Avenue.
Chicago, IL 60614
312.880.8000
Customer Service
Areas served: Illinois, Indiana, Michigan, Wisconsin, Minnesota, Kansas
Provides theme party props and decorating services; Las Vegas nights and casino equipment rentals; catering equipment and

antique food cart rentals; entertainment, music, specialty and animal acts; balloons: decorating, printing, helium and supplies; amusements, kiddy rides and carnival games; full service events, corporate picnics and parties; tents, tables, chairs, BBQs and general rentals. Specializing in corporate events, custom theme parties, balloon decorating, prop and decor, design and construction from in-house shops and hard-to-find rental items. Won Gala Award at Special Event Convention for Most Imaginative Use of Equipment.

FROST LIGHTING COMPANY
OF ILLINOIS, INC.
P.O. Box 750
Glenview, IL 60025
708.729.8200
David Kelly
Areas served: Chicagoland/Midwest
Full service lighting and electrical rentals and production. Specializes in decorative atmospheric lighting. Numerous awards.

SECURITY

ANDY FRAIN SERVICES, INC.
310 W. Chicago
Chicago, IL 60610
312.266.6900
James Ott
Areas served: Chicago and outside suburbs
Temporary or permanent security jobs. Twenty-four hour dispatch.

TABLETOP ACCESSORIES & KITCHENWARE

COVE WAX WORKS
2311 W. Main Street
Melrose Park, IL 60160
708.344.7220
Ray Tinucci
Areas served: National, Canada, South America, The Orient
Suppliers of high quality tabletop decor and outdoor Chronella Products. Flower Float floating candles, self extinguishing.

CRATE & BARREL
646 N. Michigan Avenue
Chicago, IL 60611
312.787.5900

101 N. Wabash Avenue
Chicago, IL 60602
312.372.0100

Plaza del Lago
Wilmette, IL 60091
708.256.2723

Oakbrook Mall
Oak Brook, IL 60521
708.572.1300

Hawthorne Center
Vernon Hills, IL 60061
708.367.1333

Northbrook Court
Northbrook, IL 60062
708.272.8920

Woodfield Mall
Schaumburg, IL 60173
708.619.4200

Old Orchard Center
Skokie, IL 60077
708.674.6850
Full line of unique contemporary home furnishings and accessories featuring tabletop accessories and gourmet kitchenware.

GOLD STANDARD LIQUORS
CHALET WINE & CHEESE SHOPS
5100 W. Dempster Street
Skokie, IL 60077
708.674.4200
Dale Maple
Areas served: Chicago and suburbs
No obligation beverage planning. Custom gifts for any occasion. Wine consultations, tastings, and special offerings. Beverage serving equipment and supplies. Free monthly catalog. Over 9000 products in stock. Food trays (meat, pate, cheese, fruit and dessert). Coffees, imported cheese and pate – freshness guaranteed. Nationwide shipping service. Local delivery and pick-

CHICAGO

up. Corporate services to event planners and caterers. Sandwiches, snacks and beverages delivered to office boardrooms and break rooms. Awards include: "Best United States Retailer" from The Wine Spectator, "Award of Distinction for Retailing Excellence" from Beverage Dynamics, "Best Cheese Shop" and "Best Liquor Store" from *North Shore Magazine*, "Superstar Retail Entrepreneur in the US Wine and Spirits Industry" from *Market Watch Magazine* and "1st Place Barbara Hermann – Fine Wine Buyer" from Geja's Professional Wine Tasting competition.

TIFFANY & COMPANY
715 N. Michigan Avenue
Chicago, IL 60611
312.944.7500
The finest in engraved invitations, favors, accessories, stationery, bridal registry, fine crystal and china, Tiffany flatware and gifts for all occasions.

WILLIAMS-SONOMA
104 Oakbrook Center
Oakbrook, IL 60521
708.571.2702

Chestnut Galleria
17 E. Chestnut Street
Chicago, IL 60611
312.642.1593

Woodfield Mall, F333
Schaumburg, IL 60173
708.619.0940

271 Market Square
Lake Forest, IL 60045
708.295.7045

700 N. Michigan Avenue
Suite 202
Chicago, IL 60611
312.787.8991

2100 Northbrook Court Mall
Northbrook IL 60062
708.291.3626

121 Town Square
Wheaton, IL 60187
708.665.7250
An authoritative selection of the best for the kitchen. Complete line of cookware, baking, electrics, glassware, tabletop, kitchen furniture, cookbooks, packaged foods. Knowledgeable staff will help choose equipment, plan parties. Most of their merchandise is exclusive to Williams-Sonoma.

UNIFORMS

CHEFWEAR, INC.
2449 N. Clybourn Avenue
Chicago, IL 60614
312.871.8684
800.568.2433
Rochelle Huppin
Areas served: International
Retail and wholesale sales of chefs uniforms. Ship internationally. Mail order catalogue.

VALET PARKING

ANDY FRAIN SERVICES, INC.
310 W. Chicago Avenue
Chicago, IL 60610
312.266.6900
Lorilyn Prah
Areas served: Chicagoland area
Valet parking. Twenty-four hour dispatch.

WINE & SPIRITS

GOLD STANDARD LIQUORS
CHALET WINE & CHEESE SHOPS
5100 W. Dempster Street
Skokie, IL 60077
708.674.4200
Dale Maple
Areas served: Chicago and suburbs
No obligation beverage planning. Custom gifts for any occasion. Wine consultations, tastings, and special offerings. Beverage

serving equipment and supplies. Free
monthly catalog. Over 9000 products in
stock. Food trays (meat, pate, cheese, fruit
and dessert). Coffees, imported cheese and
pate – freshness guaranteed. Nationwide
shipping service. Local delivery and pick-
up. Corporate services to event planners
and caterers. Sandwiches, snacks and
beverages delivered to office boardrooms
and break rooms. Awards include:
"Best United States Retailer" from The
Wine Spectator, "Award of Distinction for
Retailing Excellence" from Beverage
Dynamics, "Best Cheese Shop" and "Best
Liquor Store" from *North Shore Magazine*,
"Superstar Retail Entrepreneur in the US
Wine and Spirits Industry" from *Market
Watch Magazine* and "1st Place Barbara
Hermann – Fine Wine Buyer" from Geja's
Professional Wine Tasting competition.

YACHT & BOAT CHARTERS
ODYSSEY CRUISES
> North Pier
> 401 E. Illinois Street
> Suite 425
> Chicago, IL 60611
> **312.321.7600**
> Peggy Kennedy

Chicago's newest entertaining dining mega-
yacht gives you the ultimate experience of a
luxury cruise. Odyssey offers continental
American cuisine prepared by Chicago's
three-star chef, David Koelling.
Professional service staff consists of waiters
and waitresses whose only job is to provide
first class service from the beginning to end
of your cruise. 12,500 square feet.
Interior: 8000 square feet. Receptions:
700 people. Sit down: 550 people.

DALLAS

DALLAS

AUDIOVISUAL & TECHNICAL SERVICES

AGGREKO, INC.
655 Grigsby Way
Suite A
Cedar Hill, TX 75104
214.293.0491
Eric Bartley
Areas served: National
Power and temperature rental company,
generator power, electrical distribution.

ATTRACTIONS, INC.
P.O. Box 565013
Dallas, TX 75356
214.941.6971
R. Edward Cobb, President
Areas served: International
Full service entertainment firm including
live performance entertainment such as
dance and show bands, name recording
attractions, television and movie
personalities, speakers, comics, magicians,
specialty attractions, etc.; also sound and
light production, contract and rider
consultation, audio/video support systems,
and on-site stage and production
management. Specializes in consultation
and procurement of live performance
entertainment and the equipment and
logistics to present such entertainment.

DESIGN & PRODUCTIONS
11105 Shady Trail
Suite 104
Dallas, TX 75229
214.243.4572
David Opper
Areas served: International
Full service lighting design company
providing lighting, staging, scenery, audio
and special effects. Specializes in design,
installation and production.

BALLOONS

BALLOONS TO YOU
2152-B Chennault Drive
Carrollton, TX 75006
214.788.5022
Areas served: International
Wholesale and retail large scale balloon
decor. Balloon bouquets.

PETALS AND STEMS FLORIST
13319 Montfort
Dallas, TX 75240
214.233.9037
800.530.4686
Lew & Dotty
Areas served: Dallas/Fort Worth Metroplex
Flowers, plants, centerpieces, balloons,
fruit baskets, metroplex and worldwide
delivery, rental of trees and plants.
Specializes in banquets, parties, weddings,
hotel rooms, hospitality suites. Distinctions
include designs for English royalty, designs
for last three U.S. presidents, and Top 100
Florist of two wire services.

BOOKS

WILLIAMS-SONOMA
Dallas Galleria
1500 Dallas Galleria
Dallas, TX 75240
214.960.7575

Dallas Highland
51 Highland Park Village
Dallas, TX 75205
214.696.0348
An authoritative selection of the best for the
kitchen. Complete line of cookware,
bakeware, electrics, glassware, tabletop,
kitchen furniture, cookbooks, packaged
foods. Knowledgeable staff will help choose
equipment, plan parties. Most merchandise
is exclusive to Williams-Sonoma.

CALLIGRAPHY

CALLIGRAPHIC ARTS INC.
4232 Herschel Avenue
Suite 201
Dallas, TX 75219
214.522.4731
Susie-Melissa Cherry
Areas served: National
Custom-designed invitations, favors,
accessories, name tags, place cards, awards
and calligraphy.

DALLAS

EVELYN SCHRAMM
4232 Herschel Avenue
Suite 210
Dallas, TX 75219
214.521.6668
Evelyn Schramm
Areas served: National
Custom-designed invitations, favors,
accessories and calligraphy services for all
occasions.

PAPYRUS
Dallas Galleria
13350 Dallas Pkwy.
Suite 2695
Dallas, TX 75240
214.386.8744
Areas served: National
Twenty-eight locations nationwide.
Custom-designed and catalogue invitations,
accessories, place cards, menu cards,
programs. Full calligraphy services.

WILLIAM ERNEST BROWN
Dallas Galleria
13350 Dallas Pkwy.
Dallas, TX 75240
214.392.1600

524 N. Park Centre
Dallas, TX 75225
214.691.5686
Areas served: International
Custom-designed and catalogue invitations,
seating charts, accessories, place cards and
party supplies for all special events. Full
calligraphy services. Known for their high
quality products and special services.
Clients all over the United States and
Europe.

CATERING

CATERING BY ARTHUR
3230 Towerwood
Suite A
Dallas, TX 75234
214.620.7293
Lowell Michelson
Areas served: Texas, Oklahoma, Arkansas
and New Mexico
Full service catering. Specializing in Bar
Mitzvahs, theme parties, Mexican fiestas.

CULINAIRE INTERNATIONAL
2100 Stemmons Freeway
MS160
Dallas, TX 75207
214.749.5424
Tony Cummins
Areas served: Dallas/Fort Worth Metroplex
Complete event planning, catering and
corporate dining management. Corporate
and social events. Elegant catered events
for 10 - 10,000 people at the Dallas Market
Center or other metroplex locations. "Texas
Chef of the Year," 1992, Culinary Olympic
Team.

CYNTHIA MICHAELS PRODUCTIONS
11106 Stemmons Fwy.
Dallas, TX 75229
214.243.1033
Michael Jacobson
Areas served: Southwestern United States
Excellent food from BBQ to haute cuisine,
very theatrical presentation of both food
and decor. Unique locations for events
ranging from museums and estates to sound
stages. Catered to two royal families and
numerous celebrities.

ELLIS ENTERPRISES
2700 Custer Pkwy.
Richardson, TX 75080
214.247.4747
Michael Ellis
Marcus Ellis
Areas served: National
Catering, banquet center restaurant.

PUTTING ON THE RITZ, INC.
3102 Maple Avenue
Suite 450
Dallas, TX 75201-1233
214.522.2834
Prudence Di Vincenzo
Areas served: Dallas/Forth Worth
Metroplex, will travel
Total event planning services specializing in
turnkey events, creative theme parties,
gourmet catering, entertainment,
invitations, decorations, facilities, staffing,
photography, etc. Corporate, social and
convention events.

[Continued on next page ...]

DALLAS

☙ PRIVATE CHEFS

CAPTAIN FLAME
923 Pinecrest Drive
Richardson, TX 75080
214.680.8857
Q. Coleman
Areas served: Dallas/Fort Worth, National
Private chef and service staff. Specializing
in flaming entrees, salads and desserts.

CELEBRITY ACQUISITION

ATTRACTIONS, INC.
P.O. Box 565013
Dallas, TX 75356
214.941.6971
R. Edward Cobb, President
Areas served: International
Full service entertainment firm including,
but not limited, to live performance
entertainment such as dance and show
bands, name recording attractions,
television and movie personalities,
speakers, comics, magicians, specialty
attractions, etc.; also sound and light
production, contract and rider
consultation, audio/video support systems,
and on-site stage and production
management. Specializes in consultation
and procurement of live performance
entertainment and the equipment and
logistics to present such entertainment.

CHOCOLATES & CONFECTIONS

GODIVA CHOCOLATIER
Dallas Galleria
13350 Dallas Pkwy.
Dallas, TX 75240
214.458.1821

Highland Park Village
73 Highland Park Village
Dallas, TX 75205
214.559.0397
World renowned chocolatier. Belgium-style
chocolates, gift baskets and party favors.

COSTUMES

NORCOSTCO/TEXAS COSTUME
2607 Ross Avenue
Dallas, TX 75201
214.953.1255
Woody Pyeatt
Areas served: Texas, Louisiana, Arkansas,
Oklahoma, New Mexico, Colorado
Costume rental, props, makeup, costume
accessories, hats. Stage lighting, special
effects, scenic materials.

DESTINATION MANAGEMENT

AFFAIRS EXTRAORDINAIRE
11333 N. Central Expwy.
Dallas, TX 75243-6709
214.373.9977
Gloria Solomon
Areas served: Texas
Total event planning and destination
management. Specializing in corporate
organization meetings, conventions.

EQUIPMENT RENTALS & TENTING

ABBEY PARTY RENTS
2615 W. Mockingbird Lane
Dallas, TX 75235
214.350.5373
John Jakob
Areas served: Dallas Metroplex
Equipment rental, tents, lighting and decor
for special events, parties, meetings and
trade shows.

DUCKY-BOB'S PARTY & TENT RENTALS
14500 Beltwood Pkwy. E
Dallas, TX 75244
214.702.8000
Larry Glazer, President
Areas served: Southwestern U.S.
Rental of complete line of party, meeting
and special event equipment including tents.

TEXAS PROMOS, ETC.
P.O. Box 45
McKinney, TX 75069
214.542.2805
Jim Runge
Areas served: Texas and surrounding states
Entertainment, equipment, and
entertainers. In business since 1971.

EVENT PLANNING

AFFAIRS EXTRAORDINAIRE
11333 N. Central Expwy.
Dallas, TX 75243-6709
214.373.9977
Gloria Solomon
Areas served: Texas
Total event planning and destination
management. Specializing in corporate
organization meetings, conventions.

CULINAIRE INTERNATIONAL
2100 Stemmons Fwy.
MS160
Dallas, TX 75207
214.749.5424
Tony Cummins
Areas served: Dallas/Fort Worth Metroplex
Complete event planning, catering and
corporate dining management. Corporate
and social events. Elegant catered events
for 10 - 10,000 people at the Dallas Market
Center or other metroplex locations.
"Texas Chef of the Year," 1992, Culinary
Olympic Team.

EVENTS UNLIMITED
5454 La Sieria
Suite 200
Dallas, TX 75231
214.750.7226
Sheri Pizitz
Areas served: International
Corporate special event planning,
production and management. Nominated
for Special Events Gala Award three years,
won Gala Award. Nominated Best Event
Coordinator under $30,000.

FESTIVITIES
(A Division of Meeting Management
Associates, Inc.)

4100 McEwen
Suite 101
Dallas, TX 75244
214.386.9403
Linda Hill, President
Darlene Bush
Areas served: Dallas, Forth Worth, Austin
Specializing in transportation, special
events, tours and meeting planning.

GALE SLIGER PRODUCTIONS
1261 Profit Drive
Dallas, TX 75247
214.637.5566
Gale Sliger
Areas served: Arkansas, Louisiana, New
Mexico, Oklahoma and Texas.
Predominately the Dallas/Fort Worth area.
Coordination, design, fabrication, florals,
and in-house prop rental. Custom party
decorations; complete coordination and
production of major events.

INSPIRATIONS EVENT PRODUCTIONS, INC.
P.O. Box 12323
Dallas, TX 75225
214.360.9815
Cindy Ray
Areas served: Dallas, DC, San Antonio
Full custom-designed event production for
social and corporate events. Wedding
consultant.

PUTTING ON THE RITZ, INC.
3102 Maple Avenue
Suite 450
Dallas, TX 75201-1233
214.522.2834
Prudence Di Vincenzo
Areas served: Dallas/Forth Worth
Metroplex, will travel
Total event planning services specializing in
turnkey events, creative theme parties,
gourmet catering, entertainment,
invitations, decorations, facilities, staffing,
photography, etc. Corporate, social and
convention events.

[Continued on next page.]

FAVORS

CALLIGRAPHIC ARTS INC.
4232 Herschel Avenue
Suite 201
Dallas, TX 75219
214.522.4731
Susie-Melissa Cherry
Areas served: National
Custom-designed invitations, favors,
accessories, name tags, place cards, awards
and calligraphy.

EVELYN SCHRAMM
4232 Herschel Avenue
Suite 210
Dallas, TX 75219
214.521.6668
Evelyn Schramm
Areas served: National
Custom-designed invitations, favors,
accessories and calligraphy services for all
occasions.

GODIVA CHOCOLATIER
Dallas Galleria
13350 Dallas Pkwy.
Dallas, TX 75240
214.458.1821

Highland Park Village
73 Highland Park Village
Dallas, TX 75205
214.559.0397
World renowned chocolatier. Belgium-style
chocolates, gift baskets and party favors.

TIFFANY & CO.
Dallas Galleria
13350 Dallas Pkwy.
Dallas, TX 75240
214.458.2800
The finest in engraved invitations, favors,
accessories, stationery, bridal registry, fine
crystal and china, Tiffany flatware and gifts
for all occasions.

WILLIAM ERNEST BROWN
Dallas Galleria
13350 Dallas Pkwy.
Dallas, TX 75240
214.392.1600

524 N. Park Centre

Dallas, TX 75225
214.691.5686
Areas served: International
Custom-designed and catalogue invitations,
seating charts, accessories, place cards and
party supplies for all special events. Full
calligraphy services. Known for their high
quality products and special services.
Clients all over the United States and
Europe.

FIREWORKS & SPECIAL EFFECTS

DESIGN & PRODUCTIONS
11105 Shady Trail
Suite 104
Dallas, TX 75229
214.243.4572
David Opper
Areas served: International
Full service lighting design company
providing lighting, staging, scenery, audio
and special effects. Specializes in design,
installation and production.

SAMARCO, INC.
1606 Gano Street
Dallas, TX 75215
214.421.0757
800.530.4905
Areas served: National
Lighting, staging, scenery, special effects,
design, production, rental, sales.
Theatrical solutions to lighting and staging
problems. Artistic use of light for scenic
purposes and to create ambiance.

FLORISTS & FLORAL DESIGNS

DESIGNS BEHIND THE SCENES
P.O. Box 822875
Dallas, TX 75382
214.691.7307
Debbie Williams
Kim Quigley
Areas served: Dallas/Ft. Worth Metroplex
Plant rentals and floral centerpieces
for all occasions.

GALE SLIGER PRODUCTIONS
1261 Profit Drive
Dallas, TX 75247
214.637.5566
Gale Sliger
Areas served: Arkansas, Louisiana, New Mexico, Oklahoma and Texas. Predominately the Dallas/Fort Worth area. Coordination, design, fabrication, florals, and in-house prop rental. Custom party decorations; complete coordination and production of major events.

PETALS AND STEMS FLORIST
13319 Montfort
Dallas, TX 75240
214.233.9037
800.530.4686
Lew & Dotty
Areas served: Dallas/Fort Worth Metroplex Flowers, plants, centerpieces, balloons, fruit baskets, metroplex and worldwide delivery, rental of trees and plants. Specializes in banquets, parties, weddings, hotel rooms, hospitality suites. Distinctions include designs for English royalty, designs for last three US presidents, and Top 100 Florist of two wire services.

GIFTS & GIFT BASKETS

GODIVA CHOCOLATIER
Dallas Galleria
13350 Dallas Pkwy.
Dallas, TX 75240
214.458.1821

Highland Park Village
73 Highland Park Village
Dallas, TX 75205
214.559.0397
World renowned chocolatier. Belgium-style chocolates, gift baskets and party favors.

PETALS AND STEMS FLORIST
13319 Montfort
Dallas, TX 75240
214.233.9037
800.530.4686
Lew & Dotty
Areas served: Dallas/Fort Worth Metroplex Flowers, plants, centerpieces, balloons, fruit baskets, metroplex and worldwide

delivery, rental of trees and plants. Specializes in banquets, parties, weddings, hotel rooms, hospitality suites. Distinctions include designs for English royalty, designs for last three US presidents, and Top 100 Florist of two wire services.

TIFFANY & CO.
Dallas Galleria
13350 Dallas Pkwy.
Dallas, TX 75240
214.458.2800
The finest in engraved invitations, favors, accessories, stationery, bridal registry, fine crystal and china, Tiffany flatware and gifts for all occassions.

INVITATIONS & ACCESSORIES

CALLIGRAPHIC ARTS INC.
4232 Herschel Avenue
Suite 201
Dallas, TX 75219
214.522.4731
Susie-Melissa Cherry
Areas served: National
Custom-designed invitations, favors, accessories, name tags, place cards, awards and calligraphy.

EVELYN SCHRAMM
4232 Herschel Avenue
Suite 210
Dallas, TX 75219
214.521.6668
Evelyn Schramm
Areas served: National
Custom-designed invitations, favors, accessories and calligraphy services for all occasions.

PAPYRUS
Dallas Galleria
13350 Dallas Pkwy.
Suite 2695
Dallas, TX 75240
214.386.8744
Areas served: National
Twenty-eight locations nationwide. Custom-designed and catalogue invitations, accessories, place cards, menu cards,

programs. Full calligraphy services.

TIFFANY & CO.
Dallas Galleria
13350 Dallas Pkwy.
Dallas, TX 75240
214.458.2800

The finest in engraved invitations, favors, accessories, stationery, bridal registry, fine crystal and china, Tiffany flatware and gifts for all occasions.

WILLIAM ERNEST BROWN
Dallas Galleria
13350 Dallas Pkwy.
Dallas, TX 75240
214.392.1600

524 N. Park Centre
Dallas, TX 75225
214.691.5686

Areas served: International
Custom-designed and catalogue invitations, seating charts, accessories, place cards and party supplies for all special events. Full calligraphy services. Known for their high quality products and special services. Clients all over the United States and Europe.

LIGHTING, STAGING & SOUND

ABBEY PARTY RENTS
2615 W. Mockingbird Lane
Dallas, TX 75235
214.350.5373
John Jakob

Areas served: Dallas Metroplex
Equipment rental, tents, lighting and decor for special events, parties, meetings and trade shows.

ATTRACTIONS, INC.
P.O. Box 565013
Dallas, TX 75356
214.941.6971
R. Edward Cobb, President

Areas served: International
Full service entertainment firm including, but not limited, to live performance entertainment such as dance and show

bands, name recording attractions, television and movie personalities, speakers, comics, magicians, specialty attractions, etc.; also sound and light production, contract and rider consultation, audio/video support systems, and on-site stage and production management. Specializes in consultation and procurement of live performance entertainment and the equipment and logistics to present such entertainment.

DESIGN & PRODUCTIONS
11105 Shady Trail
Suite 104
Dallas, TX 75229
214.243.4572
David Opper

Areas served: International
Full service lighting design company providing lighting, staging, scenery, audio and special effects. Specializes in design, installation and production.

SAMARCO, INC.
1606 Gano Street
Dallas, TX 75215
214.421.0757
800.530.4905

Areas served: National
Lighting, staging, scenery, special effects, design, production, rental, sales. Theatrical solutions to lighting and staging problems. Artistic use of light for scenic purposes and to create ambiance.

LIMOUSINE & TRANSPORTATION

CAREY LIMOUSINE
214.638.4828
800.336.4646

Privately chauffeured sedans, limousines, vans and mini buses in 372 cities.

DAV EL CHAUFFEURED TRANSPORTATION NETWORK
800.328.3526

Areas Served: International
Luxury chauffeured services in over 350 cities worldwide. Centralized reservations and billing. Airport concierge services.

DALLAS

FESTIVITIES
(A Division of Meeting Management
Associates, Inc.)
 4100 McEwen
 Suite 101
 Dallas, TX 75244
 214.386.9403
 Linda Hill, President
 Darlene Bush
Areas served: Dallas, Forth Worth, Austin
Specializing in transportation, special
events, tours and meeting planning.

MUSIC & ENTERTAINMENT
ATTRACTIONS, INC.
 P.O. Box 565013
 Dallas, TX 75356
 214.941.6971
 R. Edward Cobb, President
Areas served: International
Full service entertainment firm including,
but not limited, to live performance
entertainment such as dance and show
bands, name recording attractions,
television and movie personalities,
speakers, comics, magicians, specialty
attractions, etc.; also sound and light
production, contract and rider
consultation, audio/video support systems,
and on-site stage and production
management. Specializes in consultation
and procurement of live performance
entertainment and the equipment and
logistics to present such entertainment.

COHEN'S CASINO PARTIES
 3826 Shadycreek Drive
 Garland, TX 75042
 214.276.2998
 Ken Cohen
Areas served: Texas
Las Vegas night parties. In business for
over ten years.

FUN COMPANY OF THE SOUTHWEST
 14109 Rocksprings Court
 Dallas, TX 75240
 214.233.5224
 Anneta Moerbe
 Michelle Moerbe
Areas served: Texas, Oklahoma, Louisiana,

Arkansas, with National connections
Professional entertainment for special
events ranging from birthday parties to full
convention shows. Entertainment custom-
tailored for your event. Acrobats, animals,
musicians, impersonators, dancers, and
more. In business since 1976.

JOAN FRANK PRODUCTIONS
 8175 Clear Springs Road
 Dallas, TX 75240
 214.470.9500
 Brad Lee
Areas served: Texas
Music and theatrical entertainment
production. 1991-92 Cotton Bowl Parade
Advisory Board.

THE ORIGINAL BUTT SKETCH
 213 S. Tyler Street
 Dallas, TX 75208
 214.943.BUTT
 Krandel Lee Newton
Areas served: International
Custom drawings, artistry services.
Conventions, receptions and promotions.

SOUND WAVE
 337 Phillips
 Coppell, TX 75019
 214.393.2320
 Jim Garrison
Areas served: Texas
Entertainment, disk jockeys, Karoake, live
bands, clowns, mimes, magicians.

TEXAS PROMOS, ETC.
 P.O. Box 45
 McKinney, TX 75069
 214.542.2805
 Jim Runge
Areas served: Texas and surrounding states
Entertainment, equipment, and
entertainers. In business since 1971.

PARTY SITES
THE ADOLPHUS HOTEL
 1321 Commerce Street
 Dallas, TX 75202
 214.742.8200
 Terri Hahn

French Renaissance style with twenty-one foot muraled ceilings and hand blown crystal chandeliers. 5244 square feet. Receptions: 600 people. Sit down: 400 people with band and dance floor. Host hotel for Her Majesty Queen Elizabeth II and His Royal Highness Prince Philip, The Duke of Edinburgh (1991). *Conde Nast Traveler* Reader's Choice Award 1992, Top Ten Hotel in the US Received AAA Five Diamond Award for the past ten years. Rated as the "top pick in Dallas" of best hotel reception sites in the Coopwood & Field Dallas/Fort Worth Weddings Book.

AMADEUS RESTAURANT
2100 Stemmons Fwy.
Dallas, TX 75207
214.749.5424
Tony Cummins

Upscale, sophisticated catered events for up to 250 people. Received three and one half stars from *Dallas Morning News* review (highest available).

ARBORS RESTAURANT
2100 Stemmons Fwy.
MS160
Dallas, TX 75207
214.749.5424
Pete Nolasco

Restaurant offering private catered events for up to 150 guests.

BELO MANSION
2101 Ross Avenue
Dallas, TX 75207
214.749.5481
Bill Heatley

Catering and banquet services, bar and weekday luncheon buffet. Unique facility. Southern decor. Can handle up to 600 people. Five star chef. Owned by Dallas Bar Association. Used for weddings.

THE DALLAS GRAND HOTEL
1914 Commerce Street
Dallas, TX 75201
214.747.7000
800.421.0011 x3457
Melissa Soliz
Mary McCarter

710 room property. All meeting space is fully renovated as of two years ago. Two Jacuzzis on roof-top sun deck. One block from the original Neiman Marcus department store. Over 43,000 square feet of meeting space. Grand ballroom is 13,552 square feet, the Embassy ballroom is 4708 square feet and both have built-in dance floors. The larger room has a built-in stage. Receptions: 2400 people. Sit down: 1200 people for dinner, 980 people for a dinner/dance.

DALLAS MARKET CENTER
2100 Stemmons Avenue
Dallas, TX 75207
214.749.5417
Peter Cwalino

One of the largest banquet facilities in Central Texas. Full event planning and catering. Awards and distinctions include 1992 Texas Chef of the Year. Member of the Culinaire Olympic Team.

THE GRAND KEMPINSKI DALLAS
15201 N. Dallas Pkwy.
Dallas, TX 75248
214.386.6000 x4335
George Palacios

Hotel/catering services. 90,000 square feet. Receptions: 3700 people. Sit down: 2000 people. Multiple awards and recognition.

THE MANSION ON TURTLE CREEK
2821 Turtle Creek Blvd.
Dallas, TX 75219
214.559.2100
Crys Cartwright

Located two miles from Central Business District. Silk-covered walls, custom-designed carpet, crystal chandeliers, beveled glass. Over eleven private function rooms. Dining, receptions, classroom, theatre, conference facilities. Distinctions include 1992 Mobil Five Star Award, 1992 AAA Five Diamond Award, 1991 Mobil Five Star Award, *Zagat's* US Travel Survey number one, number five of *Lifestyles of the Rich and Famous* World's Best Top Ten Hotels, *Institutional Investor's* The World's Best Hotels: number three in the US, number fifteen in the world, listed on *Romantic Hideaways* Most Romantic Urban Hideaways.

DALLAS

RANCHLAND
Route 3
Box 602
Roanoke, TX 76262
817.430.0070
Linda Christenson
Large meeting and party ranch near DFW Airport. Oldest party ranch in Texas. 15,000 square feet. Receptions: 1000 people. Sit down: 650 people. In business since 1968.

PARTY SUPPLIES

WILLIAM ERNEST BROWN
Dallas Galleria
13350 Dallas Pkwy.
Dallas, TX 75240

524 N. Park Centre
Dallas, TX 75225
214.691.5686
Areas served: International
Custom-designed and catalogue invitations, seating charts, accessories, place cards and party supplies for all special events. Full calligraphy services. Known for their high quality products and special services. Clients all over the United States and Europe.

PERSONNEL & STAFFING

LADY BAR "10" DERS
AND BAR "10" DERS
3024 White Oak Lane
Bedford, TX 76021
817.498.5774
214.351.1886
Vi Garcia
Areas served: Texas
Staffing and personnel for private events and convention services. Waiters, waitresses, blackjack dealers, carvers, coat check, bartenders, hosts, hostesses, greeters, etc. Set-up, clean-up and breakdown, as well as assistance in all facets of the event.

PHOTOGRAPHY & VIDEO

ALLEN HANSLEY
214.871.2949
Areas served: International
Full photography and video services for all special events. Specializing in event photography. Clients include the Anatole Hotel for the appearance of President Aquino of the Phillipines; the Susan G. Komen Foundation for the appearances of Vice President Dan Quayle, Marilyn Quayle, Betty Ford and Nancy Reagan in Dallas and Washington, DC; the opening of the Morton H. Meyerson Symphony Center for Bozell, Inc.; Neiman Marcus for the 1989 NM Best Awards; official photographer for Ramses the Great; and the Dallas Chamber of Commerce for the appearances of Barbara Bush and Saudi Arabian Prince Bandar.

CHRISTINE BOWMAN
P.O. Box 191413
Dallas, TX 75219
214.526.9683
Full photography services for all special events. Social, private, balls, fundraisers, openings, etc. Top corporate and social clientele.

BOB MADER
500 Crescent Court
Suite 160
Dallas, TX 75201
214.871.5511
800.969.5511
Hope Hickman
Areas served: Dallas
Full event photography services for all special events – corporate, private, weddings, anniversaries, etc. Clients include major Dallas hotels and corporations.

PLANT RENTALS

DESIGNS BEHIND THE SCENES
P.O. Box 822875
Dallas, TX 75382
214.691.7307
Debbie Williams
Kim Quigley
Areas served: Dallas/Ft. Worth Metroplex

Plant rentals and floral centerpieces for all occasions.

PETALS AND STEMS FLORIST
13319 Montfort
Dallas, TX 75240
214.233.9037
800.530.4686
Lew & Dotty
Areas served: Dallas/Fort Worth Metroplex
Flowers, plants, centerpieces, balloons, fruit baskets, metroplex and worldwide delivery, rental of trees and plants. Specializes in banquets, parties, weddings, hotel rooms, hospitality suites. Distinctions include designs for English royalty, designs for last three US presidents, and Top 100 Florist of two wire services.

PROPS & DECOR

ABBEY PARTY RENTS
2615 W. Mockingbird Lane
Dallas, TX 75235
214.350.5373
John Jakob
Areas served: Dallas Metroplex
Equipment rental, tents, lighting and decor for special events, parties, meetings and trade shows.

CYNTHIA MICHAELS PRODUCTIONS
11106 Stemmons Freeway
Dallas, TX 75229
214.243.1033
Michael Jacobson
Areas served: Southwestern United States
Complete theme design and decorating services and prop rentals. Theatrically sophisticated props and decor for both indoor and outdoor special events. City of Dallas Key, decor for two royal families, numerous Fortune 500 companies, "Best Buy Awards" from *Underground Shopper Magazine*.

EVENT DESIGN PRODUCTIONS
2615 W. Mockingbird Lane
Dallas, TX 75235
214.350.5373
John Jakob

David Hall
Areas served: National
Props, custom decor, design. A division of Abbey Party Rents.

GALE SLIGER PRODUCTIONS
1261 Profit Drive
Dallas, TX 75247
214.637.5566
Gale Sliger
Areas served: Arkansas, Louisiana, New Mexico, Oklahoma and Texas. Predominately the Dallas/Fort Worth area. Coordination, design, fabrication, florals, and in-house prop rental. Custom party decorations; complete coordination and production of major events.

GARY RAY'S CREATIVE SIGNS & DISPLAYS
3712 Glade Road
Colleyville, TX 76034
817.571.4460
Gary Ray
Areas served: Dallas/Fort Worth areas
Signs, scenic displays, props, festivals.

NORCOSTCO/TEXAS COSTUME
2607 Ross Avenue
Dallas, TX 75201
214.953.1255
Woody Pyeatt
Areas served: Texas, Louisiana, Arkansas, Oklahoma, New Mexico, Colorado
Costume rental, props, makeup, costume accessories, hats. Stage lighting, special effects, scenic materials.

SAMARCO, INC.
1606 Gano Street
Dallas, TX 75215
214.421.0757
800.530.4905
Areas served: National
Lighting, staging, scenery, special effects, design, production, rental, sales. Theatrical solutions to lighting and staging problems. Artistic use of light for scenic purposes and to create ambiance.

[Continued on next page.]

SIGNAGE

GARY RAY'S CREATIVE SIGNS & DISPLAYS
3712 Glade Road
Colleyville, TX 76034
817.571.4460
Gary Ray
Areas served: Dallas/Fort Worth areas
Signs, scenic displays, props, festivals.

SPEAKERS

ATTRACTIONS, INC.
P.O. Box 565013
Dallas, TX 75356
214.941.6971
R. Edward Cobb, President
Areas served: International
Full service entertainment firm including, but not limited, to live performance entertainment such as dance and show bands, name recording attractions, television and movie personalities, speakers, comics, magicians, specialty attractions, etc.; also sound and light production, contract and rider consultation, audio/video support systems, and on-site stage and production management. Specializes in consultation and procurement of live performance entertainment and the equipment and logistics to present such entertainment.

EXECUTIVE DEVELOPMENT SYSTEMS, INC.
14135 Midway Road
Suite 250, LB
Dallas, TX 75244
214.458.8855
Linda Barrett
Areas served: International
Three day Successful Life Course (personal development, habit improvement program); on-site siminars and workshops of varying lengths; convention keynotes. Develop and maintain a wholesome, positive mental attitude; follow through and achieve goals; eliminate negative life-sapping habits; improved eating, drinking and exercise habits for a strong, healthy body; recognize and control stress; time management. Positively featured on CBS News' *60 Minutes*.

THE ZIG ZIGLAR CORPORATION
3330 Earhart Drive
Suite 204
Carrollton, TX 75006
214.233.9191
800.527.0306
Bryan Flanagan
Areas served: International
Fun, uplifting speakers; inspiring, exciting programs; enteraining sessions; spouse's and children's programs. Specialty is providing talks, programs, presentations to a wide range of audiences. Each program is customized. The Ziglar Corporation is world renowned as a leader in the "People Business."

TABLETOP ACCESSORIES & KITCHENWARE

CRATE AND BARREL
North Park Center
Dallas, TX 75225
214.696.8010

Dallas Galleria
13350 Dallas Pkwy.
Dallas, TX 75240
214.392.3411
Full line of unique contemporary home furnishings and accessories featuring tabletop accessories and gourmet kitchenware.

TIFFANY & CO.
Dallas Galleria
13350 Dallas Pkwy.
Dallas, TX 75240
214.458.2800
The finest in engraved invitations, favors, accessories, stationery, bridal registry, fine crystal and china, Tiffany flatware and gifts for all occasions.

WILLIAMS-SONOMA
Dallas Galleria
1500 Dallas Galleria
Dallas, TX 75240
214.960.7575

Dallas Highland
51 Highland Park Village

Dallas, TX 75205
214.696.0348
An authoritative selection of the best for the
kitchen. Complete line of cookware,
bakeware, electrics, glassware, tabletop,
kitchen furniture, cookbooks, packaged
foods. Knowledgeable staff will help choose
equipment, plan parties. Most merchandise
is exclusive to Williams-Sonoma.

YACHT & BOAT CHARTERS
ENGLISH ROSE CHARTERS
P.O. Box 170
Lewisville, TX 75067
214.625.1921
Nancy Carruthers
Larry Bailey
Areas served: Dallas/Fort Worth Metroplex
Yacht and boat charters for special events.
Specializing in "cheeseburgers in paradise."

MIAMI

MIAMI

AUDIOVISUAL & TECHNICAL SERVICES

AUDIO VISUAL AMERICA/STAGE SOUND
20229 N.E. Sixteenth Place
Miami, FL 33162
305.653.0008
Tim Snow
Areas served: International
Progressive production support company
dedicated to customer service and
specializing in "State of the Art" equipment
rentals, sales, service, design, installation,
consultation and professional technicians.
Full concert sound, staging and lighting
capabilities. Videowalls, laser shows and
program development capabilities. Video
projection. Large and small audience
packages. Special recognition from: Papal
visit, Formula One Grand Prix, CBS
Records International, Polygram Records,
Fiesta Bowl, Kodak, IBM, Tucson
Symphony, Telluride Bluegrass Festival,
Colorado State Fair and Meeting Concepts.

BALLOONS

OOOH's AND AAAH's, INC.
3333 S.W. 117th Avenue
Davie, FL 33330
305.473.2864
Kathy Kay
Areas served: Broward County, Dade
County, West Palm, Southern Florida
Balloon and floral decorating. Specializing
in balloon sculptures and unique designs.

BOOKS

WILLIAMS-SONOMA
2392-A E. Sunrise Blvd.
Fort Lauderdale, FL 33304
305.568.0915
An authoritative selection of the best for the
kitchen. Complete line of cookware,
bakeware, electrics, glassware, tabletop,
kitchen furniture, cookbooks, packaged
foods. Knowledgeable staff will help choose
equipment, plan parties. Most merchandise
is exclusive to Williams-Sonoma.

CAKES & BAKED GOODS

CONTEMPORARY CATERERS, INC.
275 S.W. Fourteenth Avenue
Pompano Beach, FL 33069
305.942.2617
Gary Wisotzky
Areas served: Dade, Broward and Palm
Beach Counties
Full service event planning and
productions. Full service and drop-off
catering, corporate box lunches, theme and
spouse events, and custom bakery services.
Mobil refrigeration, freezers and warmers
give them unlimited possibilities in locations
where logistics play an important role in
event execution. Mobil kitchens and
portable power make them a leader in the
film industry.

CATERING

BILL'S CATERING
P.O. Box 45-1233
Miami, FL 33245
305.858.6660
Bill Hansen
Areas served: Dade, Broward, Palm
Beach, Monroe and Collier Counties
Up-scale catering, event planning, site
selection, decor and entertainment. They
received five stars from the National
Caterers Association and Bill is a professor
of catering management at Florida
International University.

CONTEMPORARY CATERERS, INC.
275 S.W. Fourteenth Avenue
Pompano Beach, FL 33069
305.942.2617
Gary Wisotzky
Areas served: Dade, Broward and Palm
Beach Counties
Full service event planning and productions.
Full service and drop-off catering, corporate
box lunches, theme and spouse events, and
custom bakery services. Mobil refrigeration,
freezers and warmers give them unlimited
possibilities in locations where logistics play
an important role in event execution. Mobil
kitchens and portable power make them a
leader in the film industry.

MIAMI

CHOCOLATES & CONFECTIONS

GODIVA CHOCOLATIER
Dadeland Mall
305.662.2429
World renowned chocolatier. Belgium-style chocolates, gift baskets and party favors.

DESTINATION MANAGEMENT

DECO PRODUCTIONS, INC.
7711 W. 22nd Avenue
Hialiah, FL 33016
305.558.0800
Sharon Siegel
Areas served: National and Caribbean
Destination management services, entertainment, meet and greet, tours, flowers, props, stage sets, decor, linens.

PARTIES BY NEIL *
ENTERTAINMENT ETC.
2329 S.W. 31st Avenue
Hallandale, FL 33009
305.987.7991
Shirley Crane
Areas served: Miami, Ft. Lauderdale, Boca Raton, Palm Beach, Orlando, Naples, Marco Island, Florida Keys
Party decor, themed events, destination management, entertainment, Zanadu, business theater. *Special Events Magazine* 1990 Best Event Design, *Special Events Magazine* 1991 Best Tabletop Design.

EQUIPMENT RENTALS & TENTING

PARTY TIME RENTALS
7711 W. 22nd Avenue
Hialeah, FL 33016
305.558.9798
Equipment rentals, tenting, linens, glassware, tables, chairs, cooking equipment, bridal equipment.

EVENT PLANNING

BILL'S CATERING
P.O. Box 45-1233
Miami, FL 33245
305.858.6660
Bill Hansen
Areas served: Dade, Broward, Palm Beach, Monroe and Collier Counties
Up-scale catering, event planning, site selection, decor and entertainment. They received five stars from the National Caterers Association and Bill is a professor of catering management at Florida International University.

BOBBY RODRIGUEZ PRODUCTIONS, INC.
6191 N.W. 32nd Terrace
Fort Lauderdale, FL 33309-2213
305.978.8610
Emil Gunther
Special event coordination and entertainment for social and corporate affairs as well as full event production for festivals.

COMCOR
2425 E. Commercial Blvd.
Suite 406
Fort Lauderdale, FL 33308
305.491.3233
Mona Meretsky
Areas served: International
Full creative event production for special events, incentives and meetings. Create sizzle, customize, constantly surprise. Specialize in corporate events. Five nominations for "Gala Awards" through *Special Events Magazine*. 1990 winner for "Best Corporate Event" under $30,000.

CONTEMPORARY CATERERS, INC.
275 S.W. Fourteenth Avenue
Pompano Beach, FL 33069
305.942.2617
Gary Wisotzky
Areas served: Dade, Broward and Palm Beach Counties
Full service event planning and productions. Full service and drop-off catering, corporate box lunches, theme and spouse events, and custom bakery services. Mobil refrigeration, freezers and warmers give them unlimited possibilities in locations

where logistics play an important role in event execution. Mobil kitchens and portable power make them a leader in the film industry.

FAMOUS FACES ENTERTAINMENT AND SPECIAL EVENTS COMPANY
2013 Harding Street
Hollywood, FL 33020
305.922.0700
800.635.6492 (Outside FL)
Paul Levine, President
Areas served: National
Theme parties, convention planning, celebrity look-alikes, music and entertainment, novelty acts, speakers, murder mystery productions, casino night, horse and dog racing on film, theme decor, models, actors, actresses, etc.

PARTIES BY LOIS BEINHORN DBA IRV BEINHORN JEWELERS, INC.
36 N.E. First Street
Suite 229
Miami, FL 33132
305.379.0304
Lois Beinhorn
Areas served: International
Professional party planner. Invitations and accessories for conventions, Bar/Bat Mitzvahs, specializing in weddings that are socially proper and correct. Featured in *Social Magazine* for huge international wedding in Miami April 10, 1992.

PARTIES BY NEIL *
ENTERTAINMENT ETC.
2329 S.W. 31st Avenue
Hallandale, FL 33009
305.987.7991
Shirley Crane
Areas served: Miami, Ft. Lauderdale, Boca Raton, Palm Beach, Orlando, Naples, Marco Island, Florida Keys
Party decor, themed events, destination management, entertainment, Zanadu, business theater. *Special Events Magazine* 1990 Best Event Design, *Special Events Magazine* 1991 Best Tabletop Design.

FAVORS

GODIVA CHOCOLATIER
Dadeland Mall
305.662.2429
World renowned chocolatier. Belgium-style chocolates, gift baskets and party favors.

FIREWORKS & SPECIAL EFFECTS

AUDIO VISUAL AMERICA/STAGE SOUND
20229 N.E. Sixteenth Place
Miami, FL 33162
305.653.0008
Tim Snow
Areas served: International
Progressive production support company dedicated to customer service and specializing in "State of the Art" equipment rentals, sales, service, design, installation, consultation and professional technicians. Full concert sound, staging and lighting capabilities. Videowalls, laser shows and program development capabilities. Video projection. Large and small audience packages. Special recognition from: Papal visit, Formula One Grand Prix, CBS Records International, Polygram Records, Fiesta Bowl, Kodak, IBM, Tucson Symphony, Telluride Bluegrass Festival, Colorado State Fair and Meeting Concepts.

PRODUCTION DYNAMICS LIGHTING
P.O. Box 290658
Davie, FL 33329-0658
305.797.2823
Steven Pollock
Areas served: Florida, especially Miami to Palm Beach, and Caribbean
Design and implementation of lighting and special effects for theme banquets, corporate shows, meetings, fashion shows; tents, dance floors, video, landscaping, and building exteriors. Steven Pollock is the president and co-founder of the South Florida/Caribbean Chapter of ISES.

MIAMI

ZAMBELLI INTERNATIONALE FIREWORKS MFG. CO., INC.
299 W. 52nd Terrace
Suite 118
Boca Raton, FL 33487
407.994.1588
800.245.0397
Areas served: International
Manufacturer and exhibitor of fireworks
extravaganzas. Indoor and outdoor
custom-designed exhibitions electrically
choreographed to music and lasers.
Distinctions include National Victory
Celebration, the Opening Ceremonies of
The Kentucky Derby Festival, the Statue of
Liberty Celebration.

FLORISTS & FLORAL DESIGNS

ACTION PLANT RENTAL
1736 S.W. Fourth Court
Fort Lauderdale, FL 33312
305.524.1724
Philip and Wendy Hancock
Areas served: South Florida
Decorate special events with tropical plants,
water features and lighting. They specialize
in the creative use of natural foilage to
create compositions of palms and trees.

DECO PRODUCTIONS, INC.
7711 W. 22nd Avenue
Hialiah, FL 33016
305.558.0800
Sharon Siegel
Areas served: National and Caribbean
Destination management services,
entertainment, meet and greet, tours,
flowers, props, stage sets, decor, linens.

DONALD MOORE PARTY DESIGNS/DMCC DESIGN GROUP INTERNATIONAL
20855 N.E. Sixteenth Avenue
Suite 24
N. Miami Beach, FL 33179
305.652.6053
Cindy Christman
Donald Moore
Areas served: Miami, Fort Lauderdale,
Palm Beach, Orlando and Carribean
Decorating, lighting, staging and flowers.

Specializing in themed events.

OOOH's AND AAAH's, INC.
3333 S.W. 117th Avenue
Davie, FL 33330
305.473.2864
Kathy Kay
Areas served: Broward County, Dade
County, West Palm, Southern Florida
Balloon and floral decorating. Specializing
in balloon sculptures and unique designs.

GIFTS & GIFT BASKETS

GODIVA CHOCOLATIER
Dadeland Mall
305.662.2429
World renowned chocolatier. Belgium-style
chocolates, gift baskets and party favors.

INVITATIONS & ACCESSORIES

PARTIES BY LOIS BEINHORN DBA IRV BEINHORN JEWELERS, INC.
36 N.E. First Street
Suite 229
Miami, FL 33132
305.379.0304
Lois Beinhorn
Areas served: International
Professional party planner. Invitations and
accessories for conventions, Bar/Bat
Mitzvahs, specializing in weddings that are
socially proper and correct. Featured in
Social Magazine for huge international
wedding in Miami April 10, 1992.

LIGHTING, STAGING & SOUND

AUDIO VISUAL AMERICA/STAGE SOUND
20229 N.E. Sixteenth Place
Miami, FL 33162
305.653.0008
Tim Snow
Areas served: International
Progressive production support company
dedicated to customer service and

service, design, installation, consultation and professional technicians. Full concert sound, staging and lighting capabilities. Videowalls, laser shows and program development capabilities. Video projection. Large and small audience packages. Special recognition from: Papal visit, Formula One Grand Prix, CBS Records International, Polygram Records, Fiesta Bowl, Kodak, IBM, Tucson Symphony, Telluride Bluegrass Festival, Colorado State Fair and Meeting Concepts.

DONALD MOORE PARTY DESIGNS/DMCC DESIGN GROUP INTERNATIONAL
> 20855 N.E. Sixteenth Avenue
> Suite 24
> N. Miami Beach, FL 33179
> **305.652.6053**
> Cindy Christman
> Donald Moore

Areas served: Miami, Fort Lauderdale, Palm Beach, Orlando and Carribean
Decorating, lighting, staging and flowers. Specializing in themed events.

MIAMI STAGE LIGHTING
> 1839 S.W. 31st Avenue
> Pembroke Park, FL 33009
> **305.964.9016**
> Marco Rose

Areas served: South Florida, Orlando
Theatrical lighting services for events.

PRODUCTION DYNAMICS LIGHTING
> P.O. Box 290658
> Davie, FL 33329-0658
> **305.797.2823**
> Steven Pollock

Areas served: Florida, especially Miami to Palm Beach, and Caribbean
Design and implementation of lighting and special effects for theme banquets, corporate shows, meetings, fashion shows; tents, dance floors, video, landscaping, and building exteriors. Steven Pollock is the president and co-founder of the South Florida/Caribbean Chapter of ISES.

LIMOUSINE & TRANSPORTATION

CAREY LIMOUSINE
> **305.764.0615**
> **800.336.4646**

Privately chauffeured sedans, limousines, vans and mini buses in 372 cities.

DAV EL CHAUFFEURED TRANSPORTATION NETWORK
> **800.328.3526** (outside CA)
> **800.826.5779** (inside CA)

Areas Served: International
Luxury chauffeured services in over 350 cities worldwide. Centralized reservations and billing. Airport concierge services.

OLD TOWN TROLLEY TOURS
> P.O. Box 12985
> Miami, FL 33101
> **305.374.8687**

Tours, transportation, shuttle services for individuals, groups, wedding. Largest fleet operator of theme styled vehicles in the United States.

LINENS

DECO PRODUCTIONS, INC.
> 7711 W. 22nd Avenue
> Hialiah, FL 33016
> **305.558.0800**
> Sharon Siegel

Areas served: National and Caribbean
Destination management services, entertainment, meet and greet, tours, flowers, props, stage sets, decor, linens.

PARTY TIME RENTALS
> 7711 W. 22nd Avenue
> Hialeah, FL 33016
> **305.558.9798**

Equipment rentals, tenting, linens, glassware, tables, chairs, cooking equipment, bridal equipment.

TABLE TOPPERS, INC.
> 3651 N.W. 81st Street
> Miami, FL 33147
> **305.836.8807**
> Renee Fink

Areas served: National

MIAMI

Tablecloths, chair covers and napkins. Specialize in elegant design. Ship nationally. Rentals and made-to-order.

MUSIC & ENTERTAINMENT

BILL'S CATERING
P.O. Box 45-1233
Miami, FL 33245
305.858.6660
Bill Hansen

Areas served: Dade, Broward, Palm Beach, Monroe and Collier Counties
Up-scale catering, event planning, site selection, decor and entertainment. They received five stars from the National Caterers Association and Bill is a professor of catering management at Florida International University.

BOBBY RODRIGUEZ PRODUCTIONS, INC.
6191 N.W. 32nd Terrace
Fort Lauderdale, FL 33309-2213
305.978.8610
Emil Gunther

Special event coordination and entertainment for social and corporate affairs as full event production for festivals.

DECO PRODUCTIONS, INC.
7711 W. 22nd Avenue
Hialiah, FL 33016
305.558.0800
Sharon Siegel

Areas served: National and Caribbean
Destination management services, entertainment, meet and greet, tours, flowers, props, stage sets, decor, linens.

FAMOUS FACES ENTERTAINMENT AND SPECIAL EVENTS COMPANY
2013 Harding Street
Hollywood, FL 33020
305.922.0700
800.635.6492 (Outside FL)
Paul Levine, President

Areas served: National
Theme parties, convention planning, celebrity look-alikes, music and entertainment, novelty acts, speakers, murder mystery productions, casino night, horse and dog racing on film, theme decor, models, actors, actresses, etc.

LA MYSTIQUE
10285 N.W. 46th Street
Sunrise, FL 33351
305.748.1603
Rita Hymowitz

Areas served: Nationwide
Dazzling dance productions include dancing with the guests, lavish costumes, music and DJs. One of the leading entertainment troupes in the country.

LAWRENCE OF FLORIDA
10107 W. Sample Road
Coral Springs, FL 33065
305.755.0500
Larry Rodkin

Areas served: Florida, Texas, California, Illinois
Music, entertainment, disc jockeys, costumed dancers, specialty lighting effects and specialty acts for all events.

LE MASQUERADE
305.936.2446
800.666.7260
Dennis Schussel

Interactive, high energy, costumed theatrical entertainment that incorporates music and special effects. Awards and distinctions include performance at the White House, national TV and newspaper coverage. Award for entertaining all Northeast caterers.

MANHATTAN MUSIC
204 Lake Point Drive
Suite 203
Fort Lauderdale, FL 33309
305.486.7664
Howard Stewart

Areas served: Miami to Palm Beach
Full service entertainment agency, music, DJs, bands orchestras, staging and lighting. Original music created for corporate and social functions.

PARTIES BY NEIL *
ENTERTAINMENT ETC.
2329 S.W. 31st Avenue
Hallandale, FL 33009
305.987.7991
Shirley Crane

MIAMI

Areas served: Miami, Ft. Lauderdale, Boca Raton, Palm Beach, Orlando, Naples, Marco Island, Florida Keys
Party decor, themed events, destination management, entertainment, Zanadu, business theater. *Special Events Magazine* 1990 Best Event Design, *Special Events Magazine* 1991 Best Tabletop Design.

PARTY SITES

BAJA BEACH CLUB
3015 Grana Avenue
Suite 320
Coconut Grove, FL 33133
305.445.0278
Cara Smolen
Multi-entertainment center in the Cocowalk Mall. A high energy dance club available for private parties.

BILL'S CATERING
P.O. Box 45-1233
Miami, FL 33245
305.858.6660
Bill Hansen
Areas served: Dade, Broward, Palm Beach, Monroe and Collier Counties
Up-scale catering, event planning, site selection, decor and entertainment. They received five stars from the National Caterers Association and Bill is a professor of catering management at Florida International University.

DORAL HOTEL & COUNTRY CLUB
4400 N.W. 87th Avenue
Miami, FL 33178
305.592.2000
Greg Dueltzow
Golf resort offering full event, meeting and convention facilities. Receptions: 800 people. Sit down: 800 people.

MAYFAIR HOUSE HOTEL
3000 Florida Avenue
Coconut Grove, FL 33133
305.441.0000
Debra Lundy
All suite hotel. Main ballroom, meeting facilities and rooftop pool. Receptions: 400 people. Sit down: 320 people.

VILLA WOODBINE
2167 S. Bayshore Drive
Coconut Grove, FL 33133
305.858.6660
Bill's Catering
Mediterranean style mansion in Coconut Grove known for its ambiance and unique pictorial setting. The property encompasses over three acres and the house is nearly 10,000 square feet. Villa Woodbine can accommodate up to 200 guests.

WILLIAMS ISLAND COUNTRY CLUB
750 N.E. 195th Street
N. Miami Beach, FL 33179
305.651.5100
Jean Marc Maltrait
Part of the luxury residential resort community of Williams Island, an elegant facility which can accommodate private special occasions of almost any size. In addition to member events, the Country Club hosts a variety of functions, from intimate dinners to larger banquets and parties for numerous outside organizations. Overlooking the Williams Island championship golf course, the Club offers gracious function rooms for indoor events and an outdoor patio, barbecue facilities by the pool and an outdoor covered bar with grill.

PLANT RENTALS

ACTION PLANT RENTAL
1736 S.W. Fourth Court
Fort Lauderdale, FL 33312
305.524.1724
Philip and Wendy Hancock
Areas served: South Florida
Decorate special events with tropical plants, water features and lighting. They specialize in the creative use of natural foilage to create compositions of palms and trees.

PROPS & DECOR

ACTION PLANT RENTAL
1736 S.W. Fourth Court
Fort Lauderdale, FL 33312
305.524.1724

MIAMI

Areas served: South Florida
Decorate special events with tropical plants, water features and lighting. They specialize in the creative use of natural foilage to create compositions of palms and trees.

BILL'S CATERING
> P.O. Box 45-1233
> Miami, FL 33245
> **305.858.6660**
> Bill Hansen

Areas served: Dade, Broward, Palm Beach, Monroe and Collier Counties
Up-scale catering, event planning, site selection, decor and entertainment. They received five stars from the National Caterers Association and Bill is a professor of catering management at Florida International University.

DECO PRODUCTIONS, INC.
> 7711 W. 22nd Avenue
> Hialiah, FL 33016
> **305.558.0800**
> Sharon Siegel

Areas served: National and Caribbean
Destination management services, entertainment, meet and greet, tours, flowers, props, stage sets, decor, linens.

DONALD MOORE PARTY DESIGNS/DMCC DESIGN GROUP INTERNATIONAL
> 20855 N.E. Sixteenth Avenue
> Suite 24
> N. Miami Beach, FL 33179
> **305.652.6053**
> Cindy Christman
> Donald Moore

Areas served: Miami, Fort Lauderdale, Palm Beach, Orlando and Carribean
Decorating, lighting, staging and flowers. Specializing in themed events.

PARTIES BY NEIL *
ENTERTAINMENT ETC.
> 2329 S.W. 31st Avenue
> Hallandale, FL 33009
> **305.987.7991**
> Shirley Crane

Areas served: Miami, Ft. Lauderdale, Boca Raton, Palm Beach, Orlando, Naples, Marco Island, Florida Keys
Party decor, themed events, destination

management, entertainment, Zanadu, business theater. *Special Events Magazine* 1990 Best Event Design, *Special Events Magazine 1991* Best Tabletop Design.

SPEAKERS
FAMOUS FACES ENTERTAINMENT AND SPECIAL EVENTS COMPANY
> 2013 Harding Street
> Hollywood, FL 33020
> **305.922.0700**
> **800.635.6492 (Outside FL)**
> Paul Levine, President

Areas served: National
Theme parties, convention planning, celebrity look-alikes, music and entertainment, novelty acts, speakers, murder mystery productions, casino night, horse and dog racing on film, theme decor, models, actors, actresses, etc.

TABLETOP ACCESSORIES & KITCHENWARE
CRATE & BARREL
> Boca Town Center
> Boca Raton, FL 33431
> **407.305.1060**

Full line of unique contemporary home furnishings and accessories featuring tabletop accessories and gourmet kitchenware.

WILLIAMS-SONOMA
> 2392-A E. Sunrise Blvd.
> Fort Lauderdale, FL 33304
> **305.568.0915**

An authoritative selection of the best for the kitchen. Complete line of cookware, bakeware, electrics, glassware, tabletop, kitchen furniture, cookbooks, packaged foods. Knowledgeable staff will help choose equipment, plan parties. Most merchandise is exclusive to Williams-Sonoma.

MIAMI

YACHT & BOAT CHARTERS

WINDRIDGE YACHT CHARTERS, INC.
Isis II & Kathleen W
303 S.E. 17th Street
Suite 607
Fort Lauderdale, FL 33316
305.525.7724
Areas served: Palm Beach to Miami
Three yachts from 130' to 170' available for
special events. Holds up to 500 people.
Full service catering and event planners to
help coordinate.

NEW ORLEANS

NEW ORLEANS

BALLOONS

BETTY HUNLEY DESIGNS
6057 Magazine Street
New Orleans, LA 70118
504.895.2870
Betty Hunley
Areas served: New Orleans
Retail store providing custom-designed and catalogue invitations, seating charts, place cards, accessories. Huge supply of ready-made place cards, sign-in boards, balloons, tabletop accessories. Full calligraphy services, event planning and decor services. Balloon services include unique balloon decor, balloon bouquets, balloon arches.

CALLIGRAPHY

BETTY HUNLEY DESIGNS
6057 Magazine Street
New Orleans, LA 70118
504.895.2870
Betty Hunley
Areas served: New Orleans
Retail store providing custom-designed and catalogue invitations, seating charts, place cards, accessories. Huge supply of ready-made place cards, sign-in boards, balloons, tabletop accessories. Full calligraphy services, event planning and decor services. Balloon services include unique balloon decor, balloon bouquets, balloon arches.

CATERING

LONDON LADY
3037 Royal Street
New Orleans, LA 70117
504.944.1984
Alan Fisher
Yacht and boat charters. Yachts up to 100 feet, holding up to 149 people. Complete catering and event planning services on and off premises.

SOUTHERN HOSPITALITY SYSTEMS
P.O. Box 15616
New Orleans, LA 70175
504.897.1402
John Rowland

Areas served: National
Complete catering, staffing and rentals. Major caterer for Tulane University. Corporate events, weddings, cocktail receptions, political events. Full staffing services include meet and greet, waiters, bartenders, etc. Rentals include linens, tables, chairs and other party needs.

ST. CHARLES RESTAURANT AND CATERING
333 St. Charles Avenue
New Orleans, LA 70130
504.522.6600
Hank Vosbein
Areas served: New Orleans and surrounding areas
On and off site catered events. Cajun and Creole dishes with emphasis on fresh Louisiana seafood and ingredients. Banquet facilities: 5 private dining rooms, main dining room, bar area. Receptions: 400 people. Sit down: 200 people.

CHOCOLATES & CONFECTIONS

GODIVA CHOCOLATIER
Lakeside Mall
504.834.3278
World renowned chocolatier. Belgium-style chocolates, gift baskets and party favors.

MARTINS WINE CELLAR FOOD EMPORIUM AND DELI
3827 Baronne Street
New Orleans, LA 70115
504.899.7411
Marc Pelletier
Areas served: National
Fine wines, champagnes, liqueurs, cordials, custom gift baskets, wine seminars and tastings, delicacies, cheeses, patés, chocolates, confections, salmons, caviar, foie gras, coffee, teas, speakers on all areas of viticulture, holiday catalogue.

NEW ORLEANS

CLASSES & SEMINARS

MARTIN'S WINE CELLAR FOOD EMPORIUM AND DELI
3827 Baronne Street
New Orleans, LA 70115
504.899.7411
Marc Pelletier
Areas served: National
Fine wines, champagnes, liqueurs, cordials, custom gift baskets, wine seminars and tastings, delicacies, cheeses, pate´s, chocolates, confections, salmons, caviar, foie gras, coffee, teas, speakers on all areas of viticulture, holiday catalogue.

THE NEW ORLEANS SCHOOL OF COOKING AND THE LOUISIANA GENERAL STORE
620 Decautur Street
New Orleans, LA 70130
504.525.2665
800.237.4841
Joe and Karen Cahn
Three hour class for visitors to New Orleans teaching the basics of Creole cooking. Other topics offered as well. Call for information. The General Store carries all Louisiana products - food mixes, cookbooks, arts and crafts. National mail order catalogue.

PAT BERNARD
1328 Harmony Street
New Orleans, LA 70115
504.879.1862
Seminars on table design for entertaining. All seminars are custom created for any size group. "Design the Elegance of the Ages" is one of her most popular seminars. New Orleans Tour Guide. Antique shopping trips for all size groups.

COSTUMES

THE COSTUME HEADQUARTERS
3635 Banks Street
New Orleans, LA 70119
504.488.9523
Louise Genozler
Areas served: National
Costume sales and rentals. Wigs, make-up, masks, fishnet stockings, etc. Shipping available C.O.D.

DELICACIES

MARTIN'S WINE CELLAR FOOD EMPORIUM AND DELI
3827 Baronne Street
New Orleans, LA 70115
504.899.7411
Marc Pelletier
Areas served: National
Fine wines, champagnes, liqueurs, cordials, custom gift baskets, wine seminars and tastings, delicacies, cheeses, pate´s, chocolates, confections, salmons, caviar, foie gras, coffee, teas, speakers on all areas of viticulture, holiday catalogue.

EQUIPMENT RENTALS & TENTING

AMERICAN RENTAL
101 Airline Hwy.
Metairie, LA 70001
504.837.9500
Cookie Williams
Areas served: New Orleans and surrounding areas
Full service equipment rentals and tents: linens, tablecloths, napkins, tables, chairs, flatware, tents, china, chaffing dishes, arches, columns, urns, etc.

BERNARD PRODUCTIONS
2125 Highway 90
Avondale, LA 70094
504.436.8434
Jay Gernsbacher
Sound, lighting, staging, equipment, talent, MC's, artists, bands.

PERRIER PARTY RENTALS
5 Knox Road
Jefferson, LA 70121
504.834.8570
Jim Perrier
Shawn Cahill
Areas served: New Orleans
Full service equipment and tenting rentals - tents, tables, chairs, linens, silver, china, glassware, etc.

[Continued on next page]

SOUTHERN HOSPITALITY SYSTEMS
P.O. Box 15616
New Orleans, LA 70175
504.897.1402
John Rowland
Areas served: National
Complete catering, staffing and rentals.
Major caterer for Tulane University.
Corporate events, weddings, cocktail
receptions, political events. Full staffing
services include meet and greet, waiters,
bartenders, etc. Rentals include linens,
tables, chairs and other party needs.

EVENT PLANNING

BETTY HUNLEY DESIGNS
6057 Magazine Street
New Orleans, LA 70118
504.895.2870
Betty Hunley
Areas served: New Orleans
Retail store providing custom-designed and
catalogue invitations, seating charts, place
cards, accessories. Huge supply of ready-
made place cards, sign-in boards, balloons,
tabletop accessories. Full calligraphy
services, event planning and decor services.
Balloon services include unique balloon
decor, balloon bouquets, balloon arches.

LONDON LADY
3037 Royal Street
New Orleans, LA 70117
504.944.1984
Alan Fisher
Yacht and boat charters. Yachts up to 100
feet. Holds up to 149 people. Complete
catering and event planning services on and
off premises.

LONDON LIVERY
3037 Royal Street
New Orleans, LA 70117
504.944.1984
Alan Fisher
Areas served: National
Luxury sedans, limousines, mini-buses,
buses, and vans. Full event planning
services.

PERFECT PRESENTATIONS
1301 Royal Street
New Orleans, LA 70116
504.522.7442
Glenn Vesh
Areas served: New Orleans
Full service florist specializing in corporate
and convention clients. All phases of floral
design, plant rentals and decor. Full party
and event planning services. The exclusive
florist to most of New Orleans' finest hotels.

FLORISTS & FLORAL DESIGNS

MITCHE'S FLORIST
4843 Magazine
New Orleans, LA 70115
504.899.4843
Mitche Hebert
Areas served: New Orleans
Full service florist, floral decor and
centerpieces for parties and weddings.
Specializes in European and exotic flowers.

PERFECT PRESENTATIONS
1301 Royal Street
New Orleans, LA 70116
504.522.7442
Glenn Vesh
Areas served: New Orleans
Full service florist specializing in corporate
and convention clients. All phases of floral
design, plant rentals and decor. Full party
and event planning services. The exclusive
florist to most of New Orleans' finest hotels.

FORMAL WEAR

AL'S FORMALWEAR
1512 St. Charles Avenue
New Orleans, LA 70130
504.525.0239
Hiram Graza
Areas served: New Orleans and
surrounding areas
Men's formal wear rentals and sales. Two
other locations in surrounding areas.

NEW ORLEANS

GIFTS & GIFT BASKETS

MARTIN'S WINE CELLAR FOOD EMPORIUM AND DELI
3827 Baronne Street
New Orleans, LA 70115
504.899.7411
Marc Pelletier
Areas served: National
Fine wines, champagnes, liqueurs, cordials, custom gift baskets, wine seminars and tastings, delicacies, cheeses, pate´s, chocolates, confections, salmons, caviar, foie gras, coffee, teas, speakers on all areas of viticulture, holiday catalogue.

INVITATIONS & ACCESSORIES

BETTY HUNLEY DESIGNS
6057 Magazine Street
New Orleans, LA 70118
504.895.2870
Betty Hunley
Areas served: New Orleans
Retail store providing custom-designed and catalogue invitations, seating charts, place cards, accessories. Huge supply of ready-made place cards, sign-in boards, balloons, tabletop accessories. Full calligraphy services, event planning and decor services. Balloon services include unique balloon decor, balloon bouquets, balloon arches.

LIGHTING, STAGING & SOUND

BERNARD PRODUCTIONS
2125 Highway 90
Avondale, LA 70094
504.436.8434
Jay Gernsbacher
Sound, lighting, staging, equipment, talent, MC's, artists, bands.

SPANGENBURG STUDIOS
1010 Central Avenue
Matairie, LA 70001
504.834.6994
Eric Spangenburg

Areas served: Southern U.S.
Prop rentals, scenery, lighting and staging.

LIMOUSINE & TRANSPORTATION

CAREY LIMOUSINE
504.523.5466
800.336.4646
Areas served: International
Privately chauffeured sedans, limousines, vans and mini buses in 372 cities.

DAV EL CHAUFFEURED TRANSPORTATION NETWORK
800.328.3526 (outside CA)
800.826.5779 (inside CA)
Areas Served: International
Luxury chauffeured services in over 350 cities worldwide. Centralized reservations and billing. Airport concierge services.

LONDON LIVERY
3037 Royal Street
New Orleans, LA 70117
504.944.1984
Alan Fisher
Areas served: National
Luxury sedans, limousines, mini buses, buses, and vans. Full event planning services.

LINENS

AMERICAN RENTAL
101 Airline Hwy.
Metairie, LA 70001
504.837.9500
Cookie Williams
Areas served: New Orleans and surrounding areas
Full service equipment rentals and tents: linens, tablecloths, napkins, tables, chairs, flatware, tents, china, chaffing dishes, arches, columns, urns, etc.

[Continued on next page]

GOTCHA COVERED
3815 Hessmer Avenue
Metairie, LA 70002
504.522.1829
800.426.1380
Locky Pool
Angela Jones
Areas served: National
Linen rentals to special event professionals
only.

PERRIER PARTY RENTALS
5 Knox Road
Jefferson, LA 70121
504.834.8570
Jim Perrier
Shawn Cahill
Areas served: New Orleans
Full service equipment and tenting rentals -
tents, tables, chairs, linens, silver, china,
glassware, etc.

MUSIC & ENTERTAINMENT

BERNARD PRODUCTIONS
2125 Highway 90
Avondale, LA 70094
504.436.8434
Jay Gernsbacher
Sound, lighting, staging, equipment, talent,
MC's, artists, bands.

DENNY LEROUX
308 Lilac Street
Metairie, LA 70005
504.482.1502
Jimmy Maxwell
Areas served: National
Singer - Songwriter - Guitarist. Denny has
performed by request for the Bee Gees,
Frank Sinatra, Ronald Reagan, Jimi
Hendrix and Bruce Springsteen.

FAME MODEL AND TALENT AGENCY, INC.
1725 Carondolet Street
New Orleans, LA 70130
504.522.2001
Chris Calloway
Areas served: National
Exhibit hostesses and models for
tradeshows, celebrity look-a-likes, mimes,
magicians, clowns, dancers. Meet and greet

hostesses. Bartenders, product
demonstrators, MC's, interpreters.

JIMMY MAXWELL AND HIS ORCHESTRA
3530 Rue Delphine
New Orleans, LA 70131
504.391.9810
Peggy Abbas
Areas served: National
"Jimmy Maxwell plays the best music…"
says Peter Duchin. Known as heir apparent
to the Lester Lanin Dance Dynasty, Jimmy
has performed for Presidents and Royalty
across the country.

NEW ORLEANS ENTERTAINMENT AGENCY
3530 Rue Delphine
New Orleans, LA 70131
504.391.9866
Robert Hemsch
Areas served: National
Direct from the birthplace of jazz, the
N.O.E.A. knows the music and musicians
that call New Orleans home. Artists include
Al Hirt, Pete Fountain, the Neville
Brothers, Harry Connick Jr., Wynton
Marsalis and Dr. John to name a few.
Personal and professional service.

PARTY SITES

AQUARIUM OF THE AMERICAS AND WOLDERBERG PARK
P.O. Box 4327
New Orleans, LA 70178
504.861.5101
Sales Department
On Mississippi River. Connected to
Wolderberg Park. Built in 1990. Adjacent
to French Quarter. Holds up to 2000
people for events inside and up to 23,000
people outside using the park. Public
parking.

AUDUBON INSTITUTE AND ZOOLOGICAL GARDEN
6500 Magazine Street
New Orleans, LA 70118
504.861.2537
Sales Department
Located on Mississippi River. Zoo and
garden settings. Several different exhibit

areas for events. Once was the sight of a sugar plantation and the 1884 cotton centennial. Groups up to 20,000. Rare animals - only white alligators in the world. Louisiana Swamp Exhibit - man-made, complete with animals, one of the most popular exhibits for small parties (300 people).

GALLIER HALL

545 St. Charles Avenue
New Orleans, LA 70130
504.565.7457
Mr. Johnson

Built in 1845. Former City Hall. Ballroom, mayor's parlor, dining room, council chamber. Receptions: 700 people. Sit down: 285 people.

HARMONY HOUSE

1328 Harmony Street
New Orleans, LA 70115
504.899.1862
Pat Bernard

Anti-Bellum House in Garden District. Built in early 1930's. High- raised cottage, marble ballroom at ground level. Surrounded by gardens, patio and pool. Stunning roses in garden. Antiques and paintings. Both inside and outside available for events. Receptions: 200 people. Sit down: 250 people.

L'APARTEMENT DE L'EMPEREUR

500 Chartres
New Orleans, LA 70130
504.524.9752
Sal Impastato

Located in middle of French Quarter. Built by Nicholas Girod who became Mayor of New Orleans, offered home to Napoleon, who died in exile and never was able to live there. The second floor has since been renovated into a banquet and event facility. Decor is understated elegance, empire period, true old French New Orleans. 2300 square feet. Receptions: 175 people. Sit down: 60 people.

LONGVIEW HOUSE AND GARDENS

7 Bamboo Road
New Orleans, LA 70124
504.488.5488
Faye Riddick

Museum house and gardens. Listed in the National Register of Historic Places. Accredited by American Museum Association. Home of one of the Sears Heiresses - Edith Rosenwald. Eight acres of gardens and fountains. Museum for tour only. Tennis club on premises. Receptions: 150 people. Sit down: 65 people. Adjacent tennis court pavilion permanently tented. Receptions: 500 people. Sit down: 250 people. Gardens hold up to 2000, can expand with additional tents.

NEW ORLEANS MUSEUM OF ART

P.O. Box 19123
New Orleans, LA 70179-0123
504.488.2631
Kelly Harper

Fine arts museum facility. Holds up to 1500 people.

ST. CHARLES RESTAURANT AND CATERING

333 St. Charles Avenue
New Orleans, LA 70130
504.522.6600
Hank Vosbein

Areas served: New Orleans and surrounding areas
On and off site catered events. Cajun and Creole dishes with emphasis on fresh Louisiana seafood and ingredients. Banquet facilities: 5 private dining rooms, main dining room, bar area. Receptions: 400 people. Sit down: 200 people.

THE TOP OF THE MART

2925 World Trade Center
Suite 2
New Orleans, LA 70130
504.522.9795
Jed Stedman

Cocktail lounge with largest revolving top in the world. Takes one and a half hours to rotate. Receptions: 500 people. Sit down: 450 people. Overlooking French Quarter and Mississippi River.

[Continued on next page.]

PARTY SUPPLIES

ACCENT ANNEX/ MARDI GRAS HEADQUARTERS
1120 S. Jeff Davis Pkwy. New Orleans, LA 70125-9901
504.821.8885
800.322.2368
Areas served: National
Mardi Gras headquarters. Six locations in US, Mardi Gras, carnival, fair and party supplies. National mail order catalogue.

BETTY HUNLEY DESIGNS
6057 Magazine Street
New Orleans, LA 70118
504.895.2870
Betty Hunley
Areas served: New Orleans
Retail store providing custom-designed and catalogue invitations, seating charts, place cards, accessories. Huge supply of ready-made place cards, sign-in boards, balloons, tabletop accessories. Full calligraphy services, event planning and decor services. Balloon services include unique balloon decor, balloon bouquets, balloon arches.

PERSONNEL & STAFFING

FAME MODEL AND TALENT AGENCY, INC.
1725 Carondolet Street
New Orleans, LA 70130
504.522.2001
Chris Calloway
Areas served: National
Exhibit hostesses and models for trade shows, celebrity look-alikes, mimes, magicians, clowns, dancers. Meet and greet hostesses. Bartenders, product demonstrators, MC's, interpreters.

SOUTHERN HOSPITALITY SYSTEMS
P.O. Box 15616
New Orleans, LA 70175
504.897.1402
John Rowland
Areas served: National
Complete catering, staffing and rentals. Major caterer for Tulane University. Corporate events, weddings, cocktail receptions, political events. Full staffing

services include meet and greet, waiters, bartenders, etc. Rentals include linens, tables, chairs and other party needs.

PHOTOGRAPHY & VIDEO

GREVY PHOTOGRAPHY
7433 Maple Street
New Orleans, LA 70118
504.866.5093
Carroll Grevemberg
Areas served: International
Still photography for all private events. Clients include major celebrities.

PHOTOGRAPHY USA
1725 Carondelet Street
New Orleans, LA 70130
504.525.8811
Chris Calloway
Areas served: National
Photography and video for all special events. Clients include major national tradeshows.

PROPS AND DECOR

BETTY HUNLEY DESIGNS
6057 Magazine Street
New Orleans, LA 70118
504.895.2870
Betty Hunley
Areas served: New Orleans
Retail store providing custom-designed and catalogue invitations, seating charts, place cards, accessories. Huge supply of ready-made place cards, sign-in boards, balloons, tabletop accessories. Full calligraphy services, event planning and decor services. Balloon services include unique balloon decor, balloon bouquets, balloon arches.

PERFECT PRESENTATIONS
1301 Royal Street
New Orleans, LA 70116
504.522.7442
Glenn Vesh
Areas served: New Orleans
Full service florist specializing in corporate

and convention clients. All phases of floral design, plant rentals and decor. Full party and event planning services. The exclusive florist to most of New Orleans' finest hotels.

SPANGENBURG STUDIOS
1010 Central Avenue
Matairie, LA 70001
504.834.6994
Eric Spangenburg
Areas served: Southern U.S.
Prop rentals, scenery, lighting and staging.

SECURITY

ADF SECURITY
150 Baronne Street
New Orleans, LA 70112
504.522.0280
John Boyd
Areas served: New Orleans
Security guards for convention centers, department stores and private parties.

SPEAKERS

MARTIN'S WINE CELLAR FOOD EMPORIUM AND DELI
3827 Baronne Street
New Orleans, LA 70115
504.899.7411
Marc Pelletier
Areas served: National
Fine wines, champagnes, liqueurs, cordials, custom gift baskets, wine seminars and tastings, delicacies, cheeses, pate's, chocolates, confections, salmons, caviar, foie gras, coffee, teas, speakers on all areas of viticulture, holiday catalogue.

VALET PARKING

DOWNTOWN PARKING SERVICE, INC.
100 Poydras Street
New Orleans, LA 70130
504.529.5708
Kenneth Cole
Areas served: New Orleans
Valet parking for all events. Formal and informal attire. Insured.

WINE & SPIRITS

MARTIN'S WINE CELLAR FOOD EMPORIUM AND DELI
3827 Baronne Street
New Orleans, LA 70115
504.899.7411
Marc Pelletier
Areas served: National
Fine wines, champagnes, liqueurs, cordials, custom gift baskets, wine seminars and tastings, delicacies, cheeses, pate's, chocolates, confections, salmons, caviar, foie gras, coffee, teas, speakers on all areas of viticulture, holiday catalogue.

YACHT & BOAT CHARTERS

LONDON LADY
3037 Royal Street
New Orleans, LA 70117
504.944.1984
Alan Fisher
Yacht and boat charters. Yachts up to 100 feet, holding up to 149 people. Complete catering and event planning services on and off premises.

❧ ❧ ❧

NEW YORK

NEW YORK

AUDIOVISUAL & TECHNICAL SERVICES

FROST LIGHTING, INC.
P.O. Box 489
FDR Station
New York, NY 10150
212.751.0223
Peter Markowitz
Areas served: New York, New Jersey
and Connecticut
Decorative lighting and temporary electrical
needs for special events.

BALLOONS

PARTY BAZAAR
390 Fifth Avenue
New York, NY 10001
212.695.6820
Mark Fleischer
Retail store offering full range of party
supplies and services. Balloons, invitations,
calligraphy, seating charts, place cards,
napkins, pinatas, centerpieces, full event
decor, in-house designers, candlesticks, and
accessories.

BOOKS

DEAN & DELUCA
560 Broadway
New York, NY 10012
212.431.1691
James Mellgren
Areas served: International
Tabletop accessories, kitchenware,
cookbooks, gift baskets. Full service
specialty foods and catering. Cheese,
pastries, produce, caviar, smoked fish,
custom-designed chocolates, Dean & Deluca
herbs and spices, dried beans and grains,
mail order department. Deliver anywhere.

FRIENDS FOR LONG ISLAND'S HERITAGE
Old Bethpage Village Restoration
Round Swamp Road
Old Bethpage, NY 11804
516.572.8413

St. James General Store
516 Moriches Road
St. James, NY 11780
516.572.8415
Jean O'Leary, Vice President
Areas served: Long Island, New York
Book selection emphasis on Early American
and Victorian recipes.

KITCHEN ARTS & LETTERS
1435 Lexington Avenue
New York, NY 10128
212.876.5550
Nach Waxman
Bookstore specializing in food and wine.
More than 7000 titles to serve the food
professional community and advanced non-
professionals. Wide ranging stock, from
cookbooks to scholarly literature,
professional and technical works, kitchen
decorating guides, fiction with food themes.
Special features: out of print books found
without charge; imported books.

WILLIAMS-SONOMA
Stamford Town Center
100 Grayrock Place
Stamford, CT 06901
203.327.3652

Danbury Fair Mall
7 Backus Avenue
Danbury, CT 06810
203.790.9996

1175 Madison Avenue
New York, NY 10028
212.289.6832

2110-B Northern Boulevard
Manhasset, NY 11030
516.365.1650

20 E. 60th Street
New York, NY 10022
212.980.5155

110 Seventh Avenue
New York, NY 10011
212.633.2203

1309 Second Avenue
New York, NY 10021
212.288.8408
An authoritative selection of the best for the
kitchen. Complete line of cookware,

bakeware, electrics, glassware, tabletop, kitchen furniture, cookbooks, packaged foods. Knowledgeable staff will help choose equipment, plan parties. Most merchandise is exclusive to Williams-Sonoma.

CAKES & BAKED GOODS

BALDUCCI'S

424 Avenue of the Americas
New York, NY 10011
212.673.2600
Areas served: National
International delicacies, catering, gift baskets and mail order. International cheese and deli, regional Italian foods, smoked fish, fresh baked ethnic breads, homemade pastries, gourmet coffee, exotic and local produce, specialty groceries, prime meats, fresh fish.

CAKES BY DESIGN

171 W. 73rd Street
Suite 9
New York, NY 10023
212.362.5374
Michael Farace
Areas served: New York, New Jersey and Connecticut
One of a kind custom-designed cakes, specializing in sculptures and hand painted sugar decorations. Bees, dragon flies, butterflies. Over seventy-five types of lifelike flowers and animals. Nineteen years experience with hand painted and hand sculptured lifelike cake decor. Scott Clark Woodley teaches seminars on "The Art of Gum Paste Flower Making." Call for details.

E.A.T.

1064 Madison Avenue
New York, NY 10028
212.772.0022
Areas served: National
Restaurant, gourmet shop, gift shop, wholesale bread, and catering. Tabletop accessories, cheese, caviar, fresh baked pastry, custom-designed cakes. Smoked Norwegian salmon, fresh produce, gourmet salads, gift baskets. Known for their breads.

CALLIGRAPHY

ANDREA LEIGH CLASTER

212.633.0970
Areas served: National
Full event planning and design. Custom-designed and catalogue invitations, seating, charts, place cards. Full in-house calligraphy services. RSVP management. Custom-designed chocolates. Hospitality gift baskets. Gift consultation. Private seminars in etiquette and gift giving. For private and corporate groups. Author of *Modern Living and Modern Giving*.

JEN'S PEN

101 W. 55th Street
Suite 4L
New York, NY 10019
212.247.6725
Jennifer Stewart
Areas served: New York, New Jersey and Connecticut
Calligraphy for wedding invitations, announcements, certificates. Handwritten invitations at very reasonable price. Worked in New York and Paris for top couture houses, publications and companies.

PARTY BAZAAR

390 Fifth Avenue
New York, NY 10001
212.695.6820
Mark Fleischer
Retail store offering full range of party supplies and services. Balloons, invitations, calligraphy, seating charts, place cards, napkins, pinatas, centerpieces, full event decor, in-house designers, candlesticks, and accessories.

[Continued on next page.]

NEW YORK

CATERING

BALDUCCI'S
424 Avenue of the Americas
New York, NY 10011
212.673.2600
Areas served: National
International delicacies, catering, gift
baskets and mail order. International
cheese and deli, regional Italian foods,
smoked fish, fresh baked ethnic breads,
homemade pastries, gourmet coffee, exotic
and local produce, specialty groceries,
prime meats, fresh fish.

CLAMBAKES BY JIM SANFORD
212.865.8976
Jim Sanford
Areas served: New York, New Jersey
and Connecticut
Catered New England clambakes for all
occasions. Service on rooftops, terraces,
backyards, patios, beaches, etc.

DEAN & DELUCA
560 Broadway
New York, NY 10012
212.431.1691
James Mellgren
Areas served: International
Tabletop accessories, kitchenware,
cookbooks, gift baskets. Full service
specialty foods and catering. Cheese,
pastries, produce, caviar, smoked fish,
custom-designed chocolates, Dean & Deluca
herbs and spices, dried beans and grains,
mail order department. Deliver anywhere.

DEE DEE DAILEY
2315 E. Fourteenth Street
Brooklyn, NY 11229
718.615.1654
Areas served: National
Full service catering. Specializing in
Caribbean, Continental and West African
cuisine. Dee Dee is available for small
dinners as a private chef.

E.A.T.
1064 Madison Avenue
New York, NY 10028
212.772.0022
Areas served: National
Restaurant, gourmet shop, gift shop,

wholesale bread, and catering. Tabletop
accessories, cheese, caviar, fresh baked
pastry, custom-designed cakes. Smoked
Norwegian salmon, fresh produce, gourmet
salads, gift baskets. Known for their
breads.

GLORIOUS FOOD, INC.
504 E. 74th Street
New York, NY 10021
212.628.2320
Berrina Felder
Areas served: National
Full service catering on and off premises.
"Best Caterer" *Zagat* 1991 Survey.

GREAT PERFORMANCES
125 Crosby Street
New York, NY 10012
212.219.2800
Liz Neumark
Areas served: New York, New Jersey,
and Connecticut's Tri-State area
Full service caterer and event planner for
corporate and private events of all sizes.
Providing exquisite food beautifully
presented, professional waitstaff, fine china
and linens, florists, decorators,
photographers, and entertainment.
Specialists in finding unique locations;
several on videotape. Excellence in catering
standards and party personnel. Food style
is rooted in classical European tradition,
mixed with American and Asian influences,
then tailored to the host's party theme and
requirements. A thorough staff training
program, specialty workshops, and a
scholarship for outstanding service.
Members of: The James Beard Foundation,
Society of Foodservice Management,
National Association of Off-Premises
Caterers, The NY Chamber of Commerce,
and NYC Convention & Visitors Bureau. In
business for over twelve years.

MANNA CATERING
24 Harrison Street
New York, NY 10013
212.966.3449
Don Lenchner
Areas served: New York, New Jersey,
Connecticut
Full service kosher catering and event
planning. Sit down dinners to 1000 people.

NEW YORK

Top social and corporate clientele. In business since 1982.

◢ PRIVATE CHEFS
DEE DEE DAILEY
2315 E. Fourteenth Street
Brooklyn, NY 11229
718.615.1654
Areas served: National
Full service catering. Specializing in Caribbean, Continental and West African cuisine. Dee Dee is available for small dinners as a private chef.

NEW YORK RESTAURANT SCHOOL
27 W. 34th Street
New York, NY 10001
212.947.7097
800.654.CHEF
Placement Department
Areas served: Five boroughs, New Jersey, Connecticut, and Westchester County
Freelance culinary help for private or catered events. Also can provide kitchen helpers, servers and bartenders.

CELEBRITY ACQUISITION
WASHINGTON SPEAKERS BUREAU
888 Seventh Avenue
New York, NY 10106
212.541.7980
Areas served: International
Speakers for all occasions - celebrities, sports, political, motivational, business, humorous.

CHOCOLATES & CONFECTIONS
ANDREA LEIGH CLASTER
212.633.0970
Areas served: National
Full event planning and design. Custom-designed and catalogue invitations, seating, charts, place cards. Full in-house calligraphy services. RSVP management.

Custom-designed chocolates. Hospitality gift baskets. Gift consultation. Private seminars in etiquette and gift giving. For private and corporate groups. Author of *Modern Living And Modern Giving*.

BALDUCCI'S
424 Avenue of the Americas
New York, NY 10011
212.673.2600
Areas served: National
International delicacies, catering, gift baskets and mail order. International cheese and deli, regional Italian foods, smoked fish, fresh baked ethnic breads, homemade pastries, gourmet coffee, exotic and local produce, specialty groceries, prime meats, fresh fish.

THE CHOCOLATE GALLERY
34 W. 22nd Street
New York, NY 10010
212.675.CAKE
Areas served: National
Carries over 10,000 items fully stocked: cake pans in all shapes and sizes from round, square, and rectangle to characters like Big Bird and Ninja Turtles. Full assortment of cookie cutters in different shapes. Supplies to make a wedding cake, from cake stands, fountains, bridges, ushers and bridesmaids in all color dresses, to the wedding ornament to dazzle the top of the cake. Tips, pastry bags, icing colors, spatulas, and much more. A wide selection of books and videos on the latest ideas in cake decorating. Offers Wilton Cake Decorating classes in Spanish: learn how to decorate cakes for the family or to start a business selling beautifully decorated cakes.

DEAN & DELUCA
560 Broadway
New York, NY 10012
212.431.1691
James Mellgren
Areas served: International
Tabletop accessories, kitchenware, cookbooks, gift baskets. Full service specialty foods and catering. Cheese, pastries, produce, caviar, smoked fish, custom-designed chocolates, Dean & Deluca herbs and spices, dried beans and grains, mail order department. Deliver anywhere.

GODIVA CHOCOLATIER

Upstate
Albany
Crossgates Mall
518.869.7143

Buffalo
Walden Galleria
716.684.3401

New York City
Downtown
85 Broad Street
212.514.6240

33 Maiden Lane
212.809.8990

World Financial Center
212.945.2174

Midtown
560 Lexington Avenue
212.980.9810

701 Fifth Avenue
212.593.2845

Pan Am Building
212.697.9128

Uptown
245 Columbus Avenue
212.787.5804

793 Madison Avenue
212.249.9444

Long Island
Stony Brook
Stony Brook Village
516.751.2012
World renowned chocolatier. Belgium-style
chocolates, gift baskets and party favors.

CLASSES & SEMINARS

ANDREA LEIGH CLASTER
212.633.0970
Areas served: National
Full event planning and design. Custom-
designed and catalogue invitations, seating,
charts, place cards. Full in-house
calligraphy services. RSVP management.

Custom-designed chocolates. Hospitality
gift baskets. Gift consultation. Private
seminars in etiquette and gift giving. For
private and corporate groups. Author of
"Modern Living and Modern Giving."

CAKES BY DESIGN
171 W. 73rd Street
Suite 9
New York, NY 10023
212.362.5374
Michael Farace
Areas served: New York, New Jersey,
Connecticut
One of a kind custom-designed cakes,
specializing in sculptures, hand painted
sugar decorations. Bees, dragon flies,
butterflies. Over seventy-five types of
lifelike flowers and animals. Nineteen years
experience with hand painted and hand
sculptured lifelike cake decor. Scott Clark
Woodley teaches seminars on "The Art of
Gum Paste Flower Making." Call for
details.

THE CHOCOLATE GALLERY
34 W. 22nd Street
New York, NY 10010
212.675.CAKE
Areas served: National
Carries over 10,000 items fully stocked:
cake pans in all shapes and sizes from
round, square, and rectangle to characters
like Big Bird and Ninja Turtles. Full
assortment of cookie cutters in different
shapes. Supplies to make a wedding cake,
from cake stands, fountains, bridges, ushers
and bridesmaids in all color dresses, to the
wedding ornament to dazzle the top of the
cake. Tips, pastry bags, icing colors,
spatulas, and much more. A wide selection
of books and videos on the latest ideas in
cake decorating. Offers Wilton Cake
Decorating classes in Spanish: learn how to
decorate cakes for the family or to start a
business selling beautifully decorated cakes.

DEGUSTIBUS AT MACY'S
343 E. 74th Street
Suite 9G
New York, NY 10021
212.439.1714
Arlene Feltman Sailhac

Cooking classes for all levels. All classes held in the fully equipped professional kitchen on the eighth floor at Macy's Herald Square. Classes offered include: Great Cosmopolitan Chefs, Great New York Chefs, Great Cuisines with a Little Fire, Great Ideas for Eating Light, Great Home Cooking from The Mediterranean, Great Asian Fare, Great Regional Italian Cooking, Great Entertaining Weeknights or Weekends, An Elegant Dinner Party - Light & Kosher, Great Pastry Chefs, Fresh From the Herb Garden, Great Sauce is the Subject, Great Bread Baking Workshop, Mastering Wine in an Afternoon, Mastering The Legendary Bordeaux Wines.

JANE BUTEL'S NEW MEXICAN AND SOUTHWESTERN COOKING SCHOOL
P.O. Box 46
Mt. Tremper, NY 12457
914.675.2312
Jane Butel Associates
Areas served: National
Southwestern cooking classes and mail order source for Southwestern chiles, spices, and other ingredients for Southwestern cooking. All seminars are hands-on. In business since 1959.

NEW YORK RESTAURANT SCHOOL
27 W. 34th Street
New York, NY 10001
212.947.7097
800.654.CHEF
Placement Department
Areas served: Five boroughs, New Jersey, Connecticut, and Westchester County
Professional training in management, culinary and pastry arts for the food service industry. Lifetime placement services. Nationally accredited by the Accrediting Council for Continuing Education and Training. Registered by the New York State Education Department.

PETER KUMP'S NEW YORK COOKING SCHOOL
307 E. 92nd Street
New York, NY 10128
212.410.4601
800.522.4610
Tone Sforza

Professional and avocational cooking classes. Evening, daytime, weekend workshops. French, Italian, pastry, bread, spa cuisine, catering, restaurant management, etc.

THE SILO
Hunt Hill Farm
44 Upland Road
New Milford, CT 06776
203.355.0300
Ruth Henderson
Areas served: Connecticut, New York, New Jersey, Massachusetts
Retail store, cooking school and art gallery. Custom group cooking classes, gallery lectures, private shopping tours. Receptions in art gallery depending on availability. Receptions: 75 people. Celebrating their twentieth anniversary.

COSTUMES

GORDON NOVELTY, INC.
933 Broadway
New York, NY 10010
212.254.8616
Mark Gordon
Costumes and prop sales. From feathered parrots to fake ice cubes. Groucho Marx glasses, 200 types of Mardi Gras masks, hats galore, fake fish, etc.

DELICACIES

BALDUCCI'S
424 Avenue of the Americas
New York, NY 10011
212.673.2600
Areas served: National
International delicacies, catering, gift baskets and mail order. International cheese and deli, regional Italian foods, smoked fish, fresh baked ethnic breads, homemade pastries, gourmet coffee, exotic and local produce, specialty groceries, prime meats, fresh fish.

[Continued on next page.]

NEW YORK

CAVIARTERIA, INC.
29 E. 60th Street
New York, NY 10022
800.4.CAVIAR
Eric Sobol
Areas served: National
Mail order and store sale of caviar, scotch salmon, fresh foie gras, gourmet foods, gift baskets. Won "Chefs in America" Gold Medal, Confrerie De Chain Des Rotisseurs, Award of Excellence.

DEAN & DELUCA
560 Broadway
New York, NY 10012
212.431.1691
James Mellgren
Areas served: International
Tabletop accessories, kitchenware, cookbooks, gift baskets. Full service specialty foods and catering. Cheese, pastries, produce, caviar, smoked fish, custom-designed chocolates, Dean & Deluca herbs and spices, dried beans and grains, mail order department. Deliver anywhere.

E.A.T.
1064 Madison Avenue
New York, NY 10028
212.772.0022
Areas served: National
Restaurant, gourmet shop, gift shop, wholesale bread and catering. Tabletop accessories, cheese, caviar, fresh baked pastry, custom-designed cakes. Smoked Norwegian salmon, fresh produce, gourmet salads, gift baskets. Known for their breads.

IDEAL CHEESE SHOP
1205 Second Avenue
New York, NY 10021
212.688.7577
800.382.0109
Edward Edelman
Areas served: National
Finest cheese. Catalogue. National delivery. Rated number one by *Zagat*, Gault Millau, awards from the French government.

DESTINATION MANAGEMENT

PASS KEY ASSOCIATES
230 E. 44th Street
Suite 9K
New York, NY 10017
212.697.4070
Jane Celler
Areas served: New York Metro
Full service, custom-designed destination management, meeting and event planning for corporations, associations and incentive groups. Theme and site selection services. Music and entertainment bookings. Celebrity look-alikes. Live props and decor.

EQUIPMENT RENTALS & TENTING

DARIEN RENTAL SERVICE CO.
365 Post Road
Darien, CT 06820
203.655.3931
Ceil
Tents, tables, chairs, silver, china and linen. Indoor and outdoor parties and gatherings, specializing in tents and party goods.

KARAOKE CONNECTION
201 E. 25th Street
Suite 3C
New York, NY 10010
212.518.4075
Peter Cummings
Areas served: New York, New Jersey, Connecticut, Pennsylvania, Massachusetts
Karaoke: equipment rentals, Master of Ceremonies, entertainers, audiotapes and videotapes as party favors. Recording booths: portable, indoor, outdoor. Lipsync videos: all equipment rental and personnel.

PARTY RENTAL LTD.
22 E. 72nd Street
New York, NY 10021
212.594.8510
Marianne Wunsch
Areas served: New York, New Jersey, Connecticut, Pennsylvania

Established in 1972, Party Rental Ltd. has been servicing the Northeast for over twenty years. Extensive assortments of fine china, hand blown glassware, distinctive place plates, and flatware. Chairs are available in over a dozen colors and counting. Table linens and cushions from taffeta to bengaline to moire and beyond. Clients can expect to obtain the impossible, whether it's importing special flatware from overseas for an event, to matching chair paint color with fabric choice. Events can range from 30 to 3000 plus guests. Deliver almost anywhere. Clientele includes all the major museums, Fortune 500 companies, and society and celebrity events in and around the tri-state area.

PROPS FOR TODAY
121 W. Nineteenth
New York, NY 10011
212.206.0330
Dyann Klein
Areas served: New York and surrounding areas
Equipment and prop rentals for all. Events: linens, tenting, chairs, tables, silverware, furniture, antiques, china, houseware.

STAMFORD TENT & PARTY RENTAL
54 Research Drive
Stamford, CT 06906
203.324.6222
Stephen Frost
Areas served: New York, New Jersey, Connecticut and beyond
Tents, dance floors, canopies, full line of party rentals. Specializing in large complex installations requiring special attention to details.

EVENT PLANNING

ANDREA LEIGH CLASTER
212.633.0970
Areas served: National
Full event planning and design. Custom-designed and catalogue invitations, seating, charts, place cards. Full in-house calligraphy services. RSVP management. Custom-designed chocolates. Hospitality gift baskets. Gift consultation. Private seminars in etiquette and gift giving. For private and corporate groups. Author of *Modern Living and Modern Giving*.

CHRISTATOS & KOSTER
201 E. 64th Street
New York, NY 10021
212.838.0022
Ann Unger
Areas served: Manhattan
Full service florist and floral design. Event planning. Plant and tree rentals. Extensive personal service.

E.J.M. ENTERTAINMENT, INC.
345 W. John Street
Hicksville, NY 11801
516.935.4210
800.EJM.IS4U
Don Mirabel
Areas served: Continental US and Puerto Rico, Canada
Live entertainment with recorded music, light systems, special effects, video taping and video projection, party favors, costume designs and changes, dance instruction, photography, music videos, etc. Bar/bat mitzvahs, weddings, corporate functions, parties for all occasions. Clients include United Way, AIDS benefits, Special Olympics, Juvenile Diabetes, Cancer Society, numerous corporate organizations.

GLORIOUS FOOD, INC.
504 E. 74th Street
New York, NY 10021
212.628.2320
Berrina Felder
Areas served: National
Full service catering on and off premises. "Best Caterer" *Zagat* 1991 Survey.

[Continued on next page.]

NEW YORK

GREAT PERFORMANCES
125 Crosby Street
New York, NY 10012
212.219.2800
Liz Neumark
Areas served: New York, New Jersey, &
Connecticut's Tri-State Area
Full service caterer and event planner for
corporate and private events of all sizes.
Providing exquisite food beautifully
presented, professional waitstaff, fine china
and linens, florists, decorators,
photographers, and entertainment.
Specialists in finding unique locations;
several on videotape. Excellence in catering
standards and party personnel. Food style
is rooted in classical European tradition,
mixed with American and Asian influences,
then tailored to the host's party theme and
requirements. A thorough staff training
program, specialty workshops, and a
scholarship for outstanding service.
Members of: The James Beard Foundation,
Society of Foodservice Management,
National Association of Off-Premises
Caterers, The NY Chamber of Commerce,
and NYC Convention & Visitors Bureau. In
business for over twelve years.

JOHN FUNT DECORATIONS
FOR SPECIAL EVENTS
165 E. 60th Street
New York, NY 10022
212.371.6353
John Funt
Areas served: International
Full decor and event planning. Twelve
years experience. Specializing in theme
events and garden style decor.

MALLORY FACTOR INC.
275 Seventh Avenue
New York, NY 10001
212.242.0000
Richard Aaron
Areas served: National
Full event production and consultation.

MANNA CATERING
24 Harrison Street
New York, NY 10013
212.966.3449
Don Lenchner

Areas served: New York, New Jersey,
and Connecticut
Full service kosher catering and event
planning. Sit down dinners up to 1000
people. Top social and corporate clientele.
In business since 1982.

PARTY ARTISTRY
222 Park Avenue, S
New York, NY 10003
212.995.2299

24 Eisenhower Parkway
Roseland, NJ 07068
201.228.2299
Tracy and Judy Davis
Areas served: National
Special event design and coordination.
Specializing in party decor.

PASS KEY ASSOCIATES
230 E. 44th Street
Suite 9K
New York, NY 10017
212.697.4070
Jane Celler
Areas served: New York Metro
Full service, custom-designed destination
management, meeting and event planning
for corporations, associations and incentive
groups. Theme and site selection services.
Music and entertainment bookings.
Celebrity look-alikes. Live props and decor.

RENNY
159 E. 64th Street
New York, NY 10021
212.288.7000
Renny Reynolds
Areas served: National
Party design and full event planning
services. Full service florist with shops in
the Hotel Carlyle and the St. Regis Hotel.
Overall atmosphere created using lighting,
flowers and decor.

NEW YORK

FAVORS

ANDREA LEIGH CLASTER
212.633.0970
Areas served: National
Full event planning and design. Custom-designed and catalogue invitations, seating, charts, place cards. Full in-house calligraphy services. RSVP management. Custom-designed chocolates. Hospitality gift baskets. Gift consultation. Private seminars in etiquette and gift giving. For private and corporate groups. Author of *Modern Living and Modern Giving.*

GODIVA CHOCOLATIER
Upstate
Albany
Crossgates Mall
518.869.7143

Buffalo
Walden Galleria
716.684.3401

New York City
Downtown
85 Broad Street
212.514.6240

33 Maiden Lane
212.809.8990

World Financial Center
212.945.2174

Midtown
560 Lexington Avenue
212.980.9810

701 Fifth Avenue
212.593.2845

Pan Am Building
212.697.9128

Uptown
245 Columbus Avenue
212.787.5804

793 Madison Avenue
212.249.9444

Long Island
Stony Brook
Stony Brook Village
516.751.2012
World renowned chocolatier. Belgium-style chocolates, gift baskets and party favors.

TIFFANY & CO.
Fifth Avenue & 57th Street
New York, NY 10022
212.755.8000
The finest in engraved invitations, favors, accessories, stationery, bridal registry, fine crystal and china, Tiffany flatware and gifts for all occasions.

FIREWORKS & SPECIAL EFFECTS

FIREWORKS BY GRUCCI
One Grucci Lane
Brookhaven, NY 11719
516.286.0088
M. Philip Butler
Areas served: National & International
State of the art fireworks programs featuring world renowned choreography of music and fireworks. World champions of Monte Carlo Competitions.

FLORISTS & FLORAL DESIGNS

CHRISTATOS & KOSTER
201 E. 64th Street
New York, NY 10021
212.838.0022
Ann Unger
Areas served: Manhattan
Full service florist and floral design. Event planning. Plant and tree rentals. Extensive personal service.

GRACIOUS HOME
1217 & 1220 Third Avenue
New York, NY 10021
212.517.6300
Areas served: National
Invitations, party supplies, tabletop accessories and kitchenware: table cloths, napkins, napkin rings, placemats, candles, china, champagne and wine glasses, caviar bowls, trays, platters, chaffing dishes, cheese boards, cookbooks. Custom-designed and catalogue invitations, place cards,

party baskets, ribbons, wrap, gift bags, flower arrangements. Free delivery in Manhattan. Ship nationally.

JOHN FUNT DECORATIONS FOR SPECIAL EVENTS
165 E. 60th Street
New York, NY 10022
212.371.6353
John Funt
Areas served: International
Full decor and event planning. Twelve years experience. Specializing in theme events and garden style decor.

LES FLEURS DE MAXIM'S
680 Madison Avenue
New York, NY 10021
212.752.9889
Olivier Guini
Areas served: New York, Tri-state, Paris, Tokyo
Retail florist and floral designers. Owned by Pierre Cardin. Flowers and exotic orchids for weddings, birthdays, anniversaries, Bar Mitzvahs and all other functions. From small romantic centerpieces to spectacular environments. Specializing in exotic orchids set in landscaped gardens and elegant hand held and round bouquets. Won First Prize and Best of Show at the New York Orchid Show and Japan Airlines Flower Arranging Award at the New York Flower Show.

RENNY
159 E. 64th Street
New York, NY 10021
212.288.7000
Renny Reynolds
Areas served: National
Party design and full event planning services. Full service florist with shops in the Hotel Carlyle and the St. Regis Hotel. Overall atmosphere created using lighting, flowers and decor.

FORMAL WEAR

A.T. HARRIS
11 E. 44th Street
New York, NY 10017
212.682.6325
Traditional formal wear sales and rentals for men.

LEXINGTON FORMAL WEAR
12 E. 46th Street
New York, NY 10017
212.867.4420
One of the largest in-house stock of rental and sale formal wear in New York. Traditional and designer. Same day service. Free pick-up and delivery in Midtown Manhattan. In business since 1925.

GIFTS & GIFT BASKETS

ANDREA LEIGH CLASTER
212.633.0970
Areas served: National
Full event planning and design. Custom-designed and catalogue invitations, seating, charts, place cards. Full in-house calligraphy services. RSVP management. Custom-designed chocolates. Hospitality gift baskets. Gift consultation. Private seminars in etiquette and gift giving. For private and corporate groups. Author of *Modern Living and Modern Giving*.

BALDUCCI'S
424 Avenue of the Americas
New York, NY 10011
212.673.2600
Areas served: National
International delicacies, catering, gift baskets and mail order. International cheese and deli, regional Italian foods, smoked fish, fresh baked ethnic breads, homemade pastries, gourmet coffee, exotic and local produce, specialty groceries, prime meats, fresh fish.

CAVIARTERIA, INC.
29 E. 60th Street
New York, NY 10022
800.4.CAVIAR
Eric Sobol
Areas served: National

NEW YORK

Mail order and store sale of caviar, Scotch salmon, fresh foie gras, gourmet foods, gifts baskets. Won "Chefs in America Gold Medal, "Confrerie De Chain Des Rotisseurs" Award of Excellence.

DEAN & DELUCA
560 Broadway
New York, NY 10012
212.431.1691
James Mellgren
Areas served: International
Tabletop accessories, kitchenware, cookbooks, gift baskets. Full service specialty foods and catering. Cheese, pastries, produce, caviar, smoked fish, custom-designed chocolates, Dean & Deluca herbs and spices, dried beans and grains, mail order department. Deliver anywhere.

D.F. SANDERS & CO.
952 Madison Avenue
New York, NY 10021
212.879.6161
Lyle Wente
Areas served: Manhattan
Design-oriented accessories and gift items for the home. Bridal registry. Monogramming on leather and stationery products.

E.A.T.
1064 Madison Avenue
New York, NY 10028
212.772.0022
Areas served: National
Restaurant, gourmet shop, gift shop, wholesale bread and catering. Tabletop accessories, cheese, caviar, fresh baked pastry, custom-designed cakes. Smoked Norwegian salmon, fresh produce, gourmet salads, gift baskets. Known for their breads.

EMBASSY SUMNER
796 Lexington Avenue
New York, NY 10021
212.734.8200
Gil Sachs
Areas served: National
Broad spectrum of fine wines and champagnes. Full wine and liquor event consultation. Delivery available. Gift baskets delivered nationwide.

GODIVA CHOCOLATIER
Upstate
Albany
Crossgates Mall
518.869.7143

Buffalo
Walden Galleria
716.684.3401

New York City
Downtown
85 Broad Street
212.514.6240

33 Maiden Lane
212.809.8990

World Financial Center
212.945.2174

Midtown
560 Lexington Avenue
212.980.9810

701 Fifth Avenue
212.593.2845

Pan Am Building
212.697.9128

Uptown
245 Columbus Avenue
212.787.5804

793 Madison Avenue
212.249.9444

Long Island
Stony Brook
Stony Brook Village
516.751.2012
World renowned chocolatier. Belgium-style chocolates, gift baskets and party favors.

GRACIOUS HOME
1217 & 1220 Third Avenue
New York, NY 10021
212.517.6300
Areas served: National
Invitations, party supplies, tabletop accessories and kitchenware: table cloths, napkins, napkin rings, placemats, candles, china, champagne and wine glasses, caviar bowls, trays, platters, chaffing dishes, cheese boards, cookbooks. Custom-designed and catalogue invitations, place

cards, party baskets, ribbons, wrap, gift bags, flower arrangements. Free delivery in Manhattan. Ship nationally.

TIFFANY & CO.
Fifth Avenue & 57th Street
New York, NY 10022
212.755.8000
The finest in engraved invitations, favors, accessories, stationery, bridal registry, fine crystal and china, Tiffany flatware and gifts for all occasions.

ICE SERVICES
DIAMOND ICE
324 W. 16th Street
New York, NY 10011
212.675.4115
Les Hendler
Ice – dry, carving, crushed. Soda, non-alcoholic beverage catering.

GREG NACHTMANN
212.567.7169
Ice sculptures and carvings for all special events.

INVITATIONS & ACCESSORIES
ANDREA LEIGH CLASTER
212.633.0970
Areas served: National
Full event planning and design. Custom-designed and catalogue invitations, seating, charts, place cards. Full in-house calligraphy services. RSVP management. Custom-designed chocolates. Hospitality gift baskets. Gift consultation. Private seminars in etiquette and gift giving. For private and corporate groups. Author of *Modern Living and Modern Giving*.

GRACIOUS HOME
1217 & 1220 Third Avenue
New York, NY 10021
212.517.6300
Areas served: National
Invitations, party supplies, tabletop

accessories and kitchenware: table cloths, napkins, napkin rings, placemats, candles, china, champagne and wine glasses, caviar bowls, trays, platters, chaffing dishes, cheese boards, cookbooks. Custom-designed and catalogue invitations, place cards, party baskets, ribbons, wrap, gift bags, flower arrangements. Free delivery in Manhattan. Ship nationally.

JAMIE OSTROW
876 Madison Avenue
New York, NY 10021
212.734.8890
Jean Ostrow
Areas served: Nationwide
Personalized stationery and invitations engraved and thermographed. Contemporary fashion forward design.

PARTY BAZAAR
390 Fifth Avenue
New York, NY 10001
212.695.6820
Mark Fleischer
Retail store offering full range of party supplies and services. Balloons, invitations, calligraphy, seating charts, place cards, napkins, pinatas, centerpieces, full event decor, in-house designers, candlesticks, and accessories.

TIFFANY & CO.
Fifth Avenue & 57th Street
New York, NY 10022
212.755.8000
The finest in engraved invitations, favors, accessories, stationery, bridal registry, fine crystal and china, Tiffany flatware and gifts for all occasions.

LIGHTING, STAGING & SOUND
FROST LIGHTING, INC.
P.O. Box 489
FDR Station
New York, NY 10150
212.751.0223
Peter Markowitz
Areas served: New York, New Jersey and Connecticut

NEW YORK

Decorative lighting and temporary electrical needs for special events.

RENNY
159 E. 64th Street
New York, NY 10021
212.288.7000
Renny Reynolds
Areas served: National
Party design and full event planning services. Full service florist with shops in the Hotel Carlyle and the St. Regis Hotel. Overall atmosphere created using lighting, flowers and decor.

LIMOUSINE & TRANSPORTATION

CAREY LIMOUSINE
212.599.1122
800.336.4646
Areas served: National
Privately chauffeured sedans, limousines, vans and mini buses in 372 cities.

DAV EL CHAUFFEURED TRANSPORTATION NETWORK
800.328.3526 (outside CA)
800.826.5779 (inside CA)
Areas Served: International
Luxury chauffeured services in over 350 cities worldwide. Centralized reservations and billing. Airport concierge services.

FUGAZY LIMOUSINE LTD.
200 Park Avenue
New York, NY 10166
212.661.0100
Roy D. Fugazy, President
Areas served: New York City, New Jersey, Connecticut
Luxury limousine, town car and passenger vans. Service twenty-four hours a day, seven days a week. Corporate transportation, primary limo service for "Grammy's" when in New York. Twenty-five years in business.

LINENS

DARIEN RENTAL SERVICE CO.
365 Post Road
Darien, CT 06820
203.655.3931
Ceil
Tents, tables, chairs, silver, china and linen. Indoor and outdoor parties and gatherings specializing in tents and party goods.

PARTY RENTAL LTD.
22 E. 72nd Street
New York, NY 10021
212.594.8510
Marianne Wunsch
Areas served: New York, New Jersey, Connecticut, Pennsylvania
Established in 1972, Party Rental Ltd. has been servicing the Northeast for over twenty years. Extensive assortments of fine china, hand blown glassware, distinctive place plates, and flatware. Chairs are available in over a dozen colors and counting. Table linens and cushions from taffeta to bengaline to moire and beyond. Clients can expect to obtain the impossible, whether it's importing special flatware from overseas for an event, to matching chair paint color with fabric choice. Events can range from 30 to 3000 plus guests. Deliver almost anywhere. Clientele includes all the major museums, Fortune 500 companies, and society and celebrity events in and around the tri-state areas.

PROPS FOR TODAY
121 W. Nineteenth
New York, NY 10011
212.206.0330
Dyann Klein
Areas served: New York and surrounding areas
Equipment and prop rentals for all events: linens, tenting, chairs, tables, silverware, furniture, antiques, china, housewares.

TABLEWRAPS
666 Cantiague Rock Road
Jericho, NY 11753
516.334.8833

[Continued on next page.]

NEW YORK

Areas served: National
Full service linen rentals. Boutique lines,
florals, satins, lames, lace, tapestries.
Hundreds of fabrics to choose from. Ship
nationwide.

MUSIC & ENTERTAINMENT

4 STAR PRODUCTIONS
209-04 23rd Avenue
Bayside, NY 11360
718.279.2023
800.842.4044
Suzan Schuster
Areas served: National
Psychics/ Fortune Tellers for special events.
Astrologers, Numerologists, Tarot Card and
Palm Readers. All performers are
professionals in their fields. They appear
fully costumed as gypsy fortune tellers and
give brief, up-beat personal readings to
guests.

A NITE AT THE RACES, INC.
2320 Avenue "U"
Brooklyn, NY 11229
718.769.7355
Rental Department
Areas served: Nationwide
Rental of horse racing events for
entertainment and fund raising. Available
in 16mm and VHS cassettes.

ABRACADABRA PRODUCTIONS
310 E. 46th Street
New York, NY 10017
212.599.7576
Leslie Carr
Areas served: National
All aspects of entertainment. 1000
performers and psychics for parties,
conventions, trade shows, hospitality suites.
Exclusive representation of Astounding
Velma, Queen of Illusion, star of radio, TV
and commercials in U.S.A., Japan and
Europe. Velma performs in both English
and French.

AUDIENCE PLEASERS
93 N. Mountain Avenue
P.O. Box 897
Upper Montclair, NJ 07043

201.744.1916
Barbara Owens
Areas served: Nationwide
Musical and variety entertainment.
Unusual acts/ custom made productions.

BOGIE'S MYSTERY TOURS®
328 W. 86th Street
Suite 4A
New York, NY 10024
212.362.7569
Karen Palmer
Areas served: International
Mystery events - private parties, corporate
events, fund-raisers, weekends, cruises, and
incentive travel. Complete planning,
scenario development, professional actors,
pens, buttons, and prizes. Playfair
whodunits - custom-designed participatory
murder mysteries. The original mystery
events company and the first to do dinner
murder parties. The owners, Karen and
Bill Palmer, write, direct and produce all
events. Members of the Mystery Writers of
America, The Private Eye Writers of
America, The Crime Writers of England,
and The American Crime Writers League.
Packagers and editors of the Bogie's
Mystery Book imprint, with several award-
winning paperback originals. Published
authors.

**CARICATURES & FACE READINGS
BY SHERRY LANE**
155 Bank Street
Studio 404
New York, NY 10014
212.675.6224
Sherry Lane
Areas served: National
Caricatures and psychic face readings.
Group caricatures from photos. Listed in
Who's Who in the East, 1991-1994; The
World *Who's Who of Women*, 1992-1993.
Has traveled around the world for Time,
Inc. and Pan Am.

E.J.M. ENTERTAINMENT, INC.
345 W. John Street
Hicksville, NY 11801
516.935.4210
800.EJM.IS4U
Don Mirabel

NEW YORK

Areas served: Continental US & Puerto Rico, Canada

Live entertainment with recorded music, light systems, special effects, video taping and video projection, party favors, costume designs and changes, dance instruction, photography, music videos, etc. Bar/bat mitzvahs, weddings, corporate functions, parties for all occasions. Clients include United Way, AIDS benefits, Special Olympics, Juvenile Diabetes, Cancer Society, numerous corporate organizations.

KARAOKE CONNECTION
> 201 E. 25th Street
> Suite 3C
> New York, NY 10010
> **212.518.4075**
> Peter Cummings

Areas served: New York, New Jersey, Connecticut, Pennsylvania, Massachusetts

Karaoke: equipment rentals, Master of Ceremonies, entertainers, audio tapes and videotapes as party favors. Recording booths: portable, indoor, outdoor. Lip-synch videos: all equipment rental and personnel.

LE MASQUERADE
> 136 Oak Drive
> Syosset, NY 11791
> **516.496.7260** (New York)
> **213.383.1191**(Los Angeles)
> **305.936.2446** (Florida)
> **800.666.7260**
> Dennis Schussel
> Bernard Schussel

Areas served: International

Interactive high energy, costumed and theatrical entertainment with music and special effects. Interaction with the guests. Private and corporate events. Media awards and distincitons include entertaining at the White House, National TV and Newspaper Coverage Award for entertaining all northwest caterers.

MARS TALENT AGENCY
> 168 Orchid Drive
> Pearl River, NY 10965
> **914.735.4569**
> Arnie and Wendy Kay

Areas served: National

Artists - groups from the 50's and 60's era of music. Brochures available. Conventions, private parties, fund-raisers.

PASS KEY ASSOCIATES
> 230 E. 44th Street
> Suite 9K
> New York, NY 10017
> **212.697.4070**
> Jane Celler

Areas served: New York Metro

Full service, custom-designed destination management, meeting and event planning for corporations, associations and incentive groups. Theme and site selection services. Music and entertainment bookings. Celebrity look-alikes. Live props and decor.

❧ CELEBRITY LOOK-ALIKES

PASS KEY ASSOCIATES
> 230 E. 44th Street
> Suite 9K
> New York, NY 10017
> **212.697.4070**
> Jane Celler

Areas served: New York Metro

Full service, custom-designed destination management, meeting and event planning for corporations, associations and incentive groups. Theme and site selection services. Music and entertainment bookings. Celebrity look-alikes. Live props and decor.

[Continued on next page.]

NEW YORK

PARTY SITES

AMERICAN MUSEUM OF NATURAL HISTORY
Central Park West at 79th Street
New York, NY 10024
212.769.5350
Amy Rudnick

Events held in exhibition halls. Hall of Ocean Life centerpiece is a 94 foot blue whale suspended form the ceiling. The Roosevelt Rotunda is a 100 foot barrel vault with a 50 foot high Barosaurus on display. African Mammals has a herd of elephants and habitat group dioramas of African wildlife. Many other halls are available for receptions and dinners. Receptions: 2000 people. Sit down: 1000 people.

GLORIOUS FOOD, INC.
522 E. 74th Street
New York, NY 10021
212.628.2320
Bettina Felder

Contemporary design, fireplace, roof terrace garden, audiovisual facilities. Receptions: 150 people. Sit down: 70 people.

GREAT PERFORMANCES
125 Crosby Street
New York, NY 10012
212.219.2800
Liz Neumark

Areas served: New York, New Jersey, & Connecticut's Tri-State Area
Complete party planning and location selection services for private and corporate functions of all sizes. Specialists at finding New York City's most unique locations for your events. Also provide everything else the event will need, including interesting and elegantly prepared food and outstanding service. Review thirty of NYC's most sought-after locations in your home or office with Great Performances location videotape. The video includes town houses, lofts, galleries, ballrooms, mansions, billiard clubs, museums, and landmarks. This video is available for purchase and it is only the latest addition to Great Performances library of over 300 locations in the Tri-state area. Their compendium of party sites is complete with color photos, detailed descriptions of room layout, capacities, fees, logistics, dance floor, equipment, and facilities for the handicapped. Members of: The James Beard Foundation, Society of Food service Management, National Association of Off-Premises Caterers, The NY Chamber of Commerce, and NYC Convention & Visitors Bureau.

THE HOUSE OF THE REDEEMER
7 E. 95th Street
New York, NY 10128
212.289.0399
Alicia Benoist

Italian Renaissance Palazzo with original furnishings (imported) style of Buenileschi. Courtyard, reception room, dining room, library and chapel. Received Cyclical Maintenance Award from the Friends of the Upper Eastside. Receptions: 400 people. Sit down: 90 people in one room.

LAURA BELLE
120 W. 43rd Street
New York, NY 10036
212.819.1000
Joanne O'Connor

Glamorous supper club located in a three-tiered former movie theater. Dance floor featuring seven layers that fluctuate "like a string." Marble and red velvet decor. Receptions: 900 people. Sit down: 400 people without dance floor and 300 people with dance floor.

L'OMNIBUS DE MAXIM'S
61st Street at Madison Avenue
New York, NY
212.751.5111
Alain Michel
Philip Gaziano

The art deco magic of Gruolliot is portrayed in large murals dominating this sophisticated dining room. Cabaret performed nightly enlivens the dining experience. Stained glass sconces, mirrored ceilings, dramatic carpeting complemented by the floral decorations of Les Fleurs de Maxim's create the ultimate environment to party. Given three stars by Bryan Miller, *New York Times*, January 1992 for Maxim's. 2000 square feet. Receptions: 250 people. Sit down: 150 people.

NEW YORK

MAXIM'S
680 Madison Avenue at 61st
Street
New York, NY zip????
212.751.5111
Philip Gaziano

French Art Nouveau mahogany woodwork, beautiful foyer leads to the classic staircase embellished by a lit mirrored wall, with hand painted stained glass ceiling, plush banquettes, miniature pink lamps at each table, bronze wall mountings, brass trimmings, intimate lighting, beveled mirrors, gilded arabesques and murals, inverted champagne flutes behind a lavish bar, all dominated by brilliant stained glass ceiling and floral carpeting. Given three stars by Bryan Miller, *New York Times*, January 10, 1992. 4000 square feet. Receptions: 800 people. Sit down: 400 people.

PASS KEY ASSOCIATES
230 E. 44th Street
Suite 9K
New York, NY 10017
212.697.4070
Jane Celler

Areas served: New York Metro
Full service, custom-designed destination management, meeting and event planning for corporations, associations and incentive groups. Theme and site selection services. Music and entertainment bookings. Celebrity look-alikes. Live props and decor.

THE RAINBOW ROOM AND RAINBOW SUITES
30 Rockefeller Plaza
New York, NY 10112
212.632.5115
Dorothy Burdumi

Wraparound views of New York's shimmering skyline. The Rainbow Room and Rainbow Suites epitomizes glamour and sophistication showcasing its recent renovation in the classic art deco and art moderne style. Receptions: 1000 people. Sit Down: 350 people.

RESTAURANT AQUAVIT
13 W. 54th Street
New York, NY 10019
212.307.7311
Robbin Cullinen, General
Manager

First class Scandinavian restaurant with seven story atrium and waterfall. Casual cafe/ bar and formal dining room. DiRona Award, Epicurean Rendezvous. Four stars Forbes Magazine 1992. 8000 square feet. Receptions: 300 people. Sit down: 200 people.

THE SILO
Hunt Hill Farm
44 Upland Road
New Milford, CT 06776
203.355.0300
Ruth Henderson

Areas served: Connecticut, New York, New Jersey, Massachusetts
Retail store, cooking school and art gallery. Custom group cooking classes, gallery lectures, private shopping tours. Receptions in art gallery depending on availability. Receptions: 75 people. Celebrating their twentieth anniversary.

THE SUPPER CLUB
240 W. 47th Street
New York, NY 10036
212.921.1940
Raven

Classic 1940's supper club in the heart of the Theatre District. Live music and entertainment nightly. Can accommodate private events for 25 to 1001 guests. Offer three venues: the Blue Room, a private cabaret/piano room with a twenty foot bar; the Balcony with a fifteen foot bar and private salons overlooking the main dining room; and the main dining room with a thirty-six foot bar, private salons, dance floor and 15 x 36 foot stage. The Supper Club has state-of-the-art audiovisual equipment, a twenty foot projection screen and theatrical lighting. Receptions: 1001 people. Sit down: 450 people.

UNITED NATIONS PLAZA PARK HYATT HOTEL
One UN Plaza
44th Street at First Avenue
New York, NY 10017
212.355.3400
June Martinez, Director Catering

Six very different elegant and sophisticated banquet rooms for functions of 15 to 250 guests. All catering and service provided by the UN Plaza Park Hyatt Hotel. Several function rooms are on high floors with spectacular views of the skyline and East River, and have living room type furnishings. AAA Four Diamond Award and *Mobil Travel Guide* Four Stars. 7000 total square feet. Receptions: 250 people. Sit down: 180 people served dinner without dance floor and 130 people served dinner with dance floor.

WADSWORTH ATHENEUM
600 Main Street
Hartford, CT 06103
203.278.2670
Deborah Gaudet-Sticca
Art museum. Meeting space, corporate events, receptions, dinners, luncheons. No weddings.

THE WATER CLUB
The East River at 30th Street
500 E. 30th Street
New York, NY 10016
212.683.3333
Andrew Kovar
Restaurant with private dining room, all glass-enclosed with panoramic views. 10,000 square feet. Largest space: 3000 square feet. Listed in Epicurean Rendezvous. Receptions: 1000 people. Sit down: 300 people.

PARTY SUPPLIES

GRACIOUS HOME
1217 & 1220 Third Avenue
New York, NY 10021
212.517.6300
Areas served: National
Invitations, party supplies, tabletop accessories and kitchenware: table cloths, napkins, napkin rings, placemats, candles, china, champagne and wine glasses, caviar, bowls, trays, platters, chaffing dishes, cheese boards, cookbooks. Custom-designed and catalogue invitations, place cards, party baskets, ribbons, wrap, gift bags, flower arrangements. Free delivery in Manhattan. Ship nationally.

PARTY BAZAAR
390 Fifth Avenue
New York, NY 10001
212.695.6820
Mark Fleischer
Retail store offering full range of party supplies and services. Balloons, invitations, calligraphy, seating charts, place cards, napkins, pinatas, centerpieces, full event decor, in-house designers, candlesticks, and accessories.

PERSONNEL & STAFFING

LEND A HAND, INC.
200 W. 72nd Street
New York, NY 10023
212.362.8200
Joe Colacio
Areas served: New York, New Jersey and Connecticut
Personnel and staffing. Bartenders, waiters, waitresses, captains, wine stewards, butlers, clean-up staff.

NEW YORK RESTAURANT SCHOOL
27 W. 34th Street
New York, NY 10001
212.947.7097
800.654.CHEF
Placement Department
Areas served: Five boroughs, New Jersey, Connecticut, and Westchester County
Freelance culinary help for private or catered events. Also provides kitchen helpers, servers and bartenders.

PHOTOGRAPHY & VIDEO

JEANNE TRUDEAU
329 E. 63rd Street
New York, NY 10021
212.751.6965
Areas served: New York, Pennsylvania, Connecticut, Rhode Island
Full photography services for all events. Specializing in weddings, private events and Bar Mitzvahs. Top corporate and private clientele.

NEW YORK

PLANT RENTALS

CHRISTATOS & KOSTER
201 E. 64th Street
New York, NY 10021
212.838.0022
Ann Unger
Areas served: Manhattan
Full service florist and floral design. Event planning. Plant and tree rentals. Extensive personal service.

PROPS & DECOR

ANDREA LEIGH CLASTER
212.633.0970
Areas served: National
Full event planning and design. Custom-designed and catalogue invitations, seating, charts, place cards. Full in-house calligraphy services. RSVP management. Custom-designed chocolates. Hospitality gift baskets. Gift consultation. Private seminars in etiquette and gift giving. For private and corporate groups. Author of *Modern Living and Modern Giving*.

FROST LIGHTING, INC.
P.O. Box 489
FDR Station
New York, NY 10150
212.751.0223
Peter Markowitz
Areas served: New York, New Jersey and Connecticut
Decorative lighting and temporary electrical needs for special events.

GORDON NOVELTY, INC.
933 Broadway
New York, NY 10010
212.254.8616
Mark Gordon
Costumes and prop sales. From feathered parrots to fake ice cubes. Groucho Marx glasses, 200 types of Mardi Gras masks, hats galore, fake fish, etc.

JOHN FUNT DECORATIONS FOR SPECIAL EVENTS
165 E. 60th Street
New York, NY 10022
212.371.6353

John Funt
Areas served: International
Full decor and event planning. Twelve years experience. Specializing in theme events and garden style decor.

NIEDERMAIR
120 Wooster Street
New York, NY 10012
212.966.8574
Louis Marra
Areas served: National
Full service display company providing prop sales for all special events. Columns, urns, panels, banners, etc.

PARTY ARTISTRY
222 Park Avenue, S
New York, NY 10003
212.995.2299

24 Eisenhower Parkway
Roseland, NJ 07068
201.228.2299
Tracy and Judy Davis
Areas served: National
Special event design and coordination. Specializing in party decor.

PARTY BAZAAR
390 Fifth Avenue
New York, NY 10001
212.695.6820
Mark Fleischer
Retail store offering full range of party supplies and services. Balloons, invitations, calligraphy, seating charts, place cards, napkins, pinatas, centerpieces, full event decor, in-house designers, candlesticks, and accessories.

PASS KEY ASSOCIATES
230 E. 44th Street
Suite 9K
New York, NY 10017
212.697.4070
Jane Celler
Areas served: New York Metro
Full service, custom-designed destination management, meeting and event planning for corporations, associations and incentive groups. Theme and site selection services. Music and entertainment bookings. Celebrity look-alikes. Live props and decor.

PROPS FOR TODAY
121 W. Nineteenth
New York, NY 10011
212.206.0330
Dyann Klein
Areas served: New York and surrounding areas
Equipment and prop rentals for all events: linens, tenting, chairs, tables, silverware, furniture, antiques, china, houseware.

RENNY
159 E. 64th Street
New York, NY 10021
212.288.7000
Renny Reynolds
Areas served: National
Party design and full event planning services. Full service florist with shops in the Hotel Carlyle and the St. Regis Hotel. Overall atmosphere created using lighting, flowers and decor.

SIGNAGE

NIEDERMAIR
120 Wooster Street
New York, NY 10012
212.966.8574
Louis Marra
Areas served: National
Full service display company providing prop sales for all special events. Columns, urns, panels, banners, etc.

SPEAKERS

WASHINGTON SPEAKERS BUREAU
888 Seventh Avenue
New York, NY 10106
212.541.7980
Areas served: International
Speakers for all occasions - celebrities, sports, political, motivational, business, humorous.

TABLETOP ACCESSORIES & KITCHENWARE

BERNARDAUD NEW YORK
777 Madison Avenue
New York, NY 10021
212.737.7775
Mary Kaye Denning
Product selection and services include the finest collections of Bernardaud porcelain dinnerware and giftware, French and American silverware, and the finest in European crystals. Specialize in adapting clients' family crest or monogram, corporate logos and firing special colors to match wallpapers or other distinctive decorations in the home or office. Expertise is internationally recognized and their porcelains grace the tables of royal households, diplomatic missions and family gatherings across Europe, the US and the Orient.

THE CHOCOLATE GALLERY
34 W. 22nd Street
New York, NY 10010
212.675.CAKE
Areas served: National
Carries over 10,000 items fully stocked: cake pans in all shapes and sizes from round, square, and rectangle to characters like Big Bird and Ninja Turtles. Full assortment of cookie cutters in different shapes. Supplies to make a wedding cake, from cake stands, fountains, bridges, ushers and bridesmaids in all color dresses, to the wedding ornament to dazzle the top of the cake. Tips, pastry bags, icing colors, spatulas, and much more. A wide selection of books and videos on the latest ideas in cake decorating. Offers Wilton Cake Decorating classes in Spanish: learn how to decorate cakes for the family or to start a business selling beautifully decorated cakes.

DEAN & DELUCA
560 Broadway
New York, NY 10012
212.431.1691
James Mellgren
Areas served: International
Tabletop accessories, kitchenware, cookbooks, gift baskets. Full service specialty foods and catering. Cheese,

pastries, produce, caviar, smoked fish,
custom-designed chocolates, Dean & Deluca
herbs and spices, dried beans and grains,
mail order department. Deliver anywhere.

D.F. SANDERS & CO.
952 Madison Avenue
New York, NY 10021
212.879.6161
Lyle F. Wente
Areas served: Manhattan
Design oriented accessories and gift items
for the home. Bridal registry. Monogramming on leather and stationery products.

E.A.T.
1064 Madison Avenue
New York, NY 10028
212.772.0022
Areas served: National
Restaurant, gourmet shop, gift shop,
wholesale bread and catering. Tabletop
accessories, cheese, caviar, fresh baked
pastry, custom-designed cakes. Smoked
Norwegian salmon, fresh produce, gourmet
salads, gift baskets. Known for their
breads.

EUROPEAN HOME PRODUCTS, INC.
136 Washington Street
Norwalk, CT 06854
203.866.7777
800.225.0760
Robert Johnson
Areas served: United States and Canada
Full line of kitchenware specializing in parts
and repairs of food processors. Gourmet
coffees by mail order.

GRACIOUS HOME
1217 & 1220 Third Avenue
New York, NY 10021
212.517.6300
Areas served: National
Invitations, party supplies, tabletop
accessories and kitchenware: table cloths,
napkins, napkin rings, placemats, candles,
china, champagne and wine glasses, caviar
bowls, trays, platters, chaffing dishes,
cheese boards, cookbooks. Custom-
designed and catalogue invitations, place
cards, party baskets, ribbons, wrap, gift
bags, flower arrangements. Free delivery in
Manhattan. Ship nationally.

POTTERY BARN
2109 Broadway
New York, NY 10023
212.595.5573

1451 Second Avenue
New York, NY 10029
212.988.4228

1292 Lexington Avenue
New York, NY 10014
212.289.2477

51 Greenwich Avenue
New York, NY 10014
212.807.6321

231 Tenth Avenue
New York, NY 10011
212.206.8118

100 Seventh Avenue
New York, NY 10011
212.633.8405

Stamford Town Center
100 Greyrock Place
Stamford, CT 06901
203.324.4664

117 E. 59th Street
New York, NY 10022
212.753.5424

250 W. 57th Street
New York, NY 10019
212.315.1855

Danbury Fair Mall
7 Backus Avenue
Danbury, CT 06810
203.790.7677

450 Central Avenue
Scarsdale, NY 10583
914.723.0660

700 Broadway
New York, NY 10003
212.505.6377
Leading retailer of contemporary tableware
and decorative accessories for the home.
Merchandise is s100% exclusive, designed
and sold exclusively at Pottery Barn. Over
fifty stores nationally and mail order.

[Continued on next page.]

NEW YORK

TIFFANY & CO.
  Fifth Avenue & 57th Street
  New York, NY 10022
  212.755.8000
The finest in engraved invitations, favors,
accessories, stationery, bridal registry, fine
crystal and china, Tiffany flatware and gifts
for all occasions.

WILLIAM WAYNE & CO.
  324 E. Ninth Street
  New York, NY 10003
  212.477.3182
  William and Wayne
Areas served: United States and Canada
Retail home furnishings, decorator
consultants, seasonal catalogue and
newsletter. Ship nationally.

WILLIAMS-SONOMA
  Stamford Town Center
  100 Grayrock Place
  Stamford, CT 06901
  203.327.3652

  Danbury Fair Mall
  7 Backus Avenue
  Danbury, CT 06810
  203.790.9996

  1175 Madison Avenue
  New York, NY 10028
  212.289.6832

  2110-B Northern Boulevard
  Manhasset, NY 11030
  516.365.1650

  20 E. 60th Street
  New York, NY 10022
  212.980.5155

  110 Seventh Avenue
  New York, NY 10011
  212.633.2203

  1309 Second Avenue
  New York, NY 10021
  212.288.8408
An authoritative selection of the best for the
kitchen. Complete line of cookware,
bakeware, electrics, glassware, tabletop,
kitchen furniture, cookbooks, packaged
foods. Knowledgeable staff will help choose
equipment, plan parties. Most merchandise
is exclusive to Williams-Sonoma.

WINE & SPIRITS

EMBASSY SUMNER
  796 Lexington Avenue
  New York, NY 10021
  212.734.8200
  Gil Sachs
Areas served: National
Broad spectrum of fine wines and
champagnes. Full wine and liquor event
consultation. Delivery available. Gift
baskets delivered nationwide.

YACHT & BOAT CHARTERS

WORLD YACHT
  Pier 62
  W. 23rd Street
  New York, NY 10011
  212.627.2775
  Jo Ann Falco
Areas served: New York, New Jersey
Yacht charter for private parties. Two to
2000 people. Full event coordination.

❧ ❧ ❧

PALM BEACH

AUDIOVISUAL & TECHNICAL SERVICES

HY-LITE PRODUCTIONS INC.
2304 Florida Avenue
West Palm Beach, FL
33401-7810
407.820.1414
Carl Borrelli
Areas served: International
Complete lighting, sound and special effects production and design services for special events, parties, fashion shows, corporate or private theater and video production. Hy-lite productions provides both the manpower and the technology for perfect events. Specializes in event theme decor (as created with lighting) and special effects. Fully licensed and insured.

MARSHALL GRANT'S ENTERTAINMENT SOURCE, INC.
1750 N. Fla. Mango Road
Suite 103
West Palm Beach, FL 33409
407.686.7000
800.422.1522
Marshall Grant
Billy Duke
Joe Gianuzzi
Areas served: Florida's Gold Coast from Orlando south through Miami; Florida's West Coast (Naples, etc.) Private parties, etc. throughout United States
Orchestras and entertainment for private parties, charity balls, conventions, etc. Suppliers of dance music, entertainers, name speakers, etc. Providers of sound, lighting, audiovisual equipment, etc. Able to provide wide range of sophisticated entertainment needs. Upper-income clients, both private and corporate. Basically private affairs, country clubs, theme parties, music to appeal to wide variety of ages in 25-70 year-old group. Thirty-five years in Palm Beach. Twenty-one years as music directors of The Breakers Hotel, Palm Beach. Marshall Grant is first living band leader inducted into the "Big Band Hall of Fame".

BALLOONS

THE BALLOON CONNECTION, INC.
204 Live Oak Blvd.
Casselberry, FL 32707
407.830.5300
Bobbie Roberts
Areas served: Florida
Full service balloon decor. Unique centerpieces, sculptures, special effects and special written materials for conventions, trade shows and business meetings.

BOOKS

WILLIAMS-SONOMA
3101 PGA Blvd.
Suite Q217
Palm Beach, FL 33410
407.694.2068
An authoritative selection of the best for the kitchen. Complete line of cookware, bakeware, electrics, glassware, tabletop, kitchen furniture, cookbooks, packaged foods. Knowledgeable staff will help choose equipment, plan parties. Most merchandise is exclusive to Williams-Sonoma.

CAKES & BAKED GOODS

SWEET TIERS
8779 South E. Federal Highway
Hobe Sand, FL 33455
407.546.8822
Betty Baird
Areas served: Miami, Palm Beach, Stewart, Vero, Orlando
Custom-designed and traditional wedding cakes, shower cakes, Austrian fondant cakes, carved fantasy cakes, handmade flowers and other confections.

CALLIGRAPHY

ANDREA LEIGH CLASTER
4521 PGA Blvd.
Suite 297
Palm Beach, FL 33418
407.624.4350
Areas served: Palm Beach County

PALM BEACH

Full event planning and design. Custom-designed and catalogue invitations, featuring charts, place cards. Full in-house calligraphy services. RSVP Management. Custom-designed chocolates. Hospitality gift baskets. Gift consultation. Private seminars in etiquette and gift giving for private and corporate groups. Author of *Modern Living and Modern Giving*.

CORDIALLY YOURS PRINTERS AND ENGRAVERS
296 S. Country Road
Palm Beach, FL 33480
407.655.6103
407.655.6147
Blanche Rotman
Areas served: International
Invitations for all occasions, Crane's fine stationery and invitations, printed and engraved invitations. They also provide calligraphy, gift baskets, napkins, matches, place cards, etc. Delivery worldwide.

OLD TOWN FLOWER SHOPS
1930 N. Dixie Highway
West Palm Beach, FL 33407
407.655.3351
Ted Johns
Areas served: National
Full service florists, floral designers and party planner offers simple elegance and custom designs. In house invitations and calligraphy services. For three consecutive years, voted Best Florist by *Palm Beach Life Magazine*. In business for thirty-eight years.

CATERING
PALM BEACH CATERING
1109 25th Street
West Palm Beach, FL 33407
407.833.1411
407.832.3863
John Sunkel
Areas served: Palm Beach, Hobe Sound and Boca Raton
Complete party service, including in-home consultations for menu planning and party set-up; unique, original recipes prepared and served by custom-trained staff; all equipment provided: exquisite linens, silver, crystal;

air-conditioned tents, flower arrangements, musicians. Covers every request for private parties. Outstanding service by quality-conscious personnel, featuring European-trained chefs and detail-oriented management; specialties include sit-down dinners for up to 1000 guests, theme parties; fresh seafood buffets; ice carvings. Winner of Caterer, Chaine des Rotisseurs, The Palm Beach Post's "Number 1 Caterer in the Palm Beaches". In business for twenty-nine years.

THE BREAKERS
One S. Country Road
Palm Beach, FL 33480
407.659.8451
Chantal DuPuis
Areas served: Palm Beach County and surrounding areas
Complete catering (planning, coordinating, set-up and break down) of social and corporate special events, theme parties and all type meals.

THE WHITE APRON CATERING
1253 Old Okeechobee Road
Suite B8
West Palm Beach, FL 33401
407.832.7175
Charles Crawford
Areas served: Palm Beach, Brownard and Dade County
Catering, staffing and rentals. Specializing in creative cuisine and top notch service for celebrity events. Authors of *The Dessert Cookbook*.

CHOCOLATES & CONFECTIONS
ANDREA LEIGH CLASTER
4521 PGA Blvd.
Suite 297
Palm Beach, FL 33418
407.624.4350
Areas served: Palm Beach County
Full event planning and design. Custom-designed and catalogue invitations, featuring charts, place cards. Full in-house calligraphy services. RSVP Management. Custom-designed chocolates. Hospitality

[Continued on next page]

gift baskets. Gift consultation. Private seminars in etiquette and gift giving for private and corporate groups. Author of *Modern Living and Modern Giving*.

GODIVA CHOCOLATIER
The Gardens at Palm Beach
407.624.0444
World renowned chocolatier. Belgium-style chocolates, gift baskets and party favors.

NICOLE CHOCOLATIER
The Breakers
One S. County Road
Palm Beach, FL 33480
407.655.6611 ext. 1503
Jayne Josephs
Areas served: International
Gartner chocolates from Antwerp, Belgium. Gift baskets, confections, biscuits, china ware, crystal and favors. Free delivery locally. Additional store in Boca Raton.

CLASSES & SEMINARS

ANDREA LEIGH CLASTER
4521 PGA Blvd.
Suite 297
Palm Beach, FL 33418
407.624.4350
Areas served: Palm Beach County
Full event planning and design. Custom-designed and catalogue invitations, featuring charts, place cards. Full in-house calligraphy services. RSVP Management. Custom-designed chocolates. Hospitality gift baskets. Gift consultation. Private seminars in etiquette and gift giving for private and corporate groups. Author of *Modern Living and Modern Giving*.

COSTUMES

REGENCY PARTY RENTALS AND PRODUCTIONS
6615 Norton Avenue
West Palm Beach, FL 33405
407.588.7600
800.933.1333
Dan Ivancevic
Areas served: South Florida

Full party planning, decorating, floral design, tenting, rentals and costumes for Southern Florida. Warehouse filled with 30,000 square feet of props, costumes and floral accessories. Member and past Board of Director for the American Rental Association.

DELICACIES

THE COFFEE CORNER
The Breakers
One S. County Road
Palm Beach, FL 33480
407.820.9821
Stacy Tasca
Areas served: International shipping
Thirty kinds of gourmet coffee, tea, scones, pastries, cookies, light lunches, cups, mugs, specialty tins, gifts.

EQUIPMENT RENTALS & TENTING

ALDRICH PARTY RENTALS, INC.
2744 Hillsboro Road
West Palm Beach, FL 33405
407.833.1735
David Steele, President
Areas served: Palm Beach and Broward Counties
Full service party and tent rental company. Established in 1959. Has 30,500 square foot warehouse and showroom. Members of the American Rental Association, IFAC, NACE and the Hotel Sales and Marketing Association.

ATLAS PARTY RENTAL
1420 Neptune Drive
Boynton Beach, FL 33426
407.736.9100
Sam and Beatrice Horowitz
Areas served: Broward and Palm Beach Counties
Party equipment rentals.

FIESTA PARTY RENTALS
6135 B Lake Worth Road
Lake Worth, FL 33463
407.966.3388

Jane Hutton
Areas served: Southern Florida
Designer linens, tents, tables, chairs, china, flatware, silver and prop rentals. Referral and full party planning services.

REGENCY PARTY RENTALS AND PRODUCTIONS
6615 Norton Avenue
West Palm Beach, FL 33405
407.588.7600
800.933.1333
Dan Ivancevic
Areas served: South Florida
Full party planning, decorating, floral design, tenting, rentals and costumes for Southern Florida. Warehouse filled with 30,000 square feet of props, costumes and floral accessories. Member and past Board of Director for the American Rental Association.

THE WHITE APRON CATERING
1253 Old Okeechobee Road
Suite B8
West Palm Beach, FL 33401
407.832.7175
Charles Crawford
Areas served: Palm Beach, Brownard and Dade County
Catering, staffing and rentals. Specializing in creative cuisine and top notch service. For celebrity events. Authors of *The Dessert Cookbook*.

EVENT PLANNING
ANDREA LEIGH CLASTER
4521 PGA Blvd.
Suite 297
Palm Beach, FL 33418
407.624.4350
Areas served: Palm Beach County
Full event planning and design. Custom-designed and catalogue invitations, featuring charts, place cards. Full in-house calligraphy services. RSVP Management. Custom-designed chocolates. Hospitality gift baskets. Gift consultation. Private seminars in etiquette and gift giving for private and corporate groups. Author of *Modern Living and Modern Giving*.

BARRY R. EPSTEIN ASSOCIATES, INC. & FLORIDA LIMOUSINE ASSOCIATION
2255 Glades Road
Suite 324
Boca Raton, FL 33431-7383
407.241.0001
Areas served: Florida
Public relations, association management, meeting planning, conventions and limousine services.

FIESTA PARTY RENTALS
6135 B Lake Worth Road
Lake Worth, FL 33463
407.966.3388
Jane Hutton
Areas served: Southern Florida
Designer linens, tents, tables, chairs, china, flatware, silver and prop rentals. Referral and full party planning services.

OLD TOWN FLOWER SHOPS
1930 N. Dixie Highway
West Palm Beach, FL 33407
407.655.3351
Ted Johns
Areas served: National
Full service florists, floral designers and party planner offers simple elegance and custom designs. In house invitations and calligraphy services. For three consecutive years, voted Best Florist by *Palm Beach Life Magazine*. In business for thirty-eight years.

PALM BEACH CATERING
1109 25th Street
West Palm Beach, FL 33407
407.833.1411
407.832.3863
John Sunkel
Areas served: Palm Beach, Hobe Sound and Boca Raton
Complete party service, including in-home consultations for menu planning and party set-up; unique, original recipes prepared and served by custom-trained staff; all equipment provided: exquisite linens, silver, crystal; air-conditioned tents, flower arrangements, musicians. Covers every request for private parties. Outstanding service by quality-conscious personnel, featuring European-trained chefs and

[Continued on next page]

detail-oriented management; specialties
include sit-down dinners for up to 1000
guests, theme parties; fresh seafood buffets;
ice carvings. Winner of Caterer, Chaine des
Rotisseurs, The Palm Beach Post's
"Number 1 Caterer in the Palm Beaches".
In business for twenty-nine years.

**REGENCY PARTY RENTALS
AND PRODUCTIONS**
> 6615 Norton Avenue
> West Palm Beach, FL 33405
> **407.588.7600**
> **800.933.1333**
> Dan Ivancevic

Areas served: South Florida
Full party planning, decorating, floral
design, tenting, rentals and costumes for
Southern Florida. Warehouse filled with
30,000 square feet of props, costumes and
floral accessories. Member and past Board
of Director for the American Rental
Association.

**SUTKA PRODUCTIONS
INTERNATIONAL, INC.**
> 914 Fern Street
> Suite B
> West Palm Beach, FL 33401
> **407.835.8455**
> **800.933.1333**
> Bruce Sutka
> Kevin Verronneau

Areas served: International
Floral, lighting and special event
coordination. Unique themes, wedding
decor and environmental concepts create
complete ambiance enhancement. Large-
scale corporate and social clientele.
Featured in *Town and Country* as one of
the ten top party planners in the country as
well as on CNN and *Good Morning
America*. *Special Events* magazine and
other national trade publications.

FAVORS

ANDREA LEIGH CLASTER
> 4521 PGA Blvd.
> Suite 297
> Palm Beach, FL 33418
> **407.624.4350**

Areas served: Palm Beach County
Full event planning and design. Custom-
designed and catalogue invitations,
featuring charts, place cards. Full in-house
calligraphy services. RSVP Management.
Custom-designed chocolates. Hospitality
gift baskets. Gift consultation. Private
seminars in etiquette and gift giving for
private and corporate groups. Author of
Modern Living and Modern Giving.

GODIVA CHOCOLATIER
> The Gardens at Palm Beach
> **407.624.0444**

World renowned chocolatier. Belgium-style
chocolates, gift baskets and party favors.

NICOLE CHOCOLATIER
> The Breakers
> One S. Country Road
> Palm Beach, FL 33480
> **407.655.6611 ext. 1503**
> Jayne Josephs

Areas served: International
Gartner chocolates from Antwerp, Belgium.
Gift baskets, confections, biscuits, china
ware, crystal and favors. Free delivery
locally. Additional store in Boca Raton.

FIREWORKS
& SPECIAL EFFECTS

HY-LITE PRODUCTIONS INC.
> 2304 Florida Avenue
> West Palm Beach, FL
> 33401-7810
> **407.83.1414**
> Carl Borrelli

Areas served: International
Complete lighting, sound and special effects
production and design services for special
events, parties, fashion shows, corporate or
private theater and video production. Hy-
lite productions provides both the
manpower and the technology for perfect
events. Specializes in event theme decor (as
created with lighting) and special effects.
Fully licensed and insured.

PALM BEACH

FLORISTS & FLORAL DESIGN

ANDREA LEIGH CLASTER
4521 PGA Blvd.
Suite 297
Palm Beach, FL 33418
407.624.4350
Areas served: Palm Beach County
Full event planning and design. Custom-designed and catalogue invitations, featuring charts, place cards. Full in-house calligraphy services. RSVP Management. Custom-designed chocolates. Hospitality gift baskets. Gift consultation. Private seminars in etiquette and gift giving for private and corporate groups. Author of *Modern Living and Modern Giving*.

THE BREAKERS FLOWER SHOP
The Breakers
One S. County Road
Palm Beach, FL 33480
407.833.3026
Martha Morgan
Areas served: Palm Beach and surrounding areas
Distinctive and unusual floral designs. Fruit and gourmet baskets, delivery and wire service.

EXTRA TOUCH FLOWERS
319 Clematis Street
West Palm Beach, FL 33401
407.835.8000
Jerold Supernaw
Area served: Palm Beach County
Full service florist and floral designers. Huge variety of linen rentals. Custom-created centerpieces. Flowering plants and tree rentals.

OLD TOWN FLOWER SHOPS
1930 N. Dixie Highway
West Palm Beach, FL 33407
407.655.3351
Ted Johns
Areas served: National
Full service florists, floral designers and party planner offers simple elegance and custom designs. In house invitations and calligraphy services. For three consecutive years, voted Best Florist by *Palm Beach Life Magazine*. In business for thirty-eight years.

POTTED PLANT & FLOWER SHOP
249 Royal Poinciana Way
Palm Beach, FL 33480
407.659.7174
Pat Sandberg
Areas served: Palm Beach Counties
Full service florists, floral design and plant rentals for special events.

REGENCY PARTY RENTALS AND PRODUCTIONS
6615 Norton Avenue
West Palm Beach, FL 33405
407.588.7600
800.933.1333
Dan Ivancevic
Areas served: South Florida
Full party planning, decorating, floral design, tenting, rentals and costumes for Southern Florida. Warehouse filled with 30,000 square feet of props, costumes and floral accessories. Member and past Board of Director for the American Rental Association.

SUTKA PRODUCTIONS INTERNATIONAL, INC.
914 Fern Street
Suite B
West Palm Beach, FL 33401
407.835.8455
800.933.1333
Bruce Sutka
Kevin Verronneau
Areas served: International
Floral, lighting and special event coordination. Unique themes, wedding decor and environmental concepts create complete ambiance enhancement. Large-scale corporate and social clientele. Featured in *Town and Country* as one of the ten top party planners in the country as well as on *CNN* and *Good Morning America*. *Special Events* magazine and other national trade publications.

FORMAL WEAR

BILL'S TUXEDO
531 Clematis Street
West Palm Beach, FL 33401
407.832.4790
Bill Suther

PALM BEACH

Areas served: Greater Palm Beach area
Formal wear sales and rentals for men.
Complete line of accessories. In business
since 1949.

GIFTS & GIFT BASKETS
ANDREA LEIGH CLASTER
4521 PGA Blvd.
Suite 297
Palm Beach, FL 33418
407.624.4350
Areas served: Palm Beach County
Full event planning and design. Custom-
designed and catalogue invitations,
featuring charts, place cards. Full in-house
calligraphy services. RSVP Management.
Custom-designed chocolates. Hospitality
gift baskets. Gift consultation. Private
seminars in etiquette and gift giving for
private and corporate groups. Author of
Modern Living and Modern Giving.

THE BREAKERS FLOWER SHOP
The Breakers
One S. County Road
Palm Beach, FL 33480
407.833.3026
Martha Morgan
Areas served: Palm Beach and surrounding
areas
Distinctive and unusual floral designs.
Fruit and gourmet baskets, delivery and
wire service.

THE COFFEE CORNER
The Breakers
One S. Country Road
Palm Beach, FL 33480
407.820.9821
Stacy Tasca
Areas served: International shipping
Thirty kinds of gourmet coffee, tea, scones,
pastries, cookies. light lunches, cups, mugs,
specialty tins, gifts.

**CORDIALLY YOURS PRINTERS
AND ENGRAVERS**
296 S. Country Road
Palm Beach, FL 33480
407.655.6103
407.655.6147

Blanche Rotman
Areas served: International
Invitations for all occasions, Crane's fine
stationery and invitations, printed and
engraved invitations. They also provide
calligraphy, gift baskets, napkins, matches,
place cards, etc. Delivery worldwide.

GODIVA CHOCOLATIER
The Gardens at Palm Beach
407.624.0444
World renowned chocolatier. Belgium-style
chocolates, gift baskets and party favors.

NICOLE CHOCOLATIER
The Breakers
One S. Country Road
Palm Beach, FL 33480
407.655.6611 ext. 1503
Jayne Josephs
Areas served: International
Gartner chocolates from Antwerp, Belgium.
Gift baskets, confections, biscuits, china
ware, crystal and favors. Free delivery
locally. Additional store in Boca Raton.

ICE SERVICES
PALM BEACH CATERING
1109 25th Street
West Palm Beach, FL 33407
407.833.1411
407.832.3863
John Sunkel
Areas served: Palm Beach, Hobe Sound
and Boca Raton
Complete party service, including in-home
consultations for menu planning and party
set-up; unique, original recipes prepared and
served by custom-trained staff; all equipment
provided: exquisite linens, silver, crystal;
air-conditioned tents, flower arrangements,
musicians. Covers every request for private
parties. Outstanding service by quality-
conscious personnel, featuring European-
trained chefs and detail-oriented
management; specialties include sit-down
dinners for up to 1000 guests, theme parties;
fresh seafood buffets; ice carvings. Winner
of Caterer, Chaine des Rotisseurs, The Palm
Beach Post's "Number 1 Caterer in the Palm
Beaches". In business for twenty-nine years.

INVITATIONS & ACCESSORIES

ANDREA LEIGH CLASTER
4521 PGA Blvd.
Suite 297
Palm Beach, FL 33418
407.624.4350
Areas served: Palm Beach County
Full event planning and design. Custom-designed and catalogue invitations, featuring charts, place cards. Full in-house calligraphy services. RSVP Management. Custom-designed chocolates. Hospitality gift baskets. Gift consultation. Private seminars in etiquette and gift giving for private and corporate groups. Author of *Modern Living and Modern Giving.*

CORDIALLY YOURS PRINTERS AND ENGRAVERS
296 S. Country Road
Palm Beach, FL 33480
407.655.6103
407.655.6147
Blanche Rotman
Areas served: International
Invitations for all occasions, Crane's fine stationery and invitations, printed and engraved invitations. They also provide calligraphy, gift baskets, napkins, matches, place cards, etc. Delivery worldwide.

OLD TOWN FLOWER SHOPS
1930 N. Dixie Highway
West Palm Beach, FL 33407
407.655.3351
Ted Johns
Areas served: National
Full service florists, floral designers and party planner offers simple elegance and custom designs. In house invitations and calligraphy services. For three consecutive years, voted Best Florist by *Palm Beach Life Magazine.* In business for thirty-eight years.

LIGHTING, STAGING & SOUND

HY-LITE PRODUCTIONS INC.
2304 Florida Avenue
West Palm Beach, FL
33401-7810
407.820.1414
Carl Borrelli
Areas served: International
Complete lighting, sound and special effects production and design services for special events, parties, fashion shows, corporate or private theater and video production. Hy-lite productions provides both the manpower and the technology for perfect events. Specializes in event theme decor (as created with lighting) and special effects. Fully licensed and insured.

MARSHALL GRANT'S ENTERTAINMENT SOURCE, INC.
1750 N. Fla. Mango Road
Suite 103
West Palm Beach, FL 33409
407.686.7000
800.422.1522
Marshall Grant
Billy Duke
Joe Gianuzzi
Areas served: Florida's Gold Coast from Orlando south through Miami; Florida's West Coast (Naples, etc.) Private parties, etc. throughout United States
Orchestras and entertainment for private parties, charity balls, conventions, etc. Suppliers of dance music, entertainers, name speakers, etc. Providers of sound, lighting, audiovisual equipment, etc. Able to provide wide range of sophisticated entertainment needs. Upper-income clients, both private and corporate. Basically private affairs, country clubs, theme parties, music to appeal to wide variety of ages in 25-70 year-old group. Thirty-five years in Palm Beach. Twenty-one years as music directors of The Breakers Hotel, Palm Beach. Marshall Grant is first living band leader inducted into the "Big Band Hall of Fame".

SUTKA PRODUCTIONS INTERNATIONAL, INC.
914 Fern Street
Suite B
West Palm Beach, FL 33401
407.835.8455
800.933.1333
Bruce Sutka
Kevin Verronneau

[Continued on next page]

PALM BEACH

Areas served: International
Floral, lighting and special event coordination. Unique themes, wedding decor and environmental concepts create complete ambiance enhancement. Large-scale corporate and social clientele. Featured in *Town and Country* as one of the ten top party planners in the country as well as on *CNN* and *Good Morning America*, *Special Events* magazine and other national trade publications.

LIMOUSINE & TRANSPORTATION

BARRY R. EPSTEIN ASSOCIATES, INC. & FLORIDA LIMOUSINE ASSOCIATION
2255 Glades Road
Suite 324
Boca Raton, FL 33431-7383
407.241.0001
Areas served: Florida
Public relations, association management, meeting planning, conventions and limousine services.

CAREY LIMOUSINE
407.471.5466
800.336.4646
Privately chauffeured sedans, limousines, vans and mini buses in 372 cities.

DAV EL CHAUFFEURED TRANSPORTATION NETWORK
800.328.3526 (outside CA)
800.826.5779 (inside CA)
Areas Served: International
Luxury chauffeured services in over 350 cities worldwide. Centralized reservations and billing. Airport concierge services.

PARK LIMOUSINE SERVICE
139 N. County Road
Palm Beach, FL 33480
407.832.2222
Areas served: Palm Beach County
Stretch limousines, town cars, personalized VIP service for all occasions.

LINENS

EXTRA TOUCH FLOWERS
319 Clematis Street
West Palm Beach, FL 33401
407.835.8000
Jerold Supernaw
Area served: Palm Beach County
Full service florist and floral designers. Huge variety of linen rentals. Custom-created centerpieces. Flowering plants and tree rentals.

FIESTA PARTY RENTALS
6135 B Lake Worth Road
Lake Worth, FL 33463
407.966.3388
Jane Hutton
Areas served: Southern Florida
Designer linens, tents, tables, chairs, china, flatware, silver and prop rentals. Referral and full party planning services.

PIERRE DEUX
224A Worth Avenue
Palm Beach, FL 33480
407.655.6810
Susie Smithers
Areas served: International
Tabletop accessories, linens, custom tablecloths, several French Faience collections, place mats, oversize plates and cutlery, candleholders, pots of jam, delicate wine glasses, ice buckets etc. Will ship UPS anywhere.

MUSIC & ENTERTAINMENT

MARSHALL GRANT'S ENTERTAINMENT SOURCE, INC.
1750 N. Fla. Mango Road
Suite 103
West Palm Beach, FL 33409
407.686.7000
800.422.1522
Marshall Grant
Billy Duke
Joe Gianuzzi
Areas served: Florida's Gold Coast from Orlando south through Miami; Florida's West Coast (Naples, etc.) Private parties, etc. throughout United States
Orchestras and entertainment for private

parties, charity balls, conventions, etc. Suppliers of dance music, entertainers, name speakers, etc. Providers of sound, lighting, audiovisual equipment, etc. Able to provide wide range of sophisticated entertainment needs. Upper-income clients, both private and corporate. Basically private affairs, country clubs, theme parties, music to appeal to wide variety of ages in 25-70 year-old group. Thirty-five years in Palm Beach. Twenty-one years as music directors of The Breakers Hotel, Palm Beach. Marshall Grant is first living band leader inducted into the "Big Band Hall of Fame".

PARTY SITES

BICE RISTORANTE
313 Worth Avenue
Palm Beach, FL 33480
407.835.1600
Maurizio Ciminella
Areas served: Palm Beach
Northern Italian cuisine. Receptions: 220 people. Sit down: 150 people.

THE BREAKERS
One S. Country Road
Palm Beach, FL 33480
407.659.8415
Kevin Walters
Social and corporate special events, theme parties, breakfasts, lunches and dinners at The Breakers. Winner of the International Food & Wine Society Citation for Excellence. Venetian Ballroom reception: 1400. Banquet: 850. Mediterranean Ballroom: 600. Banquet: 300.

CAFE L'EUROPE
150 Worth Avenue
Palm Beach, FL 33480
407.655.4020
Norbert Goldner
Lidia Goldner
Bruce Strickland
Romantic and flower-filled; this is one of the most beautiful restaurants in the area. Primarily French in technique with a dash of contemporary American style. Recipient of the Golden Spoon Award, 1991; Florida

Trend's Top 100, 1991; South Florida Magazine Awards: Most Romantic, Best Service, Best Atmosphere and Best Decor, 1990-1991; Distinguished Restaurants of North American Award, 1991. 3739 square feet. Receptions: 80 people. Sit down: 125 people.

THE OCEAN GRAND
2800 S. Ocean Blvd.
Palm Beach, FL 33480
407.582.2800
Catering Dept.
Luxurious ocean front resort. Tennis, ocean front pool and European health spa facilities. Offering full banquet, conference and meeting facilities. Receptions: 600 people. Sit down: 450 people.

PALM BEACH POLO & COUNTRY CLUB
13198 Forest Hill Blvd.
West Palm Beach, FL 33414
407.793.1440
Mike Titlebaum
Polo events, private polo matches and demonstrations, corporate events, golf tournaments with forty-five holes - dunes course designed by Jerry Pate and Ron Garl. Cypress course designed by Pete and P.B. Dye. Corporate tennis events with twenty-four courts available. Groups up to 200. On site parking. Full catering services, weddings.

TA-BOO
221 Worth Avenue
Palm Beach, FL 33480
407.835.3500
Kim O'Dea
An American bistro and bar. Holds up to fifty guests. Not available from December through May.

PERSONNEL & STAFFING

THE WHITE APRON CATERING
1253 Old Okeechobee Road
Suite B8
West Palm Beach, FL 33401
407.832.7175
Charles Crawford

[Continued on next page]

Areas served: Palm Beach, Brownard and
Dade County
Catering, staffing and rentals. Specializing
in creative cuisine and top notch service.
For celebrity events. Authors of *The
Dessert Cookbook*.

PHOTOGRAPHY & VIDEO

AVANTI VIDEO PRODUCTIONS, INC.
2300 Palm Beach Lakes Blvd.
Suite 100
West Palm Beach, FL 33409
407.684.9426
Areas served: International
Video taping and editing services for
weddings, parties, Bar Mitzvahs, Bat
Mitzvahs and special events. Emphasis on
unobtrusive candid coverage of events.
Special editing effects and techniques. Won
1981 Journalism Award, State of Florida in
1992 Wedding Videography Excellence
Award.

LUCIEN CAPEHART PHOTOGRAPHY
336 S. Country Road
Palm Beach, FL 33480
407.833.7507
Areas served: Palm Beach
Social photography.

MORT KAY STUDIOS, INC.
313 Peruvian Avenue
Palm Beach, FL 33480
407.833.3635
Mort Kay
Areas served: International
Party, commercial and portrait
photography. Specializing in weddings and
social events.

PLANT RENTALS

EXTRA TOUCH FLOWERS
319 Clematis Street
West Palm Beach, FL 33401
407.835.8000
Jerold Supernaw
Area served: Palm Beach County
Full service florist and floral designers.
Huge variety of linen rentals. Custom-

created centerpieces. Flowering plants and
tree rentals.

POTTED PLANT & FLOWER SHOP
249 Royal Poinciana Way
Palm Beach, FL 33480
407.659.7174
Pat Sandberg
Areas served: Palm Beach Counties
Full service florists, floral design and plant
rentals for special events.

PROPS & DECOR

ANDREA LEIGH CLASTER
4521 PGA Blvd.
Suite 297
Palm Beach, FL 33418
407.624.4350
Areas served: Palm Beach County
Full event planning and design. Custom-
designed and catalogue invitations,
featuring charts, place cards. Full in-house
calligraphy services. RSVP Management.
Custom-designed chocolates. Hospitality
gift baskets. Gift consultation. Private
seminars in etiquette and gift giving for
private and corporate groups. Author of
Modern Living and Modern Giving.

FIESTA PARTY RENTALS
6135 B Lake Worth Road
Lake Worth, FL 33463
407.966.3388
Jane Hutton
Areas served: Southern Florida
Designer linens, tents, tables, chairs, china,
flatware, silver and prop rentals. Referral
and full party planning services.

HY-LITE PRODUCTIONS INC.
2304 Florida Avenue
West Palm Beach, FL
33401-7810
407.820.1414
Carl Borrelli
Areas served: International
Complete lighting, sound and special
effects production and design services for
special events, parties, fashion shows,
corporate or private theater and video
production. Hy-lite productions provides

both the manpower and the technology for perfect events. Specializes in event theme decor (as created with lighting) and special effects. Fully licensed and insured.

REGENCY PARTY RENTALS AND PRODUCTIONS
6615 Norton Avenue
West Palm Beach, FL 33405
407.588.7600
800.933.1333
Dan Ivancevic
Areas served: South Florida
Full party planning, decorating, floral design, tenting, rentals and costumes for Southern Florida. Warehouse filled with 30,000 square feet of props, costumes and floral accessories. Member and past Board of Director for the American Rental Association.

SUTKA PRODUCTIONS INTERNATIONAL, INC.
914 Fern Street
Suite B
West Palm Beach, FL 33401
407.835.8455
800.933.1333
Bruce Sutka
Kevin Verronneau
Areas served: International
Floral, lighting and special event coordination. Unique themes, wedding decor and environmental concepts create complete ambiance enhancement. Large-scale corporate and social clientele. Featured in *Town and Country* as one of the ten top party planners in the country as well as on *CNN* and *Good Morning America*. *Special Events* magazine and other national trade publications.

PUBLIC RELATIONS

BARRY R. EPSTEIN ASSOCIATES, INC. & FLORIDA LIMOUSINE ASSOCIATION
2255 Glades Road
Suite 324
Boca Raton, FL 33431-7383
407.241.0001
Areas served: Florida
Public relations, association management,

meeting planning, conventions and limousine services.

SPEAKERS

MARSHALL GRANT'S ENTERTAINMENT SOURCE, INC.
1750 N. Fla. Mango Road
Suite 103
West Palm Beach, FL 33409
407.686.7000
800.422.1522
Marshall Grant
Billy Duke
Joe Gianuzzi
Areas served: Florida's Gold Coast from Orlando south through Miami; Florida's West Coast (Naples, etc.) Private parties, etc. throughout United States
Orchestras and entertainment for private parties, charity balls, conventions, etc. Suppliers of dance music, entertainers, name speakers, etc. Providers of sound, lighting, audiovisual equipment, etc. Able to provide wide range of sophisticated entertainment needs. Upper-income clients, both private and corporate. Basically private affairs, country clubs, theme parties, music to appeal to wide variety of ages in 25-70 year-old group. Thirty-five years in Palm Beach. Twenty-one years as music directors of The Breakers Hotel, Palm Beach. Marshall Grant is first living band leader inducted into the "Big Band Hall of Fame".

TABLETOP ACCESSORIES & KITCHENWARE

CRATE & BARREL
The Gardens of the Palm Beaches
Palm Beach Gardens, FL 33410
407.627.9505
Full line of unique contemporary home furnishings and accessories featuring tabletop accessories and gourmet kitchenware.

[Continued on next page]

PALM BEACH

NICOLE CHOCOLATIER
The Breakers
One S. Country Road
Palm Beach, FL 33480
407.655.6611 ext. 1503
Jayne Josephs
Areas served: International
Gartner chocolates from Antwerp, Belgium.
Gift baskets, confections, biscuits, china
ware, crystal and favors. Free delivery
locally. Additional store in Boca Raton.

PIERRE DEUX
224A Worth Avenue
Palm Beach, FL 33480
407.655.6810
Susie Smithers
Areas served: International
Tabletop accessories, linens, custom
tablecloths, several French Faience
collections, place mats, oversize plates and
cutlery, candleholders, pots of jam, delicate
wine glasses, ice buckets etc. Will ship UPS
anywhere.

POTTERY BARN
3101 PGA Blvd.
Suite M217
Palm Beach, FL 33410
407.626.9700
Leading retailer of contemporary tableware
and decorative accessories for the home.
Merchandise is s100% exclusive, designed
and sold exclusively at Pottery Barn. Over
50 stores nationally and mail order.

WILLIAMS-SONOMA
3101 PGA Blvd.
Suite Q217
Palm Beach, FL 33410
407.694.2068
An authoritative selection of the best for the
kitchen. Complete line of cookware,
bakeware, electrics, glassware, tabletop,
kitchen furniture, cookbooks, packaged
foods. Knowledgeable staff will help choose
equipment, plan parties. Most merchandise
is exclusive to Williams-Sonoma.

VALET PARKING

PALM BEACH VALET PARKING
1830 Antigua Road
West Palm Beach, FL 33405
407.965.2843
John Kavekos
Valet parking services for private parties.

YACHT & BOAT CHARTERS

DISCOVERY CRUISES
1850 Eller Drive
Suite 402
Fort Lauderdale, FL 33316
305.525.8400
Babette Barrett
Areas served: Palm Beach, Dade and
Broward Counties
Vessel has four decks of casino gambling.
Holds over 1,250 guests. Full catering and
event planning services available. Packages
offered that include live style Vegas shows,
pool side parades, overnight packages to
Freeport and the Bahamas.

WASHINGTON D.C.

WASHINGTON D.C.

AUDIOVISUAL & TECHNICAL SERVICES

COMET PRODUCTIONS, INC.
733 Fifteenth Street, NW
Suite 700
Washington, DC 20005
202.347.3344
Halle Becker
Areas served: National
Event production, entertainment, decor,
audiovisual services. National talent/acts.
Written up in *Special Events Magazine*,
guest speaker at Special Event Eight and
Nine.

L & A TENT RENTALS
7668-B Fullerton Road
Springfield, VA 22153
703.451.3390
Gail Stafford
Areas served: Washington Metro area
including Middleburg, Eastern Shore and
Baltimore
Rental of party tents in all sizes and colors,
dance floors, staging, lighting, heaters, fans,
air conditioning.

BALLOONS

BALLOON BOUQUETS® NATIONWIDE DELIVERY INFORMATION SERVICE
500 23rd Street, NW
Washington, DC 20037
202.785.1131
800.424.2323
Joe DelVecchio
Areas served: National
Balloons, imprinting, designs, sculptures,
gifts. Originator of balloon deliveries.

BALLOONS OVER WONDERLAND/TRES JOLI WEDDINGS AND SPECIAL EVENTS
12658 Monarch Court
Lakeridge, VA 22192
703.590.7172
Lou Ilardi
Areas served: Maryland, Washington, DC,
Northern Virginia
Invitations, accessories, event planning,
floral and balloon design. Balloon arches,
drops, releases, centerpieces and stuffers.

BOOKS

WILLIAMS-SONOMA
Mazza Galleria
5300 Wisconsin Avenue, NW
Washington, DC 20015
202.244.4800

Georgetown Park
3222 "M" Street, NW
Suite W55
Washington, CA 20007
202.965.3422

An authoritative selection of the best for the
kitchen. Complete line of cookware,
bakeware, electrics, glassware, tabletop,
kitchen furniture, cookbooks, packaged
foods. Knowledgeable staff will help choose
equipment, plan parties. Most merchandise
is exclusive to Williams-Sonoma.

CATERING

ALL SEASON BUSINESS COMMUNICATION AGENCY
3 W. Nap Lane
Annapolis, MD 21401
410.974.1919
J. Steven Justice
Areas served: Maryland, Washington, DC,
Virginia, Pennsylvania, Delaware, New
Jersey, New York
Special event planning, catering,
entertainment, and printing.

BIDDLE STREET CATERING
411 N. Warwick Avenue
Baltimore, MD 21223
410.233.1344
Larry Levy
Lee Lynch
Terry Dressin
Areas served: Maryland, Metro Baltimore,
Washington, DC, Southern Pennsylvania
Full service off-premise catering. From
white glove service to box lunches and
dinners, crab feasts to old fashioned bull
roasts. Regional Chesapeake Bay seafood
specialists. Fundraisers, Bar Mitzvahs,
weddings and galas. Member Chaine des
Rotisseurs.

L'ACADEMIE DE CUISINE

5021 Wilson Lane
Bethesda, MD 20814
301.986.9490
800.445.1959
Patrice Dionot
Areas served: National
Gourmet cooking classes for private groups, cooking classes and food excursions to Gascony, France. Teacher will travel anywhere in the US. Specializing in French cuisine. Limited catering. In business sixteen years.

LA FONDA MEXICAN RESTAURANT & CATERING

1639 "R" Street, NW
Washington, DC 20009
202.232.6965
Anne Vogel
Banquet room is perfect for dinners, receptions, or meetings. Imported blue and white tiles make the room elegant yet very cozy for any occasion. Offer authentic Mexican cuisine as well as the unusual and creative in today's cuisine. 1500 square feet. Receptions: 175 people. Sit down: 80 people.

MED-CATERING

11307 Elkin Street
Wheaton, MD 20902
301.946.2230
Kamal Al-Faqih
Areas served: Maryland, Washington, DC, Virginia
Full service off-premise caterer, party planner and wedding specialist. Specialize in Mediterranean cuisine. Will UPS food throughout the US.

PARIS CATERERS & RENTALS

12260 Wilkens Avenue
Rockville, MD 20852
301.530.5402
William De Paris
Areas served: Washington, DC, Virginia, Maryland, Delaware
Full service catering, event planning, equipment rental, and floral arts. Distinctions include Presidential Inaugurals.

CHOCOLATES & CONFECTIONS

GODIVA CHOCOLATIER

Union Station
202.342.2232

Georgetown
"M" Street
202.342.2232
World renowned chocolatier. Belgium-style chocolates, gift baskets and party favors.

CLASSES & SEMINARS

L'ACADEMIE DE CUISINE

5021 Wilson Lane
Bethesda, MD 20814
301.986.9490
800.445.1959
Patrice Dionot
Areas served: National
Gourmet cooking classes for private groups, cooking classes and food excursions to Gascony, France. Teacher will travel anywhere in the US. Specializing in French cuisine. Limited catering. In business sixteen years.

DESTINATION MANAGEMENT

THE CAPITAL INFORMER, INC.

3240 Prospect Street, NW
Washington, DC 20007
202.965.7420
Valerie Sumner
Full service event, destination and meeting management services provided. Services include: special event design and implementation, corporate and exhibitor entertaining, transportation, accommodation staffing, spouse programs, entertainment, customized and general tour design, meeting content development and logistical management. Association, corporation, pharmaceutical, domestic incentive and international incentive programming. Distinctions include: SITE 1990 Co-chair awards banquet committee. Valerie Sumner member of Krisam Group since 1990. Outstanding service to 4-H

1990. SITE for contributing to the success of the SITE Board of Directors meeting and for its commitment to the incentive travel industry - July 1990. SITE Washington, DC regional activities chair - Valerie Sumner. SITE Co-chair awards banquet committee 1990 - Linda Higgison.

EQUIPMENT RENTALS & TENTING

ALLIED RENTAL CENTERS
3825 Bonney Road
Virginia Beach, VA 23452
804.340.0908

961 Reon Drive
Virginia Beach, VA 23464
804.420.1030

1020 N. Battlefield Blvd.
Chesapeake, VA 23320
804.436.0363
Karen Dickinson
Areas served: Virginia Beach, Chesapeake, Norfolk, Portsmouth, Northeast North Carolina, Eastern Shore
Tents, full line of party items and wedding accessories.

BROOKE RENTAL CENTER
150 Maple Avenue, E
Vienna, VA 22180
703.938.4807

4817 First Street, N
Arlington, VA 22043
703.243.2122
Bob Brooke
Areas served: Washington, DC, Northern Virginia, suburban Maryland
Party rentals, tents, staging, dance floors, catering equipment and high volume party goods.

L & A TENT RENTALS
7668-B Fullerton Road
Springfield, VA 22153
703.451.3390
Gail Stafford
Areas served: Washington Metro area including Middleburg, Eastern Shore and Baltimore

Rental of party tents in all sizes and colors, dance floors, staging, lighting, heaters, fans, air conditioning.

PARIS CATERERS & RENTALS
12260 Wilkens Avenue
Rockville, MD 20852
301.530.5402
William De Paris
Areas served: Washington, DC, Virginia, Maryland, Delaware
Full service catering, event planning, equipment rental, and floral arts. Distinctions include Presidential Inaugurals.

WHEATON PARTY RENTALS
4229 Howard Avenue
Kensington, MD 20895
301.564.1010
Eric Goldberg
Areas served: Baltimore, MD, and Metropolitan D.C.
Party equipment, tenting, linen rentals, tables, chairs, silver and china.

EVENT PLANNING

ALL SEASON BUSINESS COMMUNICATION AGENCY
3 W. Nap Lane
Annapolis, MD 21401
410.974.1919
J. Steven Justice
Areas served: Maryland, Washington, DC, Virginia, Pennsylvania, Delaware, New Jersey, New York
Special event planning, catering, entertainment, and printing.

BALLOONS OVER WONDERLAND/TRES JOLI WEDDINGS AND SPECIAL EVENTS
12658 Monarch Court
Lakeridge, VA 22192
703.590.7172
Lou Ilardi
Areas served: Maryland; Washington, DC; Northern Virginia
Invitations, accessories, event planning, floral and balloon design. Balloon arches, drops, releases, centerpieces and stuffers.

THE CAPITAL INFORMER, INC.
3240 Prospect Street, NW
Washington, DC 20007
202.965.7420
Valerie Sumner

Full service event, destination and meeting management services provided. Services include: special event design and implementation, corporate and exhibitor entertaining, transportation, accommodation staffing, spouse programs, entertainment, customized and general tour design, meeting content development and logistical management. Association, corporation, pharmaceutical, domestic incentive and international incentive programming. Distinctions include: SITE 1990 Co-chair awards banquet committee. Valerie Sumner member of Krisam Group since 1990. Outstanding service to 4-H 1990. SITE for contributing to the success of the SITE Board of Directors meeting and for its commitment to the incentive travel industry - July 1990. SITE Washington, DC regional activities chair - Valerie Sumner. SITE Co-chair awards banquet committee 1990 - Linda Higgison.

COMET PRODUCTIONS, INC.
733 Fifteenth Street, NW
Suite 700
Washington, DC 20005
202.347.3344
Halle Becker

Areas served: National
Event production, entertainment, decor, audiovisual services. National talent/acts. Written up in *Special Events Magazine*, guest speaker at Special Event Eight and Nine.

GALA EVENTS, INC.
4915 St. Elmo Avenue
Suite 303
Bethesda, MD 20814
301.718.2900
Linda Garner

Areas served: National
Full service event planning, design and production. Specializing in award winning creative and unique functions for corporate, government, non-profit, and social clientele.

HODGE PODGE UNLIMITED
8013 Cindyla
Bethesda, MD 20817
301.365.3708
Bobbye Horowitz

Areas served: Greater Washington, DC, Virginia, Maryland and National
Complete party planning, including decorations, site selection, music and menu selection. Event direction and supervision, and planning of every detail. Tremendous selection of invitations, stationery and party supplies. In-house artist for special theme decor. Consistently picked as one of the area's top coordinators by *Washington* and *Dossier* magazines. Many write ups in local papers including quotes and mentions in the *Washington Post*.

MED-CATERING
11307 Elkin Street
Wheaton, MD 20902
301.946.2230
Kamal Al-Faqih

Areas served: Maryland, Washington, DC, Virginia
Full service off-premise caterer, party planner and wedding specialist. Specialize in Mediterranean cuisine. Will UPS food throughout the US.

PARIS CATERERS & RENTALS
12260 Wilkens Avenue
Rockville, MD 20852
301.530.5402
William De Paris

Areas served: Washington, DC, Virginia, Maryland, Delaware
Full service catering, event planning, equipment rental, and floral arts. Distinctions include Presidential Inaugurals.

SAAVVY ASSOCIATES LTD.
P.O. Box 8011
Silver Springs, MD 20907
301.439.6866
Rita Palmer

Areas served: Metropolitan Washington, DC
Full event planning services. Specializing in spectacular receptions, banquets, holiday celebrations and organized conferences.

WASHINGTON D.C.

FAVORS

GODIVA CHOCOLATIER
Union Station
202.342.2232

Georgetown
"M" Street
202.342.2232

World renowned chocolatier. Belgium-style chocolates, gift baskets and party favors.

TIFFANY & CO.
Fairfax Square at Tyson's Corner
8045 Leesburg Pike
Vienna, VA 22182
703.893.7700

The finest in engraved invitations, favors, accessories, stationery, bridal registry, fine crystal and china, Tiffany flatware and gifts for all occasions.

GIFTS & GIFT BASKETS

GODIVA CHOCOLATIER
Union Station
202.342.2232

Georgetown
"M" Street
202.342.2232

World renowned chocolatier. Belgium-style chocolates, gift baskets and party favors.

TIFFANY & CO.
Fairfax Sq.at Tyson's Corner
8045 Leesburg Pike
Vienna, VA 22182
703.893.7700

The finest in engraved invitations, favors, accessories, stationery, bridal registry, fine crystal and china, Tiffany flatware and gifts for all occasions.

INVITATIONS & ACCESSORIES

BALLOONS OVER WONDERLAND/TRES JOLI WEDDINGS AND SPECIAL EVENTS
12658 Monarch Court
Lakeridge, VA 22192
703.590.7172

Lou Ilardi
Areas served: Maryland, Washington, DC, Northern Virginia
Invitations, accessories, event planning, floral and balloon design. Balloon arches, drops, releases, centerpieces and stuffers.

HODGE PODGE UNLIMITED
8013 Cindyla
Bethesda, MD 20817
301.365.3708
Bobbye Horowitz
Areas served: Greater Washington, DC, Virginia, Maryland and National
Complete party planning, including decorations, site selection, music and menu selection. Event direction and supervision, and planning of every detail. Tremendous selection of invitations, stationery and party supplies. In-house artist for special theme decor. Consistently picked as one of the area's top coordinators by *Washington* and *Dossier* magazines. Many write ups in local papers including quotes and mentions in the *Washington Post.*

TIFFANY & CO.
Fairfax Sq.at Tyson's Corner
8045 Leesburg Pike
Vienna, VA 22182
703.893.7700

The finest in engraved invitations, favors, accessories, stationery, bridal registry, fine crystal and china, Tiffany flatware and gifts for all occasions.

LIGHTING, STAGING & SOUND

BROOKE RENTAL CENTER
150 Maple Avenue, E
Vienna, VA 22180
703.938.4807

4817 First Street, N
Arlington, VA 22043
703.243.2122
Bob Brooke
Areas served: Washington, DC, Northern Virginia, suburban Maryland
Party rentals, tents, staging, dance floors,

catering equipment and high volume party goods.

L & A TENT RENTALS
7668-B Fullerton Road
Springfield, VA 22153
703.451.3390
Gail Stafford
Areas served: Washington Metro area including Middleburg, Eastern Shore and Baltimore
Rental of party tents in all sizes and colors, dance floors, staging, lighting, heaters, fans, air conditioning.

LIMOUSINE & TRANSPORTATION

ATLANTIC VALET, INC.
1828 "L" Street, NW
Washington, DC 20036
202.466.4300
Area served: Washington Metro area
Full valet parking service and all transportation needs: limousines, vans, buses, mini buses and driver service.

CAREY LIMOUSINE
202.362.7400
Privately chauffeured sedans, limousines, vans and mini buses in 372 cities.

DAV EL CHAUFFEURED TRANSPORTATION NETWORK
800.328.3526 (outside CA)
800.826.5779 (inside CA)
Areas Served: International
Luxury chauffeured services in over 350 cities worldwide. Centralized reservations and billing. Airport concierge services.

OLD TOWN TROLLEY TOURS
5225 Kilmer Place
Hyattsville, MD 20781
301.985.3021
Tours, transportation, shuttle services for individuals, groups and weddings. Largest fleet operator of theme styled vehicles in the United States.

LINENS

WHEATON PARTY RENTALS
4229 Howard Avenue
Kensington, MD 20895
301.564.1010
Eric Goldberg
Areas served: Baltimore, MD, and Metropolitan D.C.
Party equipment, tenting, linen rentals, tables, chairs, silver and china.

MUSIC & ENTERTAINMENT

ALL SEASON BUSINESS COMMUNICATION AGENCY
3 W. Nap Lane
Annapolis, MD 21401
410.974.1919
J. Steven Justice
Areas served: Maryland; Washington; DC; Virginia; Pennsylvania; Delaware; New Jersey and New York
Special event planning, catering, entertainment, and printing.

CELLAR DOOR ENTERTAINMENT
329 South Patrick Street
Alexandria, VA 22314
703.683.1900
Scott Clayton
Areas served: Mid Atlantic and Southeastern States
Local, regional and national entertainers for events of all sizes. A division of the Cellar Door Companies, one of the largest concert promoters in the music business.

COMET PRODUCTIONS, INC.
733 Fifteenth Street, NW
Suite 700
Washington, DC 20005
202.347.3344
Halle Becker
Areas served: National
Event production, entertainment, decor, audiovisual services. National talent/acts. Written up in *Special Events Magazine*, guest speaker at Special Event Eight and Nine.

[Continued on next page.]

SUPER STAR STUDIOS
2658 Puttman Drive
Silver Springs, MD 20910
301.588.8500
Tina Reman
Areas served: International
Interactive musical entertainment for
parties and special events. Karaoke, MTV
style music videos, portable singing booths
and the "Walking Piano" from the movie
Big.

PARTY SITES
CLYDE'S OF TYSONS CORNER
8332 Leesburg Pike
Vienna, VA 22182
703.734.1907
June Ciuba
On premise catering for parties from 2 - 200
guests. Restaurant serves 200 customers on
the first floor (main restaurant). Specialize
in salmon, crab cakes, filet mignon and
good American food. *Best Friends* was
filmed at Clyde's.

CORCORAN GALLERY OF ART
Seventeenth Street and
New York Avenue, NW
Washington, DC 20006
202.638.3211
Susan Wall
A Beaux Art building located across from
the south lawn of the White House. Large
central atrium, two stories, skylighted,
marble columns. Marble staircase leading
to rotunda. Receptions: 1000 people. Sit
down: 400 people. Street parking.
Outstanding collection of American Art.
Auditorium seats 193 people.

DECATUR HOUSE
748 Jackson Place, NW
Washington, DC 20006
202.842.0920
Page Nelson
Historic house museum built by Benjamin
Henry La Trobe in 1818 for Commodore
Stephen DeCatur. Museum property of the
National Trust for Historic Preservation.
Museum, courtyard and adjacent carriage
house. Receptions: 500 people. Sit down:

220 people. Listed in *Historic Register*.

THE FOUR SEASONS HOTEL
2800 Pennsylvania Avenue, NW
Washington, DC 20007
202.342.0444
Lynn Orlowski
Judy Sullivan
Elegant 197 room hotel, including thirty
suites. Banquet space tastefully appointed.
Excellent service. Only five diamond
award-winning hotel in Washington, DC.
Voted number three in the US, number ten
in world as best hotel by readers of *Conde
Nast Traveler Magazine*. Ranked number
five best hotel in North America by
Institutional Investor Magazine.
Receptions: 800 people. Sit down: 400
people.

THE HENLEY PARK HOTEL
926 Massachusetts Avenue, NW
Washington, DC 20001
202.638.5200
Jeff Dailey
Washington's corner of Tudor Elegance.
Home of the noted Coeur de Lion
Restaurant, Wilkes Room High Tea and
Marley's Lounge Jazz. 4000 square feet
available for functions. Listed in the
National Historic Registrar and *Zagat
Restaurant Guide's* Top Ten DC.
Receptions: 225 people. Sit down: 150
people.

LA FONDA MEXICAN RESTAURANT & CATERING
1639 "R" Street, NW
Washington, DC 20009
202.232.6965
Anne Vogel
Banquet room is perfect for dinners,
receptions, or meetings. Imported blue and
white tiles make the room elegant yet very
cozy for any occasion. Offer authentic
Mexican cuisine as well as the unusual and
creative in today's cuisine. 1500 square
feet. Receptions: 175 people. Sit down: 80
people.

THE NATIONAL MUSEUM OF WOMEN IN THE ARTS
1250 New York Avenue, NW
Washington, DC 20005

202.783.5000
Ann Kent Holton
Mary Alice Nay
Housed within a huge Renaissance-Revival
style structure are four spaces: the Martin
Marietta Great Hall located on the first
floor and mezzanine, third-floor galleries, a
fourth-floor board room and a fifth-floor
auditorium. 1987 AIA Washington
Chapter's Achievement of Excellence in
Historic Preservation and Architecture;
1987 Associate Building and Contractors
Award for Restoration and Preservation;
1988 Washington Building Congress
Awards; 1988 ASID Thomas Jefferson
Award. Receptions: 1000 people (great hall
and mezzanine), 300 people (third floor
gallery). Sit down: 500 people (great hall
and mezzanine), 125 people (third floor
gallery). Meetings: from 35 in the board
room to 197 in the theater. Performance:
197 (auditorium).

WOODROW WILSON HOUSE MUSEUM
2340 "S" Street, NW
Washington, DC 20008
202.387.4062
Karen Walsh
Neo-classical town house off of Embassy
Row. Garden and indoor facilities. W.
Wilson memorabilia, his last home after the
White House. The only Presidential
Museum in the city of Washington.
Receptions: 350 people. Sit down: 250
people.

PARTY SUPPLIES
BROOKE RENTAL CENTER
150 Maple Avenue, E
Vienna, VA 22180
703.938.4807

4817 First Street, N
Arlington, VA 22043
703.243.2122
Bob Brooke
Areas served: Washington, DC, Northern
Virginia, suburban Maryland
Party rentals, tents, staging, dance floors,
catering equipment and high volume party
goods.

HODGE PODGE UNLIMITED
8013 Cindyla
Bethesda, MD 20817
301.365.3708
Bobbye Horowitz
Areas served: Greater Washington, DC,
Virginia, Maryland and National
Complete party planning, including
decorations, site selection, music and menu
selection. Event direction and supervision,
and planning of every detail. Tremendous
selection of invitations, stationery and party
supplies. In-house artist for special theme
decor. Consistently picked as one of the
area's top coordinators by *Washington* and
Dossier magazines. Many write ups in local
papers including quotes and mentions in the
Washington Post.

PHOTOGRAPHY & VIDEO
PROGRESSIVE MARKETING, INC.
941 S. George Mason Drive
Arlington, VA 22204
703.486.1500
Fran Adams
Areas served: International
Free-standing, life-sized, mounted
photographs of public figures may be rented
locally or sold out of state. Locally, a
photographer may be sent to take Polaroid
pictures of guests with the life-sized
photograph for momentos. The portraits
may also be used as displays. Worldwide
shipping.

REFLECTIONS PHOTOGRAPHY, INC.
700 Thirteenth Street, NW
Suite 950
Washington, DC 20005
202.434.4528
Joanne Amos
Areas served: National
Charitable balls, political events, proof
distribution to all participants.

[Continued on next page.]

WASHINGTON D.C.

PLANT RENTALS

PLANTS ALIVE!
15710 Layhill RoadSilver
Springs, MD 20906
301.598.3843
Betsy Lazaroff
Areas served: Maryland; Washington, DC;
East Coast
Short term tropical plant rentals for
conventions, weddings and special events.

PROPS & DECOR

COMET PRODUCTIONS, INC.
733 Fifteenth Street, NW
Suite 700
Washington, DC 20005
202.347.3344
Halle Becker
Areas served: National
Event production, entertainment, decor,
audiovisual services. National talent/acts.
Written up in *Special Events Magazine*,
guest speaker at Special Event Eight and
Nine.

HODGE PODGE UNLIMITED
8013 Cindyla
Bethesda, MD 20817
301.365.3708
Bobbye Horowitz
Areas served: Greater Washington, DC,
Virginia, Maryland and National
Complete party planning, including
decorations, site selection, music and menu
selection. Event direction and supervision,
and planning of every detail. Tremendous
selection of invitations, stationery and party
supplies. In-house artist for special theme
decor. Consistently picked as one of the
area's top coordinators by *Washington* and
Dossier magazines. Many write ups in local
papers including quotes and mentions in the
Washington Post.

TABLETOP ACCESSORIES & KITCHENWARE

CRATE & BARREL
Tyson's Corner Center
McLean, VA 22102
703.847.8555

Fashion Centre at Pentagon City
Arlington, VA 22202
703.418.1010

Montgomery Mall
7101 Democracy Blvd.
Bethesda, MD 20817
301.365.2600
Full line of unique contemporary home
furnishings and accessories featuring tabletop
accessories and gourmet kitchenware.

POTTERY BARN
Galleria at Tyson's II
1750 - 2001 International Drive
McLean, VA 22102
703.821.8504

5345 Wisconsin Avenue, NW
Suite 8
Washington, DC 20015
202.244.9330
Leading retailer of contemporary tableware
and decorative accessories for the home.
Merchandise is 100% exclusive, designed
and sold exclusively at Pottery Barn. Over
fifty stores nationally and mail order.

TIFFANY & CO.
Fairfax Sq.at Tyson's Corner
8045 Leesburg Pike
Vienna, VA 22182
703.893.7700
The finest in engraved invitations, favors,
accessories, stationery, bridal registry, fine
crystal and china, Tiffany flatware and gifts
for all occasions.

WILLIAMS-SONOMA
Mazza Galleria
5300 Wisconsin Avenue, NW
Washington, DC 20015
202.244.4800

Georgetown Park
3222 "M" Street, NW
Suite W55

Washington, DC 20007
202.965.3422

An authoritative selection of the best for the kitchen. Complete line of cookware, bakeware, electrics, glassware, tabletop, kitchen furniture, cookbooks, packaged foods. Knowledgeable staff will help choose equipment, plan parties. Most merchandise is exclusive to Williams-Sonoma.

VALET PARKING

ATLANTIC VALET, INC.
1828 "L" Street, NW
Washington, DC 20036
202.466.4300

Area served: Washington Metro area
Full valet parking service and all transportation needs: limousines, vans, buses, mini buses and driver service.

&a &a &a

NATIONAL

AUDIOVISUAL & TECHNICAL SERVICES

ACADEMY TENT AND CANVAS, INC.
2910 S. Alameda Street
Los Angeles, CA 90058
213.234.4060
800.228.3687 (inside CA)
800.222.4535 (outside CA)
Maury Rice
Areas served: National
Provide complete facility hospitality
equipment for private, commercial,
institutional, and corporate hospitality
events nationally. Including tents, flooring,
ground covering, staging, lighting, heating,
air conditioning, and power. Founded
1981.

AGGREKO, INC.
655 Grigsby Way
Suite "A"
Cedar Hill, TX 75104
214.293.0491
Eric Bartley
Areas served: National
Power and temperature rental company,
generator power, electrical distribution.

ATLANTA MUSIC AGENCY
P.O. Box 720297
Atlanta, GA 30358
404.552.8220

10820 Shallowford Road
Roswell, GA 30075
404.552.8220
Tony N. Garstin
Areas served: National
Entertainment contractors, technical
production: sound, lights, stages, stage
sets, technical administration, labor
administration.

ATTRACTIONS, INC.
P.O. Box 565013
Dallas, TX 75356
214.941.6971
R. Edward Cobb, President
Areas served: International
Full service entertainment firm including,
but not limited, to live performance
entertainment such as dance and show
bands, name recording attractions,

television and movie personalities,
speakers, comics, magicians, specialty
attractions, etc.; also sound and light
production, contract and rider
consultation, audio/video support systems,
and on-site stage and production
management. Specializes in consultation
and procurement of live performance
entertainment and the equipment and
logistics to present such entertainment.

AUDIO VISUAL AMERICA/STAGE SOUND
20229 N.E. Sixteenth Place
Miami, FL 33162
305.653.0008
Tim Snow
Areas served: International
Progressive production support company
dedicated to customer service and
specializing in "State of the Art" equipment
rentals, sales, service, design, installation,
consultation and professional technicians.
Full concert sound, staging and lighting
capabilities. Videowalls, laser shows and
program development capabilities. Video
projection: large and small audience
packages. Special recognition from: Papal
visit, Formula One Grand Prix, CBS
Records International, Polygram Records,
Fiesta Bowl, Kodak, IBM, Tucson
Symphony, Telluride Bluegrass Festival,
Colorado State Fair and Meeting Concepts.

COMET PRODUCTIONS, INC.
733 Fifteenth Street, NW
Suite 700
Washington, DC 20005
202.347.3344
Halle Becker
Areas served: National
Event production, entertainment, decor,
audiovisual services. National talent/acts.
Written up in Special Events Magazine,
guest speaker at Special Event Eight and
Nine.

DESIGN & PRODUCTIONS
11105 Shady Trail
Suite 104
Dallas, TX 75229
214.243.4572
David Opper
Areas served: International
Full service lighting design company

providing lighting, staging, scenery, audio and special effects. Specializes in design, installation and production.

EVENT TECHNICAL SERVICES, INC.
6600 Bandini Blvd.
City of Commerce, CA 90040
800.521.8368
Chris Coe
Areas served: National
State licensed contractor. Portable restrooms, temporary plumbing, generators, power distribution, platforms, stages, portable wood floors, air conditioning, heating, pool scaffolds. Specializing in outdoor events.

MAGNUM COMPANIES
170-A Ohley Drive, NE
Atlanta, GA 30324
404.872.0553
Erik Magnuson
Areas served: National
Stage lighting, sound, video, audiovisual services. Rent, sell, produce and design lighting equipment.

MCCUNE AUDIO VISUAL
951 Howard Street
San Francisco, CA 94103
415.885.2510
Dave Molnar
Areas served: International
Complete audiovisual services, sound systems, videos, multimedia, etc., for corporate events, meetings and conventions.

THE SHOW DEPARTMENT, INC.
1555 N. Sheffield
Chicago, IL 60622
312.787.2600
Areas served: International
Complete industrial show staging: large inventory of state-of-the-art equipment for rental. Multi-image projection. Video and data projection, live audio mixing, computerized lighting systems, video recording, velour drapery system, custom scenic system. Emphasis on industrial show staging/corporate meetings.

TOTAL AUDIO VISUAL SERVICES, INC.
811 Marietta Street, NW
Atlanta, GA 30318

404.875.7555
Areas served: International
Equipment, personnel and planning expertise for all audiovisual needs. All size events.

WESTERN SCENIC STUDIOS
1470 Citrus Ridge
Escondido, CA 92025
619.943.8847
Ted Prina
Areas served: National
Full event decor including lighting, staging, and floral design. Full trade show production. Technical services. In business since 1919.

BALLOONS

BALLOON BOUQUETS® NATIONWIDE DELIVERY INFORMATION SERVICE
500 23rd Street, NW
Washington, DC 20037
202.785.1131
800.424.2323
Joe DelVecchio
Areas served: National
Balloons, imprinting, designs, sculptures, gifts. Originator of balloon deliveries.

BALLOONS BY TIC-TOCK
1601 1/2 N. La Brea Avenue
Los Angeles, CA 90028
213.874.3034
Eddie Zaratsian
Areas served: California based - available Nationwide
Elegant balloon decoration for events and parties. Custom concept, design and production. Uses 100% biodegradable balloons. Winner of several awards including Best Sculpture.

BALLOONS TO YOU
2152-B Chennault Drive
Carrollton, TX 75006
214.788.5022
Areas served: International
Wholesale and retail large scale balloon decor. Balloon bouquets.

[Continued on next page.]

NATIONAL

BOOKS

THE COOKBOOK STORE
850 Yonge Street
Toronto, Ontario Canada M4W
2H1
416.920.2665
Alison Fryer
Areas served: International
Books on food and wine. Newsletters and
mail orders.

COOKS BOOKS
34 Marine Drive
Rottingdean, Sussex, England
BN2 7HQ
0273-302707
Mike & Tessa McKirdy
Areas served: International
Out-of-print, antiquarian, rare and unusual
cookbooks, wine books, and related
subjects. Send $5.00 to receive two
catalogues each of approximately 1000
items.

DEAN & DELUCA
560 Broadway
New York, NY 10012
212.431.1691
James Mellgren
Areas served: International
Tabletop accessories, kitchenware,
cookbooks, gift baskets. Full service
specialty foods and catering. Cheese,
pastries, produce, caviar, smoked fish,
custom Marin designed chocolates, Dean &
Deluca herbs and spices, dried beans and
grains, mail order department. Deliver
anywhere.

GAZIN'S CAJUN-CREOLE CUISINE
P.O. Box 19221
2910 Toulouse Street
New Orleans, LA 70179
504.482.0302
800.262.6410 (orders only)
Earl Robinson
Areas served: Fifty United States, Puerto
Rico, US Virgin Islands, APO, FPO and
Canada
Gourmet foods, cookbooks and utensils by
mail order. Specialize in Cajun and Creole
foods of Louisiana.

GOURMET GUIDES
636 First Street
Benicia, CA 94510
707.745.3909
Jean Bullock
Areas served: International
One of the largest selections of cookbooks
available anywhere. Professional chef,
caterer, books and American regional.
Hours: Wednesday - Saturday 11:00 to
3:00; often other days as well.

HOUSEHOLD WORDS
284 Purdue
Kensington, CA 94708
510.524.8859
Kay Caughren
Cookery and wine books. Out-of-print cook
books and related ephemera.

STOREY COMMUNICATIONS
GARDEN WAY PUBLISHING
P.O. Box 445
Schoolhouse Road
Pownal, VT 05261
802.823.5811
800.827.8673 (orders)
Nick Noyes, Publicity Director
"Books for Country Living" mail order
catalog offers many cookbooks suitable for
party planners, from "Picnic!" for outdoor
parties to "Perfect Fruit Pies" for dessert to
"Satisfying Soups" for all occasions.
Specialize in wholesome, healthy recipes.

WILLIAMS-SONOMA
Mail Order Department
P.O. Box 7456
San Francisco, CA 94120-7456
800.541.2233 (Orders)
800.541.1262 (Customer
service)
Areas served: National
An authoritative selection of the best for the
kitchen. Complete line of cookware,
bakeware, electrics, glassware, tabletop,
kitchen furniture, cookbooks, packaged
foods. Knowledgeable staff will help choose
equipment, plan parties. Most merchandise
is exclusive to Williams-Sonoma.

THE WINE AND FOOD LIBRARY
1207 W. Madison Street
Ann Arbor, MI 48103

313.663.4894
Jan Longone
Areas served: International
Sell antiquarian and out-of-print
cookbooks. Consult on historical cookery.

CAKES & BAKED GOODS
BALDUCCI'S
424 Avenue of the Americas
New York, NY 10011
212.673.2600
Areas served: National
International delicacies, catering, gift
baskets and mail order. International
cheese and deli, regional Italian foods,
smoked fish, fresh baked ethnic breads,
homemade pastries, gourmet coffee, exotic
and local produce, specialty groceries,
prime meats, fresh fish.

MISS GRACE LEMON CAKE CO.
422 N. Canon Drive
Beverly Hills, CA 90210
310.281.8096
800.367.2253 (mail order)
Mindy Moss
Areas served: Los Angeles, West Side,
Valley. Ship mail order anywhere.
Highest quality baked goods made
exclusively from scratch. Known for their
lemon cake. Wedding cakes, decorated
cakes for all occasions, gift baskets.

CELEBRITY ACQUISITION
**A-1 ENTERTAINMENT
AND CONCESSIONS, INC.**
2644 N. Ashland Avenue.
Chicago, IL 60614
312.880.8000
Customer Service
Areas served: Illinois, Indiana, Michigan,
Wisconsin, Minnesota, Kansas
Provides theme party props and decorating
services; Las Vegas nights and casino
equipment rentals; catering equipment and
antique food cart rentals; entertainment,
music, specialty and animal acts; balloons:

decorating, printing, helium and supplies;
amusements, kiddy rides and carnival
games; full service events, corporate picnics
and parties; tents, tables, chairs, BBQs and
general rentals. Specializing in corporate
events, custom theme parties, balloon
decorating, prop and decor, design and
construction from in-house shops and hard-
to-find rental items. Won Gala Award at
Special Event Convention for Most
Imaginative Use of Equipment.

ATLANTA SPEAKERS BUREAU
2859 Paces Ferry Road
Suite 1830
Atlanta, GA 30339
404.432.1394
Sherry J. Conner
Speakers, celebrities, entertainers. For
meetings, parties and special events.

ATTRACTIONS, INC.
P.O. Box 565013
Dallas, TX 75356
214.941.6971
R. Edward Cobb, President
Areas served: International
Full service entertainment firm including,
but not limited, to live performance
entertainment such as dance and show
bands, name recording attractions,
television and movie personalities,
speakers, comics, magicians, specialty
attractions, etc.; also sound and light
production, contract and rider
consultation, audio/video support systems,
and on-site stage and production
management. Specializes in consultation
and procurement of live performance
entertainment and the equipment and
logistics to present such entertainment.

DAMON BROOKS ASSOCIATES
1680 N. Vine Street
Suite 910
Hollywood, CA 90028
213.465.3400
Marc Goldman
Areas served: National
Coordination of celebrity involvement with
special events. Tennis, golf, and related
sporting events. Speaking, entertainment,
auction items and personal appearances.
Recognized by California Meetings, Western

Association News, Affordable Meetings,
International Festivals Association,
American Society of Association Executives.

THE ENTERTAINMENT CONNECTION, INC.
204 S. Clark Drive
Beverly Hills, CA 90211
310.652.1996
Penny Bigelow
Areas served: International
Special event production and coordination,
entertainment, catering, decoration, sound
systems, lighting, special effects, laser
shows, press/special event photographers,
limousine service, bus charters, parking
attendants, security. Entertainment at
every price level – celebrities, singers,
dancers, bands, musical groups, comics,
speakers, sports stars, complete shows.

KUSHNER AND ASSOCIATES
1104 S. Robertson Blvd.
Los Angeles, CA 90035
310.274.8819
Linda Kushner
Areas served: Southern California
Corporate event, meeting and full service
destination management company. Handle
transportation, sight seeing, companion
programs, sports and special events, music,
novelty entertainment, celebrity
acquisition, registration and hospitality
staff. Theme parties and technical support.

LORDLY & DAME
51 Church Street
Boston, MA 02116
617.482.3596
Sam Dame
Areas served: International
Full event planning, music and
entertainment, speakers, celebrity
acquisition.

MARCI WEINER
450 S. Maple Drive
Suite 204
Beverly Hills, CA 90212
310.276.5070
Areas served: Beverly Hills, Los Angeles,
Bel Air, Malibu, Palm Springs, San Diego
and Santa Barbara.
Columnist with many newspapers and

publications serving the affluent West Side
and Beverly Hills areas. She can provide
copy in any of her various publications as
well as celebrity acquisition services for
special events.

MIKE VACCARO PRODUCTIONS, INC.
3848-A Atlantic Avenue
Suite 4
Long Beach, CA 90807
310.424.4958
Mike Vaccaro
Areas served: International
Music, entertainment, theme parties, party
planning, site selection, celebrity
entertainment, etc.

STANDING OVATIONS
8380 Miramar Mall
Suite 225
San Diego, CA 92121
619.455.1850
Nan Pratt
P.J. Fox
Areas served: International
International full service speaker bureau
serving associations and corporate clients.
Quality speakers, trainers, celebrities,
entertainers and sports stars for keynotes,
general sessions, seminars and workshops.

WASHINGTON SPEAKERS BUREAU
888 Seventh Avenue
New York, NY 10106
212.541.7980
Areas served: International
Speakers for all occasions - celebrity's,
sports, political, motivation, business,
humorous.

WEST COAST COMEDY CONTACT
11362 Reagan Street
Los Alamitos, CA 90720
310.431.6122
Mariana Tilton
Areas served: Southern California
Top notch entertainers, name and novelty
acts, comics, magicians and clowns for
parties, hotels and roasts.

CALLIGRAPHY

See listings in individual cities

CHOCOLATES & CONFECTIONS

ANDREA LEIGH CLASTER
212.633.0970
Areas served: National
Full event planning and design. Custom-designed and catalogue invitations, seating, charts, place cards. Full in-house calligraphy services. RSVP management. Custom-designed chocolates. Hospitality gift baskets. Gift consultation. Private seminars in etiquette and gift giving. For private and corporate groups. Author of *Modern Living and Modern Giving*.

BALDUCCI'S
424 Avenue of the Americas
New York, NY 10011
212.673.2600
Areas served: National
International delicacies, catering, gift baskets and mail order. International cheese and deli, regional Italian foods, smoked fish, fresh baked ethnic breads, homemade pastries, gourmet coffee, exotic and local produce, specialty groceries, prime meats, fresh fish.

THE CHOCOLATE GALLERY
34 W. 22nd Street
New York, NY 10010
212.675.CAKE
Areas served: National
Carries over 10,000 items fully stocked: cake pans in all shapes and sizes from round, square, and rectangle to characters like Big Bird and Ninja Turtles. Full assortment of cookie cutters in different shapes. Supplies to make a wedding cake, from cake stands, fountains, bridges, ushers and bridesmaids in all color dresses, to the wedding ornament to dazzle the top of the cake. Tips, pastry bags, icing colors, spatulas, and much more. A wide selection of books and videos on the latest ideas in cake decorating. Offers Wilton Cake Decorating classes in Spanish: learn how to decorate cakes for the family or to start a business selling beautifully decorated cakes.

THE CHOCOLATE TRUFFLE
200 W. Cummings Park
Woburn, MA 01801
617.933.4616
Norma Herscott
Barbara Yankovich
Areas served: Continental U.S.
Specializing in swiss chocolate truffles, corporate gifts in theme chocolate, wedding favors, chocolate roses, swans, and baskets. Won *Boston Magazine*'s "Best" Chocolate Award 1990 and 1991. Muscular Dystrophy People's Choice Silver medal award.

COMPARTE'S OF CALIFORNIA
925 Montana Avenue
Santa Monica, CA 90403
310.395.2297
Jill Barker
Areas served: Courier service available for Los Angeles area, UPS available to anywhere in U.S.
Hand dipped chocolates, stuffed fruits (individually wrapped dried fruit with nuts), gift tins, custom gift baskets, molded chocolates, candies. Examples of party items: molded chocolate basket with chocolate strawberries and raspberries or assorted truffles, individual boxes (with 2 chocolates) with names to be used as place cards, chocolates with decorations (holiday, floral), theme gifts (chocolate tennis racket or golf balls). Written up in *Bon Apetit*, English toffee called "Best in Town" *Los Angeles Magazine*.

DEAN & DELUCA
560 Broadway
New York, NY 10012
212.431.1691
James Mellgren
Areas served: International
Tabletop accessories, kitchenware, cookbooks, gift baskets. Full service specialty foods and catering. Cheese, pastries, produce, caviar, smoked fish, custom designed chocolates, Dean & Deluca herbs and spices, dried beans and grains, mail order department. Deliver anywhere.

[Continued on next page.]

E.A.T.

1064 Madison Avenue
New York, NY 10028
212.772.0022
Areas served: National
Restaurant, gourmet shop, gift shop, wholesale bread, and catering. Tabletop accessories, cheese, caviar, fresh baked pastry, custom-designed cakes. Smoked Norwegian salmon, fresh produce, gourmet salads, gift baskets. Known for their breads.

EDELWEISS CHOCOLATES

444 N. Canon Drive
Beverly Hills, CA 90210
310.275.0341
Sam Rosen
Areas served: National
Finest handmade chocolates, marshmallows, fresh nuts, specially designed nuts, chocolate favors, place cards, specialty mints, gift boxes, custom designed candy plates, monogrammed mint disks, eighty varieties of chocolates and truffles handmade on the premises, chocolate seating cards. Clients all over the country, featured in *The Chocolate Bible*, over twenty magazine articles, TV shows, etc. In business over fifty years.

JOSEPH SCHMIDT CONFECTIONS

3489 16th Street
San Francisco, CA 94114
415.861.8682
Audrey Ryan
Areas served: U.S. and Canada
Custom-designed chocolates for all events. They create and sculpt anything in chocolate. They love to create one-of-a-kind things and also provide custom-designed gift baskets. Catalogue available.

JUDI KAUFMAN AND COMPANY

400 S. Beverly Drive
Suite 214
Beverly Hills, CA 90212
310.858.7787
Judi Kaufman
Areas served: National
Grand Chocolate Pizzas™ mail order. Choice of fifty-two toppings. Start at $20.00.

KARL BISSINGER'S CHOCOLATE CATALOGUE

3983 Gratiot
St. Louis, MO 63110
800.325.8881
Areas served: International
Custom and specialty mints and bars. Hand-crafted mints and/or bars with customer's name, monogram, logo, etc.

LEE GELFOND CHOCOLATES

275 S. Robertson Blvd.
Beverly Hills, CA 90211
310.854.3524
Lee Gelfond
Areas served: National
Custom-designed chocolates for all occasions — favors, gift baskets, corporate gifts, etc.

NICOLE CHOCOLATIER

The Breakers
One S. Country Road
Palm Beach, FL 33480
407.655.6611 ext. 1503
Jayne Josephs
Areas served: International
Gartner chocolates from Antwerp, Belgium. Gift baskets, confections, biscuits, china ware, crystal and favors. Free delivery locally. Additional store in Boca Raton.

PINK WHALE CHOCOLATIERS

699 Serramonte Blvd.
Suite 202
Daly City, CA 94015
415.997.3865 (collect calls accepted)
Tom Beyerle, Chocolatier
Areas served: National
Manufacturers of gourmet chocolates. Mail order and wholesale. Hand-dipped fresh chocolate made in small batches. Company produces 10,000 pounds per year. Number one swimming whale gift box, chocolate madeleine bar, "sparklers", humpback whale and bottlenose dolphin, monthly mail order specials (e.g., chocolate-covered strawberries, confectionary brownies, Easter baskets, etc.). Wedding favors. One percent gross sales donation to the American Cetacean Society for the preservation and research of whales and dolphins.

NATIONAL

MARTINS WINE CELLAR FOOD EMPORIUM AND DELI
3827 Baronne Street
New Orleans, LA 70115
504.899.7411
Marc Pelletier
Areas served: National
Fine wines, champagnes, liqueurs, cordials, custom gift baskets, wine seminars and tastings, delicacies, cheeses, pates, chocolates, confections, salmons, caviar, foie gras, coffee, teas, speakers on all areas of viticulture, holiday catalogue.

PSEUDIOS ARTISTIC EDIBLES
2117 Glendale Galleria
Glendale, CA 91210
818.240.422
Jeanne Goraleski
Areas served: National
Sculptured chocolates, nuts, gourmet food gifts, sugar free and novelty candy.

TEUSCHER CHOCOLATES
9548 Brighton Way
Beverly Hills, CA 90210
310.276.2776
Aviva Covitz, Owner
Janet Surmi, Manager
Areas served: International
Imported truffles, pralines, gianduja and marzipan chocolates from Zurich, Switzerland. Known for their champagne truffles filled with a center of Dom Perignon creme, handmade decorated gift boxes from Switzerland, gift baskets and elegant packaging with personalized service. They provide local and international delivery. Specialty is champagne truffle filled with a center of Dom Perignon creme. Handmade, decorated gift boxes from Switzerland, colorful bouquets and assorted characters, birds and animals. Unique and elegant packaging with personalized service. "...the best all-around chocolatier.", Gael Greene, *New York Magazine*; "for chocolate lovers...many connoisseurs consider Teuscher to be the world's finest", Mimi Sheraton, *New York Times*; "the most meltingly marvelous of all chocolate creations.", *Bon Apetit*.

ULTIMATE NUT & CANDY CO.
11849 Ventura Blvd.
Studio City, CA 91604
818.772.8267
Jerry Donath
Areas served: Southern California
Hand-dipped highest quality chocolates. All natural and no artificial preservatives. Named Best in Southern California by *MGM Grand Air Magazine*. Shipping and delivery.

CLASSES & SEMINARS
ANDREA LEIGH CLASTER
212.633.0970
Areas served: National
Full event planning and design. Custom-designed and catalogue invitations, seating, charts, place cards. Full in-house calligraphy services. RSVP management. Custom-designed chocolates. Hospitality gift baskets. Gift consultation. Private seminars in etiquette and gift giving. For private and corporate groups. Author of *Modern Living and Modern Giving*.

L'ACADEMIE DE CUISINE
5021 Wilson Lane
Bethesda, MD 20814
301.986.9490
800.445.1959
Patrice Dionot
Areas served: National
Gourmet cooking classes for private groups, cooking classes and food excursions to Gascony, France. Teacher will travel anywhere in the U.S. Specializing in French cuisine. Limited catering. In business sixteen years.

[Continued on next page.]

COSTUMES

BOB MANDELL'S COSTUME SHOP, INC.
  1137 Mission Street
  San Francisco, CA 94103
  415.863.7755
  Bob Mandell
Areas served: International
Northern California's largest costume
rental shop. 5000 costumes for sale. 40,000
costumes for rent. Novelties, masks, wigs,
beards, makeup. Makeup artist on staff
during Halloween week.

BROADWAY COSTUMES, INC.
  954 W. Washington Blvd.
  4th Floor
  Chicago, IL 60607-2217
  312.829.6400
Areas served: National
Costume rental and sales. Providing
masquerade party costumes since 1886.

COSTUME ARCHITECTS
  1536 Monroe Drive, NE
  Atlanta, GA 30324
  404.875.6275
Areas served: National
Costume rentals, custom made costumes,
wigs, make-up, masks, mascots, hats.
Make-up artist and staff during holidays
and Mardi Gras.

THE COSTUME HEADQUARTERS
  3635 Banks Street
  New Orleans, LA 70119
  504.488.9523
  Louise Genozler
Areas served: National
Costume sales and rentals. Wigs, make-up,
masks, fishnet stockings, etc. Shipping
available C.O.D.

GLENDALE COSTUMES
  315 N. Brand Blvd.
  Glendale, CA 91203
  818.244.1161
  Jeanne Reith, Costume
  Coordinator & Designer
  Bryan Leder, Theatrical Rentals
  Robin Kissner, Masquerade
  Rentals
Areas served: National
Costuming, makeup and costume

construction. Stock of 60,000 costumes.
complete costuming. All time periods,
including animal walk-abouts and novelties.
All categories. Clowns to grapes, soldiers
to gypsies, Romeo's to Draculas. Costume
coordination for theme parties, weddings,
etc. Resident designer holds Drama Critics
Circle and *Dramalogue* Awards for
Costume Design.

DELICACIES

APPLESOURCE
  Route 1
  Chapin, IL 62628
  217.245.7589
  Tom or Jill Vorbeck
Areas served: National
Packs of specialty apples – antique and
modern – via mail order. Over eighty
varieties were offered in 1991. Note: can
ship from late October to first week of
January only. Specialize in apple tasting
parties. "The Sampler" – twelve apples,
one each of twelve varieties, can be used for
an informal apple tasting party for six
guests. For larger groups of eight or more
(garden clubs, botanical gardens, historical
societies, etc.), they will help plan the event
and select varieties of apples.

BALDUCCI'S
  424 Avenue of the Americas
  New York, NY 10011
  212.673.2600
Areas served: National
International delicacies, catering, gift
baskets and mail order. International
cheese and deli, regional Italian foods,
smoked fish, fresh baked ethnic breads,
homemade pastries, gourmet coffee, exotic
and local produce, specialty groceries,
prime meats, fresh fish.

BEL-AIR WINE MERCHANT
  10421 Santa Monica Blvd.
  W. Los Angeles, CA 90025
  310.474.9518
  Bob Gold
Areas served: Los Angeles, International
Old vintage wines. Fresh Russian caviar.
Full bar supplies. Delivery, ship worldwide.

NATIONAL

BEST REGARDS

7898 Ostrow
Suite F
San Diego, CA 92111
619.560.9040
800.544.6234
Alan Aegerter
Areas served: National
Quality wines and champagnes with your
personal message on the label. Gourmet
foods, personalized gift baskets. Great
holiday selections. No minimum.

THE C.S. STEEN SYRUP MILL, INC.

119 N. Main Street
P.O. Box 339
Abbeville, LA 70511-0339
318.893.1654
Manufacture and package 100% pure cane
syrup, molasses and cane vinegar. In
business since 1910. 100% pure. Call or
write for free brochure. Ship via UPS or
truckline to all states and overseas

CABOT CREAMERY

P.O. Box 128
Cabot, VT 05647
802.563.2650
Connie Gould
Areas served: National
Award winning white Vermont cheddar
cheese and a complete line of reduced fat
cheddar. Fast and efficient mail order.
Awarded Best Cheddar in the US and best
low fat cheddar in the US by the US Cheese
Maker Association.

CAVIAR EXPRESS

4397 W. Bethany Home Road
Glendale, AZ 85301-5401
800.326.5777
Areas served: International
Sell fresh Malossol Black Russian Beluga
Caviar.

CAVIARTERIA, INC.

29 E. 60th Street
New York, NY 10022
800.4.CAVIAR
Eric Sobol
Areas served: United States, Puerto Rico
and Mexico
Mail order and store sale of caviar, Scotch
salmon, fresh foie gras, gourmet foods, gift
baskets, champagne shipped anywhere in
California. Won Chefs in America Gold
Medal, Confrerie De Chain Des Rotisseurs
Award Of Excellence.

CHILI PEPPER EMPORIUM

328 San Felipe Road, NW
Albuquerque, NM 87104
505.242.7538
Areas served: National
New Mexico largest and most complete chili
gift shops (three). Free mail order catalog.
Chili specialty, chili ristras, salsa, chile
jams, ground chili powders, t-shirts and
chili serving dishes. Provides all varieties.
Listed as the source for chili cooks in *Sunset
Magazine*, *Aib Journal*, *New York Times*
and many other publications throughout the
country.

THE COFFEE CORNER

The Breakers
One S. Country Road
Palm Beach, FL 33480
407.820.9821
Stacy Tasca
Areas served: International shipping
Thirty kinds of gourmet coffee, tea, scones,
pastries, cookies. light lunches, cups, mugs,
specialty tins, gifts.

COMPARTE'S OF CALIFORNIA

925 Montana Avenue
Santa Monica, CA 90403
310.395.2297
Jill Barker
Areas served: Courier service available for
Los Angeles area, UPS available anywhere
in US.
Hand dipped chocolates, stuffed fruits
(individually wrapped dried fruit with
nuts), gift tins, custom gift baskets, molded
chocolates, candies. Examples of party
items: molded chocolate basket with
chocolate strawberries and raspberries or
assorted truffles, individual boxes (with 2
chocolates) with names to be used as place
cards, chocolates with decorations (holiday,
floral), theme gifts (chocolate tennis racket
or golf balls). Articles in *Bon Apetit*,
English toffee called "Best in Town" *Los
Angeles Magazine*.

[Continued on next page.]

NATIONAL

COOK FLAVORING COMPANY
200 Sherwood Road
Paso Robles, CA 93446
805.238.3400
Josephine Lochhead
Areas served: National
Baking, spices, extracts, flavors. Flavoring
consultants provide the customer with the
very finest flavors available. Flavors are all
natural and pure. Can also create a flavor
to suit the customer's specific needs.
Specialize in vanilla extract.

D'ARTAGNAN INC.
399 St. Paul Avenue
Jersey City, NJ 07306
201.792.0748
800.DARTAGNan
Ariane Daguin
Areas served: National
Mail order foie gras, entrees, smoked game,
game sausages, game pates, fresh game and
specialty birds.

DEAN & DELUCA
560 Broadway
New York, NY 10012
212.431.1691
James Mellgren
Areas served: International
Tabletop accessories, kitchenware,
cookbooks, gift baskets. Full service
specialty foods and catering. Cheese,
pastries, produce, caviar, smoked fish,
custom designed chocolates, Dean & Deluca
herbs and spices, dried beans and grains,
mail order department. Deliver anywhere.

GAZIN'S CAJUN-CREOLE CUISINE
P.O. Box 19221
2910 Toulouse Street
New Orleans, LA 70179
504.482.0302
800.262.6410 (orders only)
Earl Robinson
Areas served: 50 United States, Puerto
Rico, Virgin Islands, Canada
Gourmet foods, cookbooks and utensils by
mail order. Specialize in Cajun and Creole
foods of Louisiana.

IDEAL CHEESE SHOP
1205 Second Avenue
New York, NY 10021

212.688.7577
800.382.0109
Edward Edelman
Areas served: National
Finest cheese. Catalogue. National
delivery. Rated Number One by *Zagat*,
Gault Millau, Awards from the French
government.

MO HOTTA - MO BETTA, INC.®
P.O. Box 4136
San Luis Obispo, CA 93403
805.544.4051
Tim Eidson
Areas served: International (one day UPS
service to Los Angeles)
Mail order catalog specializing in hot and
spicy food, clothing and accessories. Strong
emphasis on hot sauces. Chosen by
Entrepeneur Magazine as one of the twenty-
one hottest new businesses of 1991. Mail
order provides supplies for any "hot food"
party.

**THE NEW ORLEANS SCHOOL OF COOKING
AND THE LOUISIANA GENERAL STORE**
620 Decautur Street
New Orleans, LA 70130
504.525.2665
800.237.4841
Joe and Karen Cahn
Three hour class for visitors to New Orleans
teaching the basics of Creole cooking.
Other topics offered as well. Call for
information. The General Store carries all
Louisiana products - food mixes,
cookbooks, arts and crafts. National mail
order catalogue.

OMAHA STEAKS INTERNATIONAL
10909 John Galt Blvd.
P.O. Box 3300
Omaha, NE 68103
800.228.2778, Ext. 8135
Areas served: National
Unconditional guarantee, two-day express
delivery, gift card enclosures, free "Gold
Life Guide & Cookbook, " special 800 line
for customer service and home economists.
For seventy-five years, Omaha Steaks
International has specialized in the finest
cuts of corn-fed, naturally-aged Midwestern
beef. Steaks, as ordered, are of equal

weight and size. Steaks of all sizes and combinations, entrees of lamb, pork, veal, seafood and poultry; appetizers and desserts. The 1991 Zagat's New York Marketplace Survey ranked Omaha Steaks in the top five mail order companies for quality, variety, service and best buys.

PARADIGM FOODWORKS, INC.
5775 SW Jean Road
Suite 106-A
Lake Oswego, OR 97035
503.636.4880
800.234.0250
Lynne Barra
Areas served: National
Haute fudge sauce, lemon curd, Belgian waffle mixes, scone mixes. Mail order catalogue. Finalist 1990 NASFT for lemon curd. 1990 Washington Red Raspberry Comm. winner of "Best Red Raspberry Product."

PFAELZER BROTHERS
281 W. 83rd Street
Burr Ridge, IL 60521
708.325.9700
800.621.0226 (orders)
Sue Kristy
Areas served: National
Catalog source for fine quality gourmet foods. Everything from appetizers to desserts. Famous for specially selected and trimmed steaks, roasts and chops. Butter-smooth, meltingly tender filet mignon a specialty.

PORT CHATHAM SMOKED SEAFOOD
632 NW Forty-sixth Street
Seattle, WA 98107
206.783.8200
800.8.SALMON
(800.872.5666)
Areas served: National
Smoked salmon in ready-to-serve whole fillets. Pre-sliced lox and cater cut kipper. High quality smoked salmon. The only smokehouse that uses Copper River King Salmon, the world's finest salmon, for its lox. High in natural oil, with a deep red color – it can't be beat. Orders ship via Federal Express.

PSEUDIOS ARTISTIC EDIBLES
2117 Glendale Galleria
Glendale, CA 91210
818.240.422
Jeanne Goraleski
Areas served: National
Sculptured chocolates, nuts, gourmet food gifts, sugar free and novelty candy.

TABASCO COUNTRY STORE
c/o McIlhenny Company
Avery Island, LA 70513
800.634.9599
Angie Schaubert
Areas served: National
Tabasco logo sportswear, linenwear, kitchenware, food product, giftware. Cajun foods.

TEA IMPORTERS, INC.
47 Riverside Avenue
Westport, CT 06880
203.226.3301
Areas served: International
Mail order. Import of teas.

ULTIMATE NUT & CANDY CO.
11849 Ventura Blvd.
Studio City, CA 91604
818.772.8267
Jerry Donath
Areas served: Southern California
Hand-dipped highest quality chocolates. All natural and no artificial preservatives. Named Best in Southern California by *MGM Grand Air Magazine*. Shipping and delivery.

DESTINATION MANAGEMENT
DAME ASSOCIATES, INC.
51 Church Street
Boston, MA 02116
617.482.3596
Douglas Dame
Areas served: International
Destination management, trade show production, convention coordination, exhibit and display rentals, corporate seminars.

FAVORS

ANDREA LEIGH CLASTER
212.633.0970
Areas served: National
Full event planning and design. Custom-designed and catalogue invitations, seating, charts, place cards. Full in-house calligraphy services. RSVP management. Custom-designed chocolates. Hospitality gift baskets. Gift consultation. Private seminars in etiquette and gift giving. For private and corporate groups. Author of *Modern Living and Modern Giving*.

CALLIGRAPHIC ARTS INC.
4232 Herschel Avenue
Suite 201
Dallas, TX 75219
214.522.4731
Susie-Melissa Cherry
Areas served: National
Custom-designed invitations, favors, accessories, name tags, place cards, awards and calligraphy.

COMPARTE'S OF CALIFORNIA
925 Montana Avenue
Santa Monica, CA 90403
310.395.2297
Jill Barker
Areas served: Courier service available for Los Angeles area, UPS available to anywhere in US
Hand dipped chocolates, stuffed fruits (individually wrapped died fruit with nuts), gift tins, custom gift baskets, molded chocolates, candies. Examples of party items: molded chocolate basket with chocolate strawberries and raspberries or assorted truffles, individual boxes (with 2 chocolates) with names to be used as place cards, chocolates with decorations (holiday, floral), theme gifts (chocolate tennis racket or golf balls). Written up in *Bon Apetit*, English toffee called "Best in Town" *Los Angeles Magazine*.

ELEGANT ADVERTISING GRAPHICS
7280-A Carrara Place
San Diego, CA 92122
619.457.3232
Peter Turner
Areas served: International

Custom-designed and catalogue invitations, lighting and sound effects, die-cuts, foiled, embossed, special paper folds, pop-ups, place cards, favors, sign-in boards, full calligraphy services.

LINENS ET AL
165 N. Robertson Blvd.
Beverly Hills, CA 90211
310.652.7970
Marilyn Snyder
Areas served: National
Fine tabletop accessories and linens, favors and gift items. Engraving and monogramming.

EVELYN SCHRAMM
4232 Herschel Avenue
Suite 210
Dallas, TX 75219
214.521.6668
Evelyn Schramm
Areas served: National
Custom-designed invitations, favors, accessories and calligraphy services for all occasions.

NICOLE CHOCOLATIER
The Breakers
One S. Country Road
Palm Beach, FL 33480
407.655.6611 ext. 1503
Jayne Josephs
Areas served: International
Gartner chocolates from Antwerp, Belgium. Gift baskets, confections, biscuits, china ware, crystal and favors. Free delivery locally. Additional store in Boca Raton.

SIGNATURE WEDDING MINTS
1529 W. Meeker
Suite 106
Kent, WA
800.447.2993, Ext. 500
Sherrie Brockavich
Manufacturer of big, round, pastel butter mints individually wrapped in glittering silk foil and custom imprinted for all events. Call for brochure.

A SPECIAL FAVOR
617 N. Beverly Drive
Beverly Hills, CA 90210
310.273.3010

Maxx Komack
Gretchen DiNapoli
Areas served: National
Custom-designed party favors, invitations,
bridal attendant gifts, hostess gifts and
elegant accessories for all special occasions.
Previous clients include Lee Iacoca, The
Beverly Hills Hotel, The Bistro Garden and
many more.

TEUSCHER CHOCOLATES
9548 Brighton Way
Beverly Hills, CA 90210
310.276.2776
Aviva Covitz, Owner
Janet Surmi, Manager
Areas served: International
Imported truffles, pralines, gianduja and
marzipan chocolates from Zurich,
Switzerland. Known for their champagne
truffles filled with a center of Dom Perignon
creme, handmade decorated gift boxes from
Switzerland, gift baskets and elegant
packaging with personalized service. They
provide local and international delivery.

ULTIMATE NUT & CANDY CO.
11849 Ventura Blvd.
Studio City, CA 91604
818.772.8267
Jerry Donath
Areas served: Southern California
Hand-dipped highest quality chocolates. All
natural and no artificial preservatives.
Named Best in Southern California by
MGM Grand Air Magazine. Shipping and
delivery.

WILLIAM ERNEST BROWN
442 N. Canon Drive
Beverly Hills, CA 90210
310.278.5620
Areas served: International
Custom-designed and catalogue invitations,
seating charts, accessories, place cards and
party supplies for all special events. They
also provide calligraphy services. Known
for their high quality products and special
services. Clients all over the United States
and Europe.

FIREWORKS & SPECIAL EFFECTS

AUDIO VISUAL AMERICA/STAGE SOUND
20229 N.E. Sixteenth Place
Miami, FL 33162
305.653.0008
Tim Snow
Areas served: International
Progressive production support company
dedicated to customer service and
specializing in "State of the Art" equipment
rentals, sales, service, design, installation,
consultation and professional technicians.
Full concert sound, staging and lighting
capabilities. Videowalls, laser shows and
program development capabilities. Video
projection: large and small audience
packages. Special recognition from: Papal
visit, Formula One Grand Prix, CBS
Records International, Polygram Records,
Fiesta Bowl, Kodak, IBM, Tucson
Symphony, Telluride Bluegrass Festival,
Colorado State Fair and Meeting Concepts.

CLASSIC FIREWORKS BY EVENTS, INC.
P.O. Box 205
Mandeville, LA 70470-0205
504.893.8800
800.783.2513
David Spear
Areas served: International
Indoor pyrotechnic productions and aerial
fireworks displays. Produced pyrotechnics
at last three Super Bowls.

DESIGN & PRODUCTIONS
11105 Shady Trail
Suite 104
Dallas, TX 75229
214.243.4572
David Opper
Areas served: International
Full service lighting design company
providing lighting, staging, scenery, audio
and special effects. Specializes in design,
installation and production.

FIREWORKS BY GRUCCI
One Grucci Lane
Brookhaven, NY 11719
516.286.0088
M. Philip Butler
Areas served: International

State of the art fireworks programs featuring world renowned choreography of music and fireworks. World champions of Monte Carlo Competitions.

HY-LITE PRODUCTIONS INC.
2304 Florida Avenue
West Palm Beach, FL 33401-7810
407.820.1414
Carl Borrelli
Areas served: International
Complete lighting, sound and special effects production and design services for special events, parties, fashion shows, corporate or private theater and video production. Hy-lite productions provides both the manpower and the technology for perfect events. Specializes in event theme decor (as created with lighting) and special effects. Fully licensed and insured.

IMAGES EVENT PRODUCTION
1649 Twelfth Street
Santa Monica, CA 90404
310.392.4240
Jerry Astourian
Areas served: International
Event design, lighting design, set and prop construction. Specializing in Hollywood premiere parties, corporate galas, fundraising events, private affairs. Special Events Magazine Gala Awards: Best Decorated Theme Event, Most Imaginative Use of Lighting & Special Effects (four years), Most Imaginative Use Of A Tent, Most Imaginative Use of Equipment, Special Logistic Award.

PARTY LIGHTS OF CALIFORNIA
8656 Sky Rim Drive
Suite 110
Lakeside, CA 92040
619.443.9949
M. White
Areas served: International
Complete line of Cyalume Lightstick products. Lighters, necklaces, cocktail stirrers, bracelets, earrings. Worldwide shipping.

PYRO SPECTACULARS
P.O. Box 2329
Rialto, CA 92377
800.322.7732

Kevin Kelley
Areas served: International
Aerial fireworks, displays choreographed to music, low level displays and special effects. Clients include Chinese New Year, Hong Kong (annually), Los Angeles Olympics, Rolling Stones Steel Wheel Tour, America Fest, Statue of Liberty, Macy's, Dodgers, Angels, Giants, A's Super Bowls, Hollywood Bowl, Magic Mountain and LA County Fair.

SAMARCO, INC.
1606 Gano Street
Dallas, TX 75215
214.421.0757
800.530.4905
Areas served: National
Lighting, staging, scenery, special effects, design, production, rental, sales. Theatrical solutions to lighting and staging problems. Artistic use of light for scenic purposes and to create ambiance.

ZAMBELLI INTERNATIONALE FIREWORKS MFG. CO., INC.
299 W. 52nd Terrace
Suite 118
Boca Raton, FL 33487
407.994.1588
800.245.0397
Areas served: International
Manufacturer and exhibitor of fireworks extravaganzas. Indoor and outdoor custom-designed exhibitions electrically choreographed to music and lasers. Distinctions include National Victory Celebration, the Opening Ceremonies of The Kentucky Derby Festival, the Statue of Liberty Celebration.

GIFTS & GIFT BASKETS
ANN FIEDLER CREATIONS
10544 W. Pico Blvd.
Los Angeles, CA 90064
310.838.1857
Ann Fiedler
Areas served: International
Fine quality invitations, calligraphy, personalized gifts, place cards, accessories, corporate and charity invites. Unique custom designs with a creative flair at every

price. One of the largest retailers of invitations in the United States with a huge selection of catalogues.

BALDUCCI'S

424 Avenue of the Americas
New York, NY 10011
212.673.2600

Areas served: National
International delicacies, catering, gift baskets and mail order. International cheese and deli, regional Italian foods, smoked fish, fresh baked ethnic breads, homemade pastries, gourmet coffee, exotic and local produce, specialty groceries, prime meats, fresh fish.

BALLOONS BY TIC-TOCK

1601 1/2 N. La Brea Avenue
Los Angeles, CA 90028
213.874.3034
Eddie Zaratsian

Areas served: National
Custom corporate and personal gift baskets for all occasions

BEST REGARDS

7898 Ostrow
Suite F
San Diego, CA 92111
619.560.9040
800.544.6234
Alan Aegerter

Areas served: National
Quality wines and champagnes with your personal message on the label. Gourmet foods, personalized gift baskets. Great holiday selections. No minimum.

THE BEST TO YOU

7915 Silverton Avenue
Suite 307
San Diego, CA 92126
Linda Gorin
619.578.2740

Areas served: International
Custom-designed gift baskets: theme, holiday, corporate gifts. Showroom viewing by appointment only.

CALIFORNIA BASKET COMPANY & WINE SHOP

20 S. Raymond Avenue
Old Pasadena, CA 91105
800.992.9992

818.577.9292
Jack Daniel Smith

Areas served: International
Custom-made gift baskets, can handle large volumes with ease. Baskets can be made on short notice and can include customer supplied products and goods for special events (company mugs, pens, etc.). Specialize in unique gourmet foods, coffees and teas, chocolates, cheeses and meats, bath products. Also feature a large selection of wines and imported beers. One of the largest gift basket companies in California, but each basket is made to order. All bows are hand-made and can be color coordinated for any color scheme. Have a sixteen page full color catalog free of charge.

COMPARTE'S OF CALIFORNIA

925 Montana Avenue
Santa Monica, CA 90403
310.395.2297
Jill Barker

Areas served: Courier service available for Los Angeles area, UPS available to anywhere in U.S.
Hand dipped chocolates, stuffed fruits (individually wrapped died fruit with nuts), gift tins, custom gift baskets, molded chocolates, candies. Examples of party items: molded chocolate basket with chocolate strawberries and raspberries or assorted truffles, individual boxes (with 2 chocolates) with names to be used as place cards, chocolates with decorations (holiday, floral), theme gifts (chocolate tennis racket or golf balls). Written up in *Bon Apetit*, English toffee called "Best in Town" *Los Angeles Magazine*.

THE COFFEE CORNER

The Breakers
One S. Country Road
Palm Beach, FL 33480
407.820.9821
Stacy Tasca

Areas served: International shipping
Thirty kinds of gourmet coffee, tea, scones, pastries, cookies. light lunches, cups, mugs, specialty tins, gifts.

[Continued on next page.]

DEAN & DELUCA

560 Broadway
New York, NY 10012
212.431.1691
James Mellgren
Areas served: International
Tabletop accessories, kitchenware,
cookbooks, gift baskets. Full service
specialty foods and catering. Cheese,
pastries, produce, caviar, smoked fish,
custom designed chocolates, Dean & Deluca
herbs and spices, dried beans and grains,
mail order department. Deliver anywhere.

E.A.T.

1064 Madison Avenue
New York, NY 10028
212.772.0022
Areas served: National
Restaurant, gourmet shop, gift shop,
wholesale bread, and catering. Tabletop
accessories, cheese, caviar, fresh baked
pastry, custom-designed cakes. Smoked
Norwegian salmon, fresh produce, gourmet
salads, gift baskets. Known for their
breads.

EMBASSY SUMNER

796 Lexington Avenue
New York, NY 10021
212.734.8200
Gil Sachs
Areas served: National
Broad spectrum of fine wines and
champagnes. Full wine and liquor event
consultation. Delivery available. Gift
baskets delivered nationwide.

ENCHANTED BASKETS

1645 N. Vine Street
Suite 606
Hollywood, CA 90028
213.467.2171
800.BASKETS
Phyllis Solomon
Areas served: International
Gift baskets and corporate gifts. Unique
basket styles, gourmet, specialty foods,
coffees, teas, chocolate, bath baskets, baby
baskets, etc. Baskets for all holidays and
occasions. Theme baskets - Italian, sport,
Southwestern, etc. Customized baskets
tailored to specifications and budget.

GRACIOUS HOME

1217 & 1220 Third Avenue
New York, NY 10021
212.517.6300
Areas served: National
Invitations, party supplies, tabletop
accessories and kitchenware: table cloths,
napkins, napkin rings, placemats, candles,
china, champagne and wine glasses, caviar
bowls, trays, platters, chaffing dishes,
cheese boards, cookbooks. Custom-
designed and catalogue invitations, place
cards, party baskets, ribbons, wrap, gift
bags, flower arrangements. Free delivery in
Manhattan. Ship nationally.

MISS GRACE LEMON CAKE CO.

16571 Ventura Blvd.
Encino, CA 91436
818.885.1987
Mindy Moss
Areas served: Los Angeles, West Side,
Valley. Ship mail order anywhere.
Highest quality baked goods made
exclusively from scratch. Known for their
lemon cake. Wedding cakes, decorated
cakes for all occasions, gift baskets.

JOSEPH SCHMIDT CONFECTIONS

3489 16th Street
San Francisco, CA 94114
415.861.8682
Audrey Ryan
Areas served: U.S. and Canada
Custom-designed chocolates for all events.
They create and sculpt anything in
chocolate. They love to create one-of-a-
kind things and also provide custom-
designed gift baskets. Catalogue available.

NICOLE CHOCOLATIER

The Breakers
One S. Country Road
Palm Beach, FL 33480
407.655.6611 ext. 1503
Jayne Josephs
Areas served: International
Gartner chocolates from Antwerp, Belgium.
Gift baskets, confections, biscuits, china
ware, crystal and favors. Free delivery
locally. Additional store in Boca Raton.

PSEUDIOS ARTISTIC EDIBLES
2117 Glendale Galleria
Glendale, CA 91210
818.240.4222
Jeanne Goraleski
Areas served: National
Sculptured chocolates, nuts, gourmet food gifts, sugar free and novelty candy.

ULTIMATE NUT & CANDY CO.
11849 Ventura Blvd.
Studio City, CA 91604
818.772.8267
Jerry Donath
Areas served: Southern California
Hand-dipped highest quality chocolates. All natural and no artificial preservatives. Named Best in Southern California by MGM Grand Air Magazine. Shipping and delivery.

INVITATIONS & ACCESSORIES

See listings in individual cities

LIGHTING, STAGING & SOUND

ACADEMY TENT AND CANVAS, INC.
2910 S. Alameda Street
Los Angeles, CA 90058
213.234.4060
800.228.3687 (inside CA)
800.222.4535 (outside CA)
Maury Rice
Areas served: National
Provide complete facility hospitality equipment for private, commercial, institutional, and corporate hospitality events nationally. Including tents, flooring, ground covering, staging, lighting, heating, air conditioning, and power. Founded 1981.

ATLANTA MUSIC AGENCY
P.O. Box 720297
Atlanta, GA 30358

404.552.8220

10820 Shallowford Road
Roswell, GA 30075
404.552.8220
Tony N. Garstin
Areas served: National
Entertainment contractors, technical production: sound, lights, stages, stage sets, technical administration, labor administration.

ATTRACTIONS, INC.
P.O. Box 565013
Dallas, TX 75356
214.941.6971
R. Edward Cobb, President
Areas served: International
Full service entertainment firm including, but not limited, to live performance entertainment such as dance and show bands, name recording attractions, television and movie personalities, speakers, comics, magicians, specialty attractions, etc.; also sound and light production, contract and rider consultation, audio/video support systems, and on-site stage and production management. Specializes in consultation and procurement of live performance entertainment and the equipment and logistics to present such entertainment.

AUDIO VISUAL AMERICA/STAGE SOUND
20229 N.E. Sixteenth Place
Miami, FL 33162
305.653.0008
Tim Snow
Areas served: International
Progressive production support company dedicated to customer service and specializing in "State of the Art" equipment rentals, sales, service, design, installation, consultation and professional technicians. Full concert sound, staging and lighting capabilities. Videowalls, laser shows and program development capabilities. Video projection: large and small audience packages. Special recognition from: Papal visit, Formula One Grand Prix, CBS Records International, Polygram Records, Fiesta Bowl, Kodak, IBM, Tucson Symphony, Telluride Bluegrass Festival, Colorado State Fair and Meeting Concepts.

DESIGN & PRODUCTIONS
11105 Shady Trail
Suite 104
Dallas, TX 75229
214.243.4572
David Opper
Areas served: International
Full service lighting design company
providing lighting, staging, scenery, audio
and special effects. Specializes in design,
installation and production.

HDO PRODUCTIONS
1465 N. Gordon Avenue
Burlingame, CA 94010
415.375.0331
415.375.1200
800.225.1471
Areas served: National
Tents, canopies, freestanding structures,
floors, lights, heat. Outdoor event
planning. Offices in Washington, DC
and Chicago.

HY-LITE PRODUCTIONS INC.
2304 Florida Avenue
West Palm Beach, FL 33401-
7810
407.820.1414
Carl Borrelli
Areas served: International
Complete lighting, sound and special effects
production and design services for special
events, parties, fashion shows, corporate or
private theater and video production. Hy-
lite productions provides both the
manpower and the technology for perfect
events. Specializes in event theme decor (as
created with lighting) and special effects.
Fully licensed and insured.

IMAGES EVENT PRODUCTION
1649 Twelfth Street
Santa Monica, CA 90404
310.392.4240
Jerry Astourian
Areas served: International
Event design, lighting design, set and prop
construction. Specializing in Hollywood
premiere parties, corporate galas,
fundraising events, private affairs. Special
Events Magazine Gala Awards: Best
Decorated Theme Event, Most Imaginative
Use of Lighting & Special Effects (four
years), Most Imaginative Use Of A Tent,
Most Imaginative Use of Equipment, Special
Logistic Award.

MAGNUM COMPANIES
170-A Ohley Drive, NE
Atlanta, GA 30324
404.872.0553
Erik Magnuson
Areas served: National
Stage lighting, sound, video, audiovisual
services. Rent, sell, produce and design
lighting equipment.

RENNY
159 E. 64th Street
New York, NY 10021
212.288.7000
Renny Reynolds
Areas served: National
Party design and full event planning
services. Full service florist with shops in
the Hotel Carlyle and the St. Regis Hotel.
Overall atmosphere created using lighting,
flowers and decor.

SAMARCO, INC.
1606 Gano Street
Dallas, TX 75215
214.421.0757
800.530.4905
Areas served: National
Lighting, staging, scenery, special effects,
design, production, rental, sales.
Theatrical solutions to lighting and staging
problems. Artistic use of light for scenic
purposes and to create ambiance.

THE SHOW DEPARTMENT, INC.
1555 N. Sheffield
Chicago, IL 60622
312.787.2600
Areas served: International
Complete industrial show staging: large
inventory of state-of-the-art equipment for
rental. Multi-image projection. Video and
data projection, live audio mixing,
computerized lighting systems, video
recording, velour drapery system, custom
scenic system. Emphasis on industrial show
staging/corporate meetings.

NATIONAL

SUTKA PRODUCTIONS INTERNATIONAL, INC.
914 Fern Street
Suite B
West Palm Beach, FL 33401
407.835.8455
800.933.1333
Bruce Sutka
Kevin Verronneau
Areas served: International
Floral, lighting and special event coordination. Unique themes, wedding decor and environmental concepts create complete ambiance enhancement. Large-scale corporate and social clientele. Featured in *Town and Country* as one of the ten top party planners in the country as well as on *CNN* and *Good Morning America*. *Special Events Magazine* and other national trade publications.

VISUAL DESIGN ASSOCIATES
25 East Street
Cambridge, MA 02141
617.868.9200
Len Schnabel
Areas served: National, Offshore
Corporate meeting stages, theme party scenics, lighting and audio systems. Custom and stock inventory of stages, creative lighting.

WESTERN SCENIC STUDIOS
1470 Citrus Ridge
Escondido, CA 92025
619.943.8847
Ted Prina
Areas served: National
Full event decor including lighting, staging, and floral design. Full trade show production. Technical services. In business since 1919.

LIMOUSINE & TRANSPORTATION

CAREY LIMOUSINE
305.764.0615
800.336.4646
Privately chauffeured sedans, limousines, vans and mini buses in 372 cities.

DAV EL CHAUFFEURED TRANSPORTATION NETWORK
800.328.3526
Areas Served: International
Luxury chauffeured services in over 350 cities worldwide. Centralized reservations and billing. Airport concierge services.

LINENS

ACCENT PARTY LINEN RENTALS
270 N. Canon Drive
Suite 1328
Beverly Hills, CA 90210
310.273.8191
Debbie Baker
Areas served: National
Local and nationwide rental of fancy overlay tablecloths. Wholesale only to special event professionals.

CAROUSEL LINEN RENTAL, INC.
454 Sheridan Road
Highwood, IL 60040
708.432.8182
800.238.8182
Scott, Pari, Anna Marie
Areas served: National
Linen rental for special events. Theme prints, florals, lame, lurex, solid colors. In business for 27 years.

GOTCHA COVERED
3815 Hessmer Avenue
Metairie, LA 70002
504.522.1829
800.426.1380
Locky Pool
Angela Jones
Areas served: National
Linen rentals to special event professionals only.

LADY OF THE CLOTHS
13837 Ventura Blvd.
Suite 6
Sherman Oaks, Ca 91423
818.986.2843
Shirley LaBossiere
Areas served: Ship anywhere
Linen rentals.

[Continued on next page.]

LINEN EFFECTS AND BBJ BOUTIQUE
7020 Lawndale
Lincolnwood, IL 60645
708.679.9200
Steven Handelman
Areas served: International
Fine linen rentals. Patterned, formal, metallic and theme linens. First Place Award Winner for Table Design 1992 Special Events Convention.

PIERRE DEUX
224A Worth Avenue
Palm Beach, FL 33480
407.655.6810
Susie Smithers
Areas served: International
Tabletop accessories, linens, custom tablecloths, several French Faience collections, place mats, oversize plates and cutlery, candleholders, pots of jam, delicate wine glasses, ice buckets etc. Will ship UPS anywhere.

SUR LA TABLE
800.243.0852
Shirley Collins
BJ Osterloh
Areas served: National
Cooking equipment and linens for the table. Federal Express shipping or regular UPS. Gift wrap and bridal registry.

TABLETOPPERS, INC.
450-B Lake Cook Road
Deerfield, IL 60015
708.945.4470
Areas served: United States
Quality linen rental. Thirty-one solid colors and over seventy prints and specialty cloths, chair covers, laces and table skirtings. One of the Midwest's largest linen rental companies, with in-house sewing department and over 20,000 yards of material. Serviced last three US Opens, Ryder Cup and last two Super Bowls. Weddings their specialty. Set-up crews available if needed, for that special touch.

TABLE TOPPERS, INC.
3651 N.W. 81st Street
Miami, FL 33147
305.836.8807
Renee Fink

Areas served: National
Tablecloths, chair covers and napkins. Specialize in elegant design. Ship nationally. Rentals and made-to-order.

TABLEFASHIONS, LTD.
116 Will Drive
Canton, MA 02021
617.821.1160
Sandi Chudnow
Areas served: International
Specialty linens, chair covers, upscale specialty table treatments (all manufacturing and processing is handled in-house).

TABLEWRAPS
666 Cantiague Rock Road
Jericho, NY 11753
516.334.8833
Areas served: National
Full service linen rentals. Boutique linens, florals, satins, lames, lace, tapestries. Hundreds of fabrics to choose from. Ship nationwide.

MAGAZINES, NEWSLETTERS & PUBLICATIONS

ART CULINAIRE
P.O. Box 238
Madison, NJ 07940
201.993.5500
Mitchell Davis, Editor
Franz Mitterer, Publisher
Quarterly publication: $59 for one year (four issues); $108 for two years (eight issues); $147 for three years (twelve issues). Add $6 per year for delivery outside the USA. Payable in US funds.

CELEBRITY – SOCIETY
188 Santa Elena Lane
Montecito, CA 93108
805.969.3377
Chevy Foster, Publisher/Editor
Published monthly. Photo-journalistic presentation of charity, cultural, philanthropic and social events. Subscription rate is $36 per year. Awards and distinctions include congratulatory letters from President Reagan, Mayor Tom

Bradley and Governor Pete Wilson which were published in the magazine.

CHILE PEPPER MAGAZINE

P.O. Box 4278
Albuquerque, NM 87196
505.266.8322
Robert Spiegel, Publisher
Dave DeWitt, Editor

Bi-monthly food magazine devoted to spicy foods from all over the world, including recipes and text describing Cajun, Southwestern, Mexican, Caribbean, Asian and more. $15.95 per year. Hottest magazine in America.

COOKING LIGHT
THE MAGAZINE OF FOOD AND FITNESS

P.O. Box 1748
Birmingham, AL 35201
205.877.6000
Jeffrey Ward, Publisher
Katherine Eakin, Editor

Bi-monthly plus one holiday issue in December. America's favorite guide to healthy living featuring a mainstream approach for combining the ideas of in-home preparation of nutritious, appetizing recipes with regular, sensible exercise as the basis for a healthier lifestyle. Six issues for $15; twelve issues for $28; eighteen issues for $39.

DELICIOUS! MAGAZINE

1301 Spruce Street
Boulder, CO 80302
303.939.8440
Sue Frederick, Editor

Published eight times yearly by New Hope Communications. Health and nutrition news; recipes. Subscription: $17 per year.

FARE SHARE

4709 Weyhill Drive
Arlington, TX 76013
817.457.2273

Food letter. Bread baking classes. Cookbooks. Community, regional cookbooks. Breads. IACP member.

THE HERB QUARTERLY

P.O. Box 548
Boiling Springs, PA 17007
717.245.2764

Linda Sparrowe, Editor
Published by Long Mountain Press, Inc. four times a year (quarterly). Beautiful quarterly magazine dedicated to all things herbal, including seasonal menus highlighting fresh herbs and edible flowers. Subscriptions are $24 for one year; $45 for two years. Oldest herb magazine in publication. Called "the most elegant of herb magazines" by *Harrowsmith Magazine*.

PALATE PLEASERS MAGAZINE

420 Boyd Street
Suite 502
Los Angeles, CA 90013
213.680.9101
Dorre Higashi, Editor

Published by Apcon International, Inc. twice a year. Includes lavishly illustrated, in-depth features on seasonal festivals and events, the origin and preparation of traditional foods, simple and colorful recipes as well as a national food store directory, ten-city restaurant guide and much more. A one year postpaid subscription (two issues) is $17.90.

SPECIAL EVENTS MAGAZINE

6133 Bristol Parkway
P.O. Box 3640
Culver City, CA 90231-3640
310.337.9717
800.543.4116
Liese Gardner, Editor
Lisa Voested, Publisher

Trade publication serving all disciplines in the special events industry with quality editorial and four-color photos of national and international events. Subscriptions are $36 a year. The magazine also sponsors the Special Event, the only convention and trade show for everyone involved in the industry. The Special Event offers business and trend seminars as well as demonstrations and exhibits.

[Continued on next page.]

TEA TALK, A NEWSLETTER ON THE PLEASURES OF TEA

419 N. Larchmont Blvd.
Suite 225
Los Angeles, CA 90004
310.659.9650
Diana Rosen, Editor

Quarterly national newsletter focusing on entertaining with tea. Directories of B&Bs, hotels and tearooms that serve afternoon tea; reviews of books, restaurants, new products. Articles on caterers, teapot collectors and artists, and tea blenders.

THE TEA QUARTERLY

2210 Wilshire Blvd.
Suite 634
Santa Monica, CA 90403
310.479.7370
Wendy Rasmussen Moore, Editor

Areas served: International
Newsletter devoted to tea for both consumers and the industry. Regular features include reviews of afternoon tea services around the states, and interviews with personal-teas. Emphasis on the specialty tea market, enjoyment of high-quality tea and accompaniments. Published for over ten years. Catalogues and mail order.

THE UNDERGROUND WINE JOURNAL AND RARITIES

1654 Amberwood Drive
Suite A
So. Pasadena, CA 91030
818.441.6617
818.441.6765
Christine Graham, Publisher
John Tilson, Editor

Wine Journal published monthly. Definitive guide to fine wines currently available. Subscription: $48 per year. *Rarities* published quarterly. Gourmet's guide to rare wine, great dining and sophisticated travel. Subscription: $45 per year.

WHO'S WHO IN PROFESSIONAL SPEAKING MEMBERSHIP DIRECTORY FOR THE NATIONAL SPEAKERS ASSOCIATION

1500 S. Priest Drive
Tempe, AZ 85281
602.968.2552
Lisa Iverson, Editor

Stacy Tetschner, Editor
Published annually by National Speakers Association. Picture and brief description of all members of the National Speakers Association; also divided into speaking topics and geographical location. Subscription rate: meeting planners NSA members, no charge. $25, all others.

WINE & SPIRITS MAGAZINE

P.O. Box 1548
Princeton, NJ 08542
415.255.7736
Joshua Greene, Editor

Published seven times a year. Consumer-oriented, wine enthusiast magazine featuring results from the American Wine Competition, exclusive restaurant and retail polls, and colorful features by top writers. Subscription rate: $18 per year.

MUSIC & ENTERTAINMENT

4 STAR PRODUCTIONS

209-04 Twenty-third Avenue
Bayside, NY 11360
718.279.2023
800.842.4044
Suzan Schuster

Areas served: National
Psychics/ Fortune Tellers for special events. Astrologers, Numerologists, Tarot Card and Palm Readers. All performers are professionals in their fields. They appear fully costumed as gypsy fortune tellers and give brief, up-beat personal readings to guests.

ABRACADABRA PRODUCTIONS

310 E. 46th Street
New York, NY 10017
212.599.7576
Leslie Carr

Areas served: National
All aspects of entertainment. 1000 performers and psychics for parties, conventions, trade shows, hospitality suites. Exclusive representation of Astounding Velma, Queen of Illusion, star of radio, TV and commercials in U.S.A., Japan and Europe. Velma performs in both English and French.

ATLANTA MUSIC AGENCY
P.O. Box 720297
Atlanta, GA 30358
404.552.8220

10820 Shallowford Road
Roswell, GA 30075
404.552.8220
Tony N. Garstin
Areas served: National
Entertainment contractors, technical
production: sound, lights, stages, stage sets,
technical administration, labor
administration.

ATTRACTIONS, INC.
P.O. Box 565013
Dallas, TX 75356
214.941.6971
R. Edward Cobb, President
Areas served: International
Full service entertainment firm including,
but not limited, to live performance
entertainment such as dance and show
bands, name recording attractions,
television and movie personalities,
speakers, comics, magicians, specialty
attractions, etc.; also sound and light
production, contract and rider
consultation, audio/video support systems,
and on-site stage and production
management. Specializes in consultation
and procurement of live performance
entertainment and the equipment and
logistics to present such entertainment.

AUDIENCE PLEASERS
93 N. Mountain Avenue
P.O. Box 897
Upper Montclair, NJ 07043
201.744.1916
Barbara Owens
Areas served: Nationwide
Musical and variety entertainment.
Unusual acts/ custom made productions.

BOGIE'S MYSTERY TOURS®
328 W. Eighty-sixth Street
Suite 4A
New York, NY 10024
212.362.7569
Karen Palmer
Areas served: International
Mystery events - private parties, corporate
events, fund-raisers, weekends, cruises, and
incentive travel. Complete planning,
scenario development, professional actors,
pens, buttons, and prizes. Playfair
whodunits - custom designed participatory
murder mysteries. The original mystery
events company and the first to do dinner
murder parties. The owners, Karen and
Bill Palmer, write, direct and produce all
events. Members of the Mystery Writers of
America, The Private Eye Writers of
America, The Crime Writers of England,
and The American Crime Writers League.
Packagers and editors of the Bogie's
Mystery Book imprint, with several award-
winning paperback originals

**CARICATURES & FACE READINGS
BY SHERRY LANE**
155 Bank Street
Studio 404
New York, NY 10014
Sherry Lane
212.675.6224
Areas served: National
Caricatures and psychic face readings.
Group caricatures from photos. Listed in
*Who's Who in the East, 1991-1994; The
World Who's Who of Women, 1992-1993.*
Has traveled around the world for Time,
Inc. and Pan Am.

DR. BOP AND THE HEADLINERS
1220 N. State Pkwy.
Suite 709
Chicago, IL 60610
312.787.8787
Ed Engelhart
Areas served: National
Rock 'n Roll entertainment. Played for
Prince Charles.

EARL & ERNIE HECKSCHER ORCHESTRA
10 Miller Place
Suite 603
San Francisco, CA 94108
415.362.3990
Earl Heckscher
Areas served: National
Full orchestra available in any size,
providing dance music and back up for
weddings, corporate events, conventions
and private parties.

[Continued on next page.]

E.J.M. ENTERTAINMENT, INC.
345 W. John Street
Hicksville, NY 11801
516.935.4210
800.EJM.IS4U
Don Mirabel
Areas served: Continental US & Puerto
Rico, Canada
Live entertainment with recorded music,
light systems, special effects, video taping
and video projection, party favors, costume
designs and changes, dance instruction,
photography, music videos, etc. Bar/bat
mitzvahs, weddings, corporate functions,
parties for all occasions. Clients include
United Way, AIDS benefits, Special
Olympics, Juvenile Diabetes, Cancer
Society, numerous corporate organizations.

**FAMOUS FACES ENTERTAINMENT
AND SPECIAL EVENTS COMPANY**
2013 Harding Street
Hollywood, FL 33020
305.922.0700
800.635.6492 (Outside FL)
Paul Levine, President
Areas served: National
Theme parties, convention planning,
celebrity look-alikes, music and
entertainment, novelty acts, speakers,
murder mystery productions, casino night,
horse and dog racing on film, theme decor,
models, actors, actresses, etc.

JD MUSIC PRODUCTIONS
1610 W. Highland
Suite 34
Chicago, IL 60660
800.659.0762
James Hahn
Areas served: National (predominately
Midwest)
Live musical entertainment (classical, jazz,
rock, big band, Dixieland, country
western). National conventions, trade
shows, corporate hospitality parties.
Private parties.

KIM THE SONGWRITER
1219 E. Adams Avenue
Orange, CA 92667
310.288.1611
714.633.7513

Kim Olson
Areas served: International
Unique entertainment. Creates humorous
songs instantly. Warm, personable and
funny, creating on the spot songs and
writing, producing theme songs for
companies. Host for variety of club
telethons. Dream Pin Winner of Quarter,
highest award a cast member can achieve.
Call or write for information.

LA CIRCUS
7531 S. La Salle Avenue
Los Angeles, CA 90047
216.751.3486
Wini McKay
Areas served: International
Customized circus events for all occasions.
Equipment rental, seats, tenting, games,
performers, elephant ride and act as well as
complete set up. clients include Disney,
Yamaha, Pepsi International and many more.

MARS TALENT AGENCY
168 Orchid Drive
Pearl River, NY 10965
914.735.4569
Arnie and Wendy Kay
Areas served: National
Artists - groups from the 50's and 60's era
of music. Brochures available.
Conventions, private parties, fund-raisers.

LE MASQUERADE
136 Oak Drive
Syosset, NY 11791
516.496.7260 (New York)
213.383.1191(Los Angeles)
305.936.2446 (Florida)
800.666.7260
Dennis Schussel
Bernard Schussel
Areas served: International
Interactive high energy, costumed and
theatrical entertainment with music and
special effects. Interaction with the guests.
Private and corporate events. Media
awards and distincitons include entertaining
at the White House, National TV and
newspaper coverage. Award for
entertaining all northwest caterers.

NATIONAL

LORDLY & DAME
    51 Church Street
    Boston, MA 02116
    617.482.3596
    Sam Dame
Areas served: International
Full event planning, music and
entertainment, speakers, celebrity
acquisition.

MARGE GHILARDUCCI AGENCY
    724 Berkley Street
    Berkley, MA 02779
    508.822.3735
    Marge & Chris Ghilarducci
Areas served: International
Performing artists for family entertainment
in storytelling, music, juggling, physical
comedy, theatre, dance. Family
entertainment series for community events,
festivals and theatres.

MIKE VACCARO PRODUCTIONS, INC.
    3848-A Atlantic Avenue
    Suite 4
    Long Beach, CA 90807
    310.424.4958
    Mike Vaccaro
Areas served: International
Music, entertainment, theme parties, party
planning, site selection, celebrity
entertainment, etc.

A NITE AT THE RACES, INC.
    2320 Avenue "U"
    Brooklyn, NY 11229
    718.769.7355
    Rental Department
Areas served: Nationwide
Rental of horse racing events for
entertainment and fund raising. Available
in 16mm and VHS cassettes.

THE ORIGINAL BUTT SKETCH
    213 S. Tyler Street
    Dallas, TX 75208
    214.943.BUTT
    Krandel Lee Newton
Areas served: International
Custom drawings, artistry services.
Conventions, receptions and promotions.

PAM AND BILLY KAY
    10322 Mary Bell Avenue
    Sunland, CA 91040
    818.352.9774
    Pam & Billy Kay
Areas served: International
Musical and comedy entertainment is
provided.

PAINT ME A PARTY, INC.
    1035 W. Webster
    Chicago, IL 60614
    312.935.5400
    Sally Schwartz
Areas served: National
Event planning, entertainment and music
booking. Two divisions: Events As Art and
Just Entertainment. Highly visual, high-
impact parties. Subtle, layered marketing
events from concept to logo.

STANDING OVATIONS
    8380 Miramar Mall
    Suite 225
    San Diego, CA 92121
    619.455.1850
    Nan Pratt
    P.J. Fox
Areas served: International
International full service speaker bureau
serving associations and corporate clients.
Quality speakers, trainers, celebrities,
entertainers and sports stars for keynotes,
general sessions, seminars and workshops.

SUPER STAR STUDIOS
    2658 Puttman Drive
    Silver Springs, MD 20910
    301.588.8500
    Tina Reman
Areas served: International
Interactive musical entertainment for
parties and special events. Karaoke, MTV
style music videos, portable singing booths
and the "Walking Piano" from the movie *Big*.

[Continued on next page.]

❧ CARICATURES & DRAWINGS

QUICK PORTRAIT SKETCHES AND PAINTINGS BY KALAN BRUNINK
> West Nine Olvera Street
> Los Angeles, CA 90012
> **213.464.8185**
> Kalan Brunink

Areas served: International
Quick portrait sketches in charcoal in a few minutes. Very accurate likenesses produced artistically. Quick oil portrait paintings of up to 30 or 40 inches for dramatic content of the environment or as a gift to a particular person. Who's Who in California. First place ribbon Beverly Hills Art League Affaire in the Gardens Exhibit. First place ribbon Hancock Park Art League. Painting of Pope John Paul II put on calendar published in 40 countries and approved by the Vatican's Commission of Sacred Art. Has done 20,000 portraits including Bruce Willis, Ry Cooder, Lawrence Welk, Anthony Quinn for Anthony Quinn Library. Appeared on *Two on the Town* and as guest artist on game show *Break the Bank*.

CARICATURES BY TED JEWELL
> P.O. Box 69934
> Los Angeles, CA 90069
> **213.467.4822**
> Lois Jewell

Areas Served: Los Angeles, CA in particular but will go anywhere.
Caricatures as entertainment and custom art work. Work appears a lot on TV. Works with the motion picture industry
BARBARA DENNY CARICATURES
> **714.527.8503**

Areas: International
Quick sketch caricatures for all occasions

"KING SAUL"
> **818.980.6991**

Areas: International
Former Walt Disney Animator. Creates caricatures in full animation using color pastels.

❧ CELEBRITY LOOK-ALIKES

See Los Angeles under Music & Entertainment

❧ CIRCUS

LA CIRCUS
> 7531 S. La Salle Avenue
> Los Angeles, CA 90047
> **216.751.3486**
> Wini McKay

Areas served: International
Customized circus events for all occasions. Equipment rental, seats, tenting, games, performers, elephant ride and act as well as complete set up. clients include Disney, Yamaha, Pepsi International and many more.

❧ COMEDY

MICHAEL PASTERNAK AS "LT. COLUMBO"
> **818.716.5977**

Areas Served: International
Lt. Columbo at your party to deliver personalized roast written entirely around birthday honoree, anniversary couple, guests or sales force.

❧ DANCE TROUPES

LE MASQUERADE
> 136 Oak Drive
> Syosset, NY 11791
> **516.496.7260** (New York)
> **213.383.1191** (Los Angeles)
> **305.936.2446** (Florida)
> **800.666.7260**
> Dennis Schussel
> Bernard Schussel

Areas served: International
Interactive high energy, costumed and theatrical entertainment with music and special effects. Interaction with the guests. Private and corporate events. Media awards and distincitons include entertaining at the White House, National TV and Newspaper Coverage Award for entertaining all northwest caterers.

QUELLES TOMATES! PRODUCTIONS
4605 Fulton Avenue
Suite 3
Sherman Oaks, CA 91423-5125
818.981.4373
Jodi Laine
Pat Tallman
Areas served: National
Music, action, adventure and
entertainment. Also, look-a-likes and other
characters to enhance the atmosphere.
Shows are custom tailored to suite the event
or revue. The entertainment is completely
unique and original - choreography,
costumes - you name it!

PARTY SUPPLIES

ACCENT ANNEX/ MARDI GRAS HEADQUARTERS
1120 S. Jeff Davis Pkwy.
New Orleans, LA 70125-9901
504.821.8885
800.322.2368
Areas served: National
Mardi Gras headquarters. Six locations in
U.S., Mardi Gras, carnival, fair and party
supplies. National mail order catalogue.

THE BAG LADIES
4214 Glencoe Avenue
Marina Del Rey, CA 90292
310.822.1706
800.359.BAGS
Linda Hollander
Custom-printing on paper and plastic bags.
Carry festive gift bags, shred and tissue.
Metallic foil printing and bags are available
for extra.

COVE WAX WORKS
2311 W. Main Street
Melrose Park, IL 60160
708.344.7220
Ray Tinucci
Areas served: National, Canada, South
America, The Orient
Suppliers of high quality tabletop decor and
outdoor Chronella Products. Flower Float
floating candles, self extinguishing.

GRACIOUS HOME
1217 & 1220 Third Avenue
New York, NY 10021
212.517.6300
Areas served: National
Invitations, party supplies, tabletop
accessories and kitchenware: table cloths,
napkins, napkin rings, placemats, candles,
china, champagne and wine glasses, caviar
bowls, trays, platters, chaffing dishes,
cheese boards, cookbooks. Custom-
designed and catalogue invitations, place
cards, party baskets, ribbons, wrap, gift
bags, flower arrangements. Free delivery in
Manhattan. Ship nationally.

MARTIN INDUSTRIES
2081 S. Hellman Avenue
Suite D
Ontario, CA 91761
714.947.6623
800.544.9197 (outside CA)
Areas served: International
Glow-in-the-dark novelties. Necklaces,
bracelets, earrings, cocktail stirrers, stick-
on buttons with company logo. Specialties
include glow products, customized with logo
or saying, or plain!

PARTY LIGHTS OF CALIFORNIA
8656 Sky Rim Drive
Suite 110
Lakeside, CA 92040
619.443.9949
M. White
Areas served: International
Complete line of Cyalume Lightstick products.
Lighters, necklaces, cocktail stirrers,
bracelets, earrings. Worldwide shipping.

WILLIAM ERNEST BROWN
442 N. Canon Drive
Beverly Hills, CA 90210
310.278.5620
Areas served: International
Custom-designed and catalogue invitations,
seating charts, accessories, place cards and
party supplies for all special events. They
also provide calligraphy services. Known
for their high quality products and special
services. Clients all over the United States
and Europe.

[Continued on next page.]

PROPS & DECOR

ANDREA LEIGH CLASTER
212.633.0970
Areas served: National
Full event planning and design. Custom-designed and catalogue invitations, seating, charts, place cards. Full in-house calligraphy services. RSVP management. Custom-designed chocolates. Hospitality gift baskets. Gift consultation. Private seminars in etiquette and gift giving. For private and corporate groups. Author of *Modern Living and Modern Giving*.

COMET PRODUCTIONS, INC.
733 Fifteenth Street, NW
Suite 700
Washington, DC 20005
202.347.3344
Halle Becker
Areas served: National
Event production, entertainment, decor, audiovisual services. National talent/acts. Written up in Special Events Magazine, guest speaker at Special Event Eight and Nine.

DAME ASSOCIATES, INC.
51 Church Street
Boston, MA 02116
617.482.3596
Douglas Dame
Areas served: International
Destination management, trade show production, convention coordination, exhibit and display rentals, corporate seminars.

HY-LITE PRODUCTIONS INC.
2304 Florida Avenue
West Palm Beach, FL 33401-7810
407.820.1414
Carl Borrelli
Areas served: International
Complete lighting, sound and special effects production and design services for special events, parties, fashion shows, corporate or private theater and video production. Hy-lite productions provides both the manpower and the technology for perfect events. Specializes in event theme decor (as created with lighting) and special effects. Fully licensed and insured.

IMAGES EVENT PRODUCTION
1649 Twelfth Street
Santa Monica, CA 90404
310.392.4240
Jerry Astourian
Areas served: International
Event design, lighting design, set and prop construction. Specializing in Hollywood premiere parties, corporate galas, fundraising events, private affairs. Special Events Magazine Gala Awards: Best Decorated Theme Event, Most Imaginative Use of Lighting & Special Effects (four years), Most Imaginative Use Of A Tent, Most Imaginative Use of Equipment, Special Logistic Award.

JOHN FUNT DECORATIONS FOR SPECIAL EVENTS
165 E. 60th Street
New York, NY 10022
212.371.6353
John Funt
Areas served: International
Full decor and event planning. Twelve years experience. Specializing in theme events and garden style decor.

NIEDERMAIR
120 Wooster Street
New York, NY 10012
212.966.8574
Louis Marra
Areas served: National
Full service display company providing prop sales for all special events. Columns, urns, panels, banners, etc.

RENNY
159 E. 64th Street
New York, NY 10021
212.288.7000
Renny Reynolds
Areas served: National
Party design and full event planning services. Full service florist with shops in the Hotel Carlyle and the St. Regis Hotel. Overall atmosphere created using lighting, flowers and decor.

NATIONAL

SAMARCO, INC.
1606 Gano Street
Dallas, TX 75215
214.421.0757
800.530.4905
Areas served: National
Lighting, staging, scenery, special effects,
design, production, rental, sales.
Theatrical solutions to lighting and staging
problems. Artistic use of light for scenic
purposes and to create ambiance.

**SUTKA PRODUCTIONS
INTERNATIONAL, INC.**
914 Fern Street
Suite B
West Palm Beach, FL 33401
407.835.8455
800.933.1333
Bruce Sutka
Kevin Verronneau
Areas served: International
Floral, lighting and special event
coordination. Unique themes, wedding
decor and environmental concepts create
complete ambiance enhancement. Large-
scale corporate and social clientele.
Featured in *Town and Country* as one of
the ten top party planners in the country as
well as on *CNN* and *Good Morning
America. Special Events Magazine* and
other national trade publications.

VISUAL DESIGN ASSOCIATES
25 East Street
Cambridge, MA 02141
617.868.9200
Len Schnabel
Areas served: National, Offshore
Corporate meeting stages, theme party
scenics, lighting and audio systems. Custom
and stock inventory of stages, creative
lighting.

WESTERN SCENIC STUDIOS
1470 Citrus Ridge
Escondido, CA 92025
619.943.8847
Ted Prina
Areas served: National
Full event decor including lighting, staging,
and floral design. Full trade show
production. Technical services. In
business since 1919.

SIGNAGE
NIEDERMAIR
120 Wooster Street
New York, NY 10012
212.966.8574
Louis Marra
Areas served: National
Full service display company providing
prop sales for all special events. Columns,
urns, panels, banners, etc.

SPEAKERS
ATLANTA SPEAKERS BUREAU
2859 Paces Ferry Road
Suite 1830
Atlanta, GA 30339
404.432.1394
Sherry Conner
Speakers, celebrities, entertainers. For
meetings, parties and special events.

ATTRACTIONS, INC.
P.O. Box 565013
Dallas, TX 75356
214.941.6971
R. Edward Cobb
Areas served: International
Full service entertainment firm including,
but not limited, to live performance
entertainment such as dance and show
bands, name recording attractions,
television and movie personalities,
speakers, comics, magicians, specialty
attractions, etc.; also sound and light
production, contract and rider
consultation, audio/video support systems,
and on-site stage and production
management. Specializes in consultation
and procurement of live performance
entertainment and the equipment and
logistics to present such entertainment.

**CALIFORNIA LEISURE CONSULTANTS
OF LOS ANGELES**
3605 Long Beach Blvd.
Suite 201
Long Beach, CA 90807-4013
310.427.0414
Ilene Reinhart
Creative approach to total destination

management services. Specialize in
innovative theme party productions,
customized tour coordination, sporting
events, speakers, entertainment, specialty
gift items and expert service for corporate,
association and incentive meetings and
conventions.

DAMON BROOKS ASSOCIATES
1680 N. Vine Street
Suite 910
Hollywood, CA 90028
213.465.3400
Marc Goldman

Areas served: National
Coordination of celebrity involvement with
special events. Tennis, golf, and related
sporting events. Speaking, entertainment,
auction items and personal appearances.
Recognized by California Meetings, Western
Association News, Affordable Meetings,
International Festivals Association,
American Society of Association Executives.

DUKE OF BOURBON
20908 Roscoe Blvd.
Canoga Park, CA 91304
818.341.1234
David Breitstein
Ron Breitstein

Areas served: San Fernando Valley,
Beverly Hills, West Los Angeles, Malibu,
Westlake Village, Thousand Oaks, Agoura
Wine tasting seminars, executive wine
seminars, party and event planning with
delivery of wine, spirits, beer, wine
collecting consultation, speakers, gift
baskets, newsletter. Specialize in
personalized service. Commendations from
City and County of Los Angeles for twenty-
five years of successful business. Chosen by
The Wine Spectator and *Market Watch* as
one of top twelve wine and spirits shops in
America for 1990. *Beverage Dynamics*
Retailer of the Year 1991.

FAMOUS FACES ENTERTAINMENT AND SPECIAL EVENTS COMPANY
2013 Harding Street
Hollywood, FL 33020
305.922.0700
800.635.6492 (Outside FL)
Paul Levine, President

Areas served: National
Theme parties, convention planning,
celebrity look-alikes, music and
entertainment, novelty acts, speakers,
murder mystery productions, casino night,
horse and dog racing on film, theme decor,
models, actors, actresses, etc.

HUMOR DYNAMICS
P.O. Box 2140
Santa Maria, CA 93457
805.934.3232
John Kinde

Areas served: National
John Kinde is a full-time humorist and
professional speaker. Comedy or magic
programs provided. An emphasis on
programs that have a message of humor for
success and life enrichment.

HY-LITE PRODUCTIONS INC.
2304 Florida Avenue
West Palm Beach, FL 33401-7810
407.820.1414
Carl Borrelli

Areas served: International
Complete lighting, sound and special effects
production and design services for special
events, parties, fashion shows, corporate or
private theater and video production. Hy-
lite productions provides both the
manpower and the technology for perfect
events. Specializes in event theme decor (as
created with lighting) and special effects.
Fully licensed and insured.

LORDLY & DAME
51 Church Street
Boston, MA 02116
617.482.3596
Sam Dame

Areas served: International
Full event planning, music and
entertainment, speakers, celebrity
acquisition.

MARTIN'S WINE CELLAR FOOD EMPORIUM AND DELI
3827 Baronne Street
New Orleans, LA 70115
504.899.7411
Marc Pelletier

Areas served: National
Fine wines, champagnes, liqueurs, cordials, custom gift baskets, wine seminars and tastings, delicacies, cheeses, pate´s, chocolates, confections, salmons, caviar, foie gras, coffee, teas, speakers on all areas of viticulture, holiday catalogue.

MARSHALL GRANT'S ENTERTAINMENT SOURCE, INC.

1750 N. Fla. Mango Road
Suite 103
West Palm Beach, FL 33409
407.686.7000
800.422.1522
Marshall Grant
Billy Duke
Joe Gianuzzi

Areas served: Florida's Gold Coast from Orlando south through Miami; Florida's West Coast (Naples, etc.) Private parties, etc. throughout United States
Orchestras and entertainment for private parties, charity balls, conventions, etc. Suppliers of dance music, entertainers, name speakers, etc. Providers of sound, lighting, audiovisual equipment, etc. Able to provide wide range of sophisticated entertainment needs. Upper-income clients, both private and corporate. Basically private affairs, country clubs, theme parties, music to appeal to wide variety of ages in 25-70 year-old group. Thirty-five years in Palm Beach. Twenty-one years as music directors of The Breakers Hotel, Palm Beach. Ohall Grant is first living band leader inducted into the "Big Band Hall of Fame".

SPEAK, INC.

6540 Lusk Blvd.
San Diego, CA 92121
619.457.9880
Jennifer Walker
Ruth Levin
Richard Gibbons

Areas served: International
Full service speaker and trainer bureau. Over 1000 internationally known motivational speakers, sports stars, business and entertainment speakers.

STANDING OVATIONS

8380 Miramar Mall
Suite 225
San Diego, CA 92121
619.455.1850
Nan Pratt
P.J. Fox

Areas served: International
International full service speaker bureau serving associations and corporate clients. Quality speakers, trainers, celebrities, entertainers and sports stars for keynotes, general sessions, seminars and workshops.

WALTERS INTERNATIONAL SPEAKERS BUREAU

P.O. Box 1120
Glendora, CA 91740
818.335.8069
Lilley Walters

Areas served: International
Humorists, motivational speakers, magicians.

WASHINGTON SPEAKERS BUREAU

888 Seventh Avenue
New York, NY 10106
212.541.7980

Areas served: International
Speakers for all occasions - celebrity's, sports, political, motivation, business, humorous.

THE WINESELLAR

9550 Waples Street
Suite 115
San Diego, CA 92121
619.455.1414
David Clark
Terry Hudson

Areas served: National
Retail store specializing in small production, high quality, handcrafted wines. Foreign and domestic wines. Wine storage facilities. Speakers on wine. Tastings in adjoining restaurant every Saturday (reservations in advance). Produce custom-designed wine tasting parties at outside locations. Custom-designed gift baskets.

[Continued on next page.]

THE ZIG ZIGLAR CORPORATION
3330 Earhart Drive
Suite 204
Carrollton, TX 75006
214.233.9191
800.527.0306
Bryan Flanagan
Areas served: International
Fun, uplifting speakers; inspiring, exciting
programs; entertaining sessions; spouse's
and children's programs. Specialty is
providing talks, programs, presentations to
a wide range of audiences. Each program is
customized. The Ziglar Corporation is
world renowned as a leader in the "People
Business."

TABLETOP ACCESSORIES & KITCHENWARE

A COOK'S WARES
211 37th Street
Beaver Falls, PA 15010
412.846.5194
Areas served: National, Alaska, Hawaii,
APO, FPO (for extra charge)
Cookware, bakeware, gadgets, cutlery for
the serious cook at great savings.

COVE WAX WORKS
2311 W. Main Street
Melrose Park, IL 60160
708.344.7220
Ray Tinucci
Areas served: National, Canada, South
America, The Orient
Suppliers of high quality tabletop decor and
outdoor Chronella Products. Flower Float
floating candles, self extinguishing.

DEAN & DELUCA
560 Broadway
New York, NY 10012
212.431.1691
James Mellgren
Areas served: International
Tabletop accessories, kitchenware,
cookbooks, gift baskets. Full service
specialty foods and catering. Cheese,
pastries, produce, caviar, smoked fish,
custom designed chocolates, Dean & Deluca

herbs and spices, dried beans and grains,
mail order department. Deliver anywhere.

E.A.T.
1064 Madison Avenue
New York, NY 10028
212.772.0022
Areas served: National
Restaurant, gourmet shop, gift shop,
wholesale bread, and catering. Tabletop
accessories, cheese, caviar, fresh baked
pastry, custom-designed cakes. Smoked
Norwegian salmon, fresh produce, gourmet
salads, gift baskets. Known for their
breads.

EUROPEAN HOME PRODUCTS, INC.
136 Washington Street
Norwalk, CT 06854
203.866.7777
800.225.0760
Robert Johnson
Areas served: U.S. & Canada
Full line of kitchenware specializing in parts
and repairs of food processors. Gourmet
coffees by mail order.

FIORI
448 South Coast Highway
Suite A
Laguna Beach, CA 92651
714.494.2553
Bonnie Wolin
Areas served: International
Specializing in fine quality Italian and
Greek handpainted ceramics known as
Majolica. Pieces have been featured in the
following publications: *Gourmet,
Metropolitan Home, China Glass &
Tabletop* and *Laguna Magazine. The Los
Angeles Times* selected Fiori under the Best
in Southern California in the Sunday,
November 1990, magazine edition.

GRACIOUS HOME
1217 & 1220 Third Avenue
New York, NY 10021
212.517.6300
Areas served: National
Invitations, party supplies, tabletop
accessories and kitchenware: table cloths,
napkins, napkin rings, placemats, candles,
china, champagne and wine glasses, caviar
bowls, trays, platters, chaffing dishes,

cheese boards, cookbooks. Custom-designed and catalogue invitations, place cards, party baskets, ribbons, wrap, gift bags, flower arrangements. Free delivery in Manhattan. Ship nationally.

NICOLE CHOCOLATIER
The Breakers
One S. Country Road
Palm Beach, FL 33480
407.655.6611 ext. 1503
Jayne Josephs
Areas served: International
Gartner chocolates from Antwerp, Belgium. Gift baskets, confections, biscuits, china ware, crystal and favors. Free delivery locally. Additional store in Boca Raton.

OLD TOWN FLOWER SHOPS
1930 N. Dixie Highway
West Palm Beach, FL 33407
407.655.3351
Ted Johns
Full service florists, floral designers and party planner offers simple elegance and custom designs. In house invitations and calligraphy services for three consecutive years and voted Best Florist by Palm Beach Life Magazine. This shop has been in business for thirty-eight years.

PIERRE DEUX
224A Worth Avenue
Palm Beach, FL 33480
407.655.6810
Susie Smithers
Areas served: International
Tabletop accessories, linens, custom tablecloths, several French Faience collections, place mats, oversize plates and cutlery, candleholders, pots of jam, delicate wine glasses, ice buckets etc. Will ship UPS anywhere.

POTTERY BARN
Mail Order Department
P.O. Box 7044
San Francisco, CA 94120-7044
800.922.5507 (Orders)
800.922.9934 (Customer service)
Areas served: National
Over fifty stores and mail order. The county's leading retailer of contemporary tableware and decorative accessories for the

home. Tabletop items and decorative accessories, casual furniture. Merchandise is 100% exclusive, designed and sold exclusively at Pottery Barn.

REPLACEMENTS, LTD.
1089 Knox Road
P.O. Box 26029
Greensboro, NC 27420
919.697.3000
Areas served: International
World's largest supplier of discontinued china, crystal and flatware. Over 1,400,000 pieces in 40,000 patterns available.

SUR LA TABLE
800.243.0852
Shirley Collins
BJ Osterloh
Areas served: National
Cooking equipment and linens for the table. Federal Express shipping or regular UPS. Gift wrap and bridal registry.

THE CHEF'S CATALOG
3215 Commercial Avenue
Northbrook, IL 60062
800.338.3232
Tina Berkovitz
Areas served: National
Gourmet kitchenware used by America's great chefs. Cookware, cutlery, small appliances, "tools-of-the-trade", bakeware, microwave accessories, cookbooks, dinnerware, cleaning and storage. Professional quality, over 1001 discoveries for cooking, entertaining, gift giving. New York Design Award For Premier Issue.

WILLIAM-WAYNE & COMPANY
324 E. Ninth Street
New York, NY 10003
212.477.3182
William or Wayne
Areas served: National and Canada
Retail home furnishings for the home decorator consultant. Seasonal newsletter/catalogue. Monkey Decorative Association prints, etchings, tabletop, etc. Some one-of-a-kind. Metal wall sconces. Frequent editorial coverage.

[Continued on next page.]

WILLIAMS-SONOMA
> Mail Order Department
> P.O. Box 7456
> San Francisco, CA 94120-7456
> **800.541.2233** (Orders)
> **800.541.1262** (Customer service)

Areas served: National
106 stores and mail order
An authoritative selection of the best for the kitchen. Complete line of kitchenware –cookware, baking, electrics, plus packaged foods, glassware, tabletop, kitchen furniture, cookbooks. Knowledgeable staff will help choose equipment, plan parties. Catalog consistently wins gold medals in competitions in its class; Chuck William, founder and vice chairman and guiding spirit, imbues the selection with his standard of excellence and integrity.

UNIFORMS

CHEFWEAR, INC.
> 2449 N. Clybourn Avenue
> Chicago, IL 60614
> **312.871.8684**
> **800.568.2433**
> Rochelle Huppin

Areas served: International
Retail and wholesale sales of chefs uniforms. Ship internationally. Mail order catalogue.

FUN UNIFORM SUPPLY
> 4104 24th Street
> San Francisco, CA 94114
> **800.723.8726**
> Joanne Fusco

Areas served: International
Manufactures and distributes chef's uniforms for men and women. Variety of creative, colorful designs. Catalogue available.

ﾞ ﾞ ﾞ

TIPS FROM THE PROS

Safari parties and sports themes are very hot right now. Sports themes are big among the Bar Mitzvah clientele while safari can transform itself into anything – a wild nightclub, an Out of Africa look or a rain forest.

Aroma therapy and New Age music are being used more at events and not just at New Age theme events, but for futuristic.

The environment continues to be important as people begin to use potted plants at events instead of cut flowers, or use reusable foam board props for centerpieces.

Lighting is still a popular way to create a big decor look although the trend seems to be toward brighter color washes. People are becoming more bold with colors and with the use of neon to accent a room.

Liese Gardner
Special Events Magazine

ಶಾಶಾಶಾ

When you design a party, you want to consider all the "power points" of an event. Every event has its own areas of importance, but usually a power point is a place where your guests directly interact with the party, i.e., the entrance, the buffets, the table where they sit, the stage and dance floor. Each of these areas is a place where you can concentrate your design efforts effectively.

Walk through your party location like a guest arriving for the first time. Use the existing landscape or architectural elements of the party site to help guide you through the design. If there is a great looking tree in the center of your cocktail area, use that as a centerpiece to the party. Light it with strands of white twinkle lights or hang a series of Japanese lanterns like ornaments from the branches. The best place to start decorating your party is at the front door; let people know this is where "the party's at!" A standard house has natural elements that can be enhanced. The front steps can be lined with blooming potted plants, glowing paper luminarios, or funny signs that cue the guest to the party. If a themed character is being used, make them part of your entrance treatment so that they can directly interact with your guests right from the start.

Jerry Astourian
Images Event Production

ಶಾಶಾಶಾ

Simple elegance and traditional styles are making a comeback. No one wants to appear garish or flamboyant during an economic downturn – perception is critical and outrageous events that run the risk of criticism are in less demand.

Chantal DuPois
The Breakers
Off-Premises Catering Manager

ಶಾಶಾಶಾ

We will continue to see the trends of the 1990s be a blend of international cuisines and traditional recipes that create exciting new food styles and tastes. But this is only part of what makes an evening of dining successful. Overall ambiance and great service are vital to the creation of a memorable evening. So it is not just the food it is the quality of the entire experience that the hosts of the 1990s need to address.

Mary Micucci, 1992
Along Came Mary, Inc.

৯৯৯৯

It is imperative to have enough help at any party. You must be a guest – not a servant – at your own parties. The rule of thumb is to have one in help for every 20 people. Don't expect your friends to act as bartenders or slave labor.

The most important word in your social vocabulary is RECIPROCATION. If you go, you owe!

The following are "no-no's" for party guests: drinking Bud from a can; saving the swizzle stick for a souvenir; wrapping the hors d'oeuvres to take home for dinner; sipping champagne from yours or anyone else's slippers; taking home the bottle of wine you brought – or even worse, taking home a more expensive bottle; bragging about your wealth or complaining about your poverty; trying to promote business goods or services. A party is meant to be a social experience, not a market place.

Marci Weiner
Beverly Hills Society Columnist and Confidant to the Stars

৯৯৯৯

The dining adventure should be the ultimate socially-shared sensual experience – a feast for the senses. The more senses celebrated in harmony, the richer and more memorable the occasion.

Shelby Goodman
Designer of Interiors and Extraordinary Parties

৯৯৯৯

In order for an event to be outstanding, the location must be unique and comfortable (no matter what the weather is like), the lighting and decor should set the tone for the evening's activities, the food and service need to be impeccable and food selections should never be chosen from a pre-planned menu, the entertainment exciting and participatory, and a specially-designed gift should be handed out or, better yet, uniquely delivered (if guests are staying at a hotel) that will remind them always of the event attended.

Mona S. Meretsky
Comcor

৯৯৯৯

❧❧❧❧

For a quality special event, be sure to invite a fascinating mixture of guests and utilize a consistent theme, including the food. Be sure the room is comfortable, and that there is a steady flow of activity and food service. The service should be well organized and parking should be handled with ease. To obtain optimal publicity at a special event, target the proper press to attend, and process their requests immediately. The bottom line is to be very professional, yet be sure to be relaxed and enjoy yourself during the event.

Joan Luther
Joan Luther & Associates
Public Relations

❧❧❧❧

The secret to successful entertaining is to make everyone feel that they're the guest of honor.

Diane Abramson
International fashion designer
and hostess to the rich and famous

❧❧❧❧

Just a ♪ 2 say...

A great party is like a symphony. Every ♪, every word, every person is filled with the magic of the song!

Carol Connors
Award winning songwriter who co-wrote theme song of
Robin Leach's "Lifestyles of the Rich and Famous" -
"Champagne Wishes and Caviar Dreams" sung by Dionne Warwick

INDEX

INDEX

INDEX

INDEX

INDEX

INDEX

INDEX

INDEX

❧ ❧ ❧

ABOUT THE AUTHOR

Jan Roberts, author of The Beverly Hills Party Planner is founder, owner and sole operator of Rent An Event, a full service event planning company based in Beverly Hills, California.

Founded in 1988 as an entertainment booking and production company, it has since expanded into a full event and party planning production company whose clients include major hotels, corporations and organizations.

In addition to planning events, Jan also teaches seminars on "The Art of Entertaining" at local schools and colleges as well as devoting her time and talents to helping non-profit and charitable organizations.

ORDER FORM

For additional copies of The Beverly Hills Party Planner, send $17.95 per copy to:

THE BEVERLY HILLS
PARTY PLANNER
139 South Beverly Drive / Suite 312
Beverly Hills, CA 90212

I would like _____ copies of The Beverly Hills Party Planner.

Name: _____

Company: _____

Address: _____

City: _____

State: _____   Zip: _____   Phone: _____

SUBTOTAL: $ _____

SHIPPING AND HANDLING ($6.50 per book): _____

SALES TAX (California residents add 8.25%): _____

TOTAL: $ _____

Please send check or money order made payable to The Beverly Hills Party Planner.
Please allow up to four weeks for delivery.
For bulk sales rates or more information, please call 310.271.7641
Thank you for your order.

NOTES

NOTES

NOTES

NOTES

NOTES